ESSENTIAL RELATIVITY

Wolfgang Rindler

Southwest Center for Advanced Studies, Dallas, Texas

ESSENTIAL

RELATIVITY

Special, General, and Cosmological

VAN NOSTRAND REINHOLD COMPANY

New York   Cincinnati   Toronto   London   Melbourne

Van Nostrand Reinhold Company Regional Offices:
Cincinnati, New York, Chicago, Millbrae, Dallas

Van Nostrand Reinhold Company Foreign Offices:
London, Toronto, Melbourne

Published by Van Nostrand Reinhold Company
450 West 33rd Street, New York, N.Y. 10001

Published simultaneously in Canada by
D. Van Nostrand Company (Canada), Ltd.

15 14 13 12 11 10 9 8 7 6 5 4 3 2 1

Preface

This book is an attempt to bring the full range of relativity theory within reach of advanced undergraduates, while containing enough new material and simplifications of old arguments so as not to bore the expert teacher. Roughly equal coverage is given to special relativity, general relativity, and cosmology. With many judicious omissions it can be taught in one semester, but it would better serve as the basis of a year's work. It is my hope, anyway, that its level and style of presentation may appeal also to wider classes of readers unrestricted by credit considerations. General relativity, the modern theory of gravitation in which free particles move along "straightest possible" lines in curved spacetime, and cosmology, with its dynamics for the whole possibly curved universe, not only seem necessary for a scientist's balanced view of the world, but offer some of the greatest intellectual thrills of modern physics. Nevertheless, considered luxuries, they are usually squeezed out of the graduate curriculum by the pressure of specialization. Special relativity escapes this tag with a vengeance, and tends to be taught as a pure service discipline, with too little emphasis on its startling ideas. What better time, therefore, to enjoy these subjects for their own sake than as an undergraduate? In spite of its forbidding mathematical reputation, even general relativity is accessible at that stage. Anyone who knows the calculus up to partial differentiation, ordinary vectors to the point of differentiating them, and that most useful method of approximation, the binomial theorem, should be able to read this book. Its mathematical level rises very gradually. Four-vectors are introduced half way through special relativity, and are then used sufficiently to leave no doubt that they are tools and not just ornaments. And, of course, no serious approach to general relativity is possible without tensors. Accordingly, these are introduced at the appropriate point (in Chapter 8), but as unobtrusively as possible, so that those who habitually skip a few paragraphs will perhaps hardly notice them. Yet the more ambitious reader, who is prepared to pause and think, will find enough tensor theory outlined here to give him a basic understanding of all relativistic tensor arguments. The experience of seeing tensors and Riemannian geometry in action may motivate him to learn more about these subjects eventually.

In its order of presentation the book breaks with tradition. With few exceptions, the usual procedure has been to accept Newton's definition of inertial frames for special relativity, and not to introduce the equivalence principle until just before it is needed in general relativity. It is then that the student suddenly learns that he has been working against the wrong background: that Newton's frames are not, after all, the frames relevant to special relativity. This is excusable only as long as general relativity, and, in particular, the equivalence principle, are regarded as doubtful. Once we accept them, as do most experts today, we should paint a consistent picture from the beginning. And so, in this book, not only the equivalence principle, but even Mach's principle (with due reservations) and some cosmology precede special relativity in order to set it in its proper perspective. Special relativity is then developed rigorously, with an eye on the physics at all times, but emphasizing ideas, not experimental detail. There is some unavoidable overlap of subject matter with my previous book "Special Relativity"* (referred to hereafter as RSR), but the actual duplication is minimal, and many common topics are treated quite differently. I trust that friends of RSR can read even

---

*Oliver and Boyd, Edinburgh and London; New York: Interscience Publishers, Inc., a Division of John Wiley & Sons, Inc., second edition, 1966.

this part of the present book with profit. There follows an "easy" chapter on general relativity, which represents about the limit to which one can go without the use of tensors. The next chapter (Chapter 8) is probably the hardest in the book, but after Section 75 it can at first be omitted, except for a "light" reading of Section 79. The last chapter, on cosmology, though rigorous and detailed, should be easier again. Those whose primary interest lies in this field can read it almost independently of the rest of the book. At the end of the text there is a collection of over 130 exercises, put together rather carefully. I would urge even the most casual reader not quite to ignore these. Though their full solution often requires ingenuity, even a mere perusal should provide some useful insights. In addition, students should give their curiosity full rein and develop the habit of continually inventing and answering their own problems. Finally a warning: in several sections the units are chosen so as to make the speed of light unity, which should be borne in mind when comparing formulas.

These remarks would not be complete without an expression of gratitude to my friend Professor Jürgen Ehlers for reading the manuscript in detail and making innumerable suggestions for improvement, which I was only too glad to accept. Furthermore, it is a pleasure to have this opportunity of thanking Professor Carlo Cattaneo and members of the Istituto Matematico "Guido Castelnuovo" of the University of Rome, where part of this book was written, for their warm hospitality and most stimulating discussions, and the authorities of the Southwest Center for Advanced Studies for granting me leave.

WOLFGANG RINDLER

Rome
April 1969

ABBREVIATIONS USED IN THIS BOOK

RSR   Rindler, "Special Relativity," 2nd ed. 1966
SR   Special relativity
GR   General relativity
AS   Absolute space
GT   Galilean transformation
LT   Lorentz transformation
RP   Relativity principle
EP   Equivalence principle
LIF   Local inertial frame
CM   Center of momentum
CP   Cosmological principle
PCP   Perfect cosmological principle
RW   Robertson-Walker

Contents

ESSENTIAL RELATIVITY

1

The Rise and Fall of Absolute Space

Originally, relativity in physics meant the abolition of absolute space. More particularly, it has come to mean either of Einstein's famous two theories, *special relativity* (SR) and *general relativity* (GR). SR abolished absolute space in its Maxwellian role as the carrier of light waves and of electromagnetic fields in general, while GR abolished absolute space also in its Newtonian role as the standard of nonacceleration. Since these ideas are fundamental, we shall devote the first chapter to a brief discussion centered on the three questions: What is absolute space? Why should it be abolished? And how can it be abolished?

A more modern and positive definition of relativity has grown *ex post facto* from the actual relativity theories; according to this view, the relativity of any physical theory expresses itself in the group of coordinate transformations that leave the laws of the theory invariant. For example, as we shall see, Newton's mechanics possesses the relativity of the so-called Galilean group, SR possesses the relativity of the Lorentz group, GR possesses the relativity of the full group of transformations, and the various cosmologies possess the relativity of the various symmetries with which the large-scale universe is credited. Even a theory valid only in one absolute Euclidean space, provided *that* is physically homogeneous and isotropic, would possess a relativity, namely the group of rotations and translations of the coordinate axes.

2   *Newton's Laws*

We recall Newton's three laws of mechanics, of which the first (Galileo's law) is really a special case of the second:

(i) Free particles move with constant vector-velocity (i.e., with zero acceleration, or, in other words, with constant speed along straight lines).

(ii) The vector-force on a particle equals the product of its mass into its vector-acceleration: $\mathbf{f} = m\mathbf{a}$.

(iii) The forces of action and reaction are equal and opposite (i.e., if a particle A exerts a force $\mathbf{f}$ on a particle B, then B exerts a force $-\mathbf{f}$ on A).

Of course, physical laws are usually stated relative to some *reference frame*, which allows physical quantities like velocity, acceleration, etc., to be measured. Preferred among reference frames are *rigid* frames, and preferred among these are the *inertial* frames. Newton's laws apply in the latter.

A rigid reference frame is an idealization, or extension, of a rigid body. For example, the earth determines a rigid frame throughout all space, consisting of all those points which remain "rigidly" at rest relative to the earth and to each other. We can associate an orthogonal Cartesian coordinate system S with such a frame in many ways, by choosing three mutually orthogonal planes within it and measuring x, y, z as distances from these planes. Also a time coordinate t must be defined in order that the system can become physically useful. A rigid frame, endowed with such coordinates, we shall call a *Cartesian* frame. Here we shall take it for granted that the geometry in such a frame is Euclidean.

Newton's first law serves as an operational test to single out inertial frames among rigid frames: a rigid frame is called inertial if free particles, *provided they are sufficiently removed from all attracting matter*, move without acceleration relative to it. Empirically, the frame of the "fixed stars" was long recognized as inertial to considerable accuracy, and it was taken as the basic reference frame for Newton's laws. Today, when our galaxy is known to rotate, and the universe is known to expand, we might substitute for the "fixed stars" that rigid frame in which all other galaxies appear to us to recede isotropically, i.e., the frame which is most symmetrical relative to the distant universe. When we talk of the frame of the "fixed stars," we shall really mean the latter.

The Galilean Transformation   3

Now consider two Cartesian frames $S(x,y,z,t)$ and $S'(x',y',z',t')$ in "standard configuration," as shown in Figure 1: S' moves in the x-direction of S with uniform velocity v and the corresponding axes of S and S' remain parallel throughout the motion, having coincided at time $t = t' = 0$. It is assumed that the same units of distance and

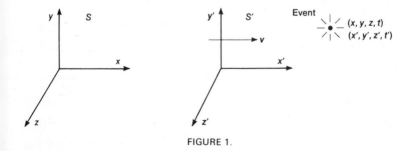

FIGURE 1.

time are adopted in both frames. Suppose an event (like the flashing of a light bulb, or the collision of two point-particles) has coordinates (x, y, z, t) relative to S and (x', y', z', t') relative to S'. Then the classical (and "common sense") relations between these two sets of coordinates are given by the so-called *Galilean transformation* (GT):

$$x' = x - vt, \quad y' = y, \quad z' = z, \quad t' = t. \qquad (3.1)$$

The last of these relations is usually taken for granted; it expresses the universality, or absoluteness, of time.

4   *The Set of All Inertial Frames*

If the frame S in Figure 1 is inertial, so is S'—since the linear equations of motion of free particles in S are transformed by (3.1) into similar linear equations in S', and a Cartesian reference frame relative to which free particles have linear equations of motion is inertial. Conversely, any inertial frame must move uniformly relative to any other such frame, since a nonuniform relative motion would make it impossible for Newton's first law to be satisfied in both frames. Hence the class of inertial frames consists precisely of the basic frame of the fixed stars plus all other frames moving uniformly (and, of course, without rotation) relative to that one. According to Newton, all these inertial frames have infinite spatial and temporal extent, i.e., x, y, z, t all range from minus to plus infinity.

5   *Newtonian Relativity*

Not only Newton's first law, but also his second and third are valid in *all* inertial frames. For in Newton's theory, both $\mathbf{f}$ and m are invariant between inertial frames by definition (and experience confirms this—at least approximately) and $\mathbf{a}$ can be seen to be invariant under the Galilean transformation. Hence the mechanics based on these three laws is identical in all inertial frames. Newton, as Galileo before him, illustrated this fact with the familiar example of a ship, in which all motions and all mechanics happen in the same way whether the ship is at rest or is moving uniformly in a straight line. This property of Newtonian mechanics is often referred to as *Newtonian* (or *Galilean*) *relativity*.

Newton's Absolute Space   6

Because of this "relativity," the uniform motion of one inertial frame relative to another cannot be detected by internal mechanical experiments subject to Newton's theory. But *acceleration* is absolute: while I may be in doubt whether my ship has sailed or is still tied to the pier, I shall be in no doubt if it suddenly hits an iceberg. According to Newton, a particle does not resist uniform motion, of whatever speed, but it does resist any change in its velocity, i.e., acceleration, both positive and negative. This is precisely expressed by Newton's second law: the coefficient m in the equation $\mathbf{f} = m\mathbf{a}$ is a measure of the particle's *inertia*, i.e., of its resistance to acceleration. And here it may well be asked: acceleration with respect to what? Empirically the answer is simple: with respect to any one of the inertial frames. Physically and aesthetically, however, this answer is quite unsatisfactory, and Newton was fully aware of this. What in the world singles out the class of inertial frames over all the others as standards of nonacceleration? Newton found no answer, and postulated instead the existence of an *absolute space* (AS). This is supposed to interact with every particle so as to resist its acceleration. Newton chose to identify AS with the center of mass frame of the solar system, and his successors identified it with the frame of the fixed stars. But clearly one could identify it with any other inertial frame just as well.

7   *Objections to Newton's Absolute Space*

Newton's concept of an absolute space has never lacked critics. From Bishop Berkeley, a near-contemporary of Newton, to Ernst Mach in the nineteenth century, to Einstein in the twentieth, cogent arguments have been brought against AS:

(a) It is purely *ad hoc* and *explains* nothing. It can be likened to Kepler's early (and possibly facetious) suggestion that angels were responsible for pushing the planets along their paths, or to Sciama's modern analogy of "demons" appropriately active in metals to explain what was until recently the mystery of superconductivity.

(b) There is no unique way of locating Newton's AS within the infinite class of inertial frames.

(c) "It conflicts with one's scientific understanding to conceive of a thing [AS] which acts but cannot be acted upon." The words are Einstein's, but he attributes the thought to Mach. In any case, this is perhaps the most powerful objection of all. It not only questions AS (which Newton's theory can do without) but also the set of all inertial frames.

The fact remains that inertial frames are very real: they play a central role in Newton's theory, and, indeed, in our experience. But Newton's theory offers no satisfactory explanation for their existence. If we fix our attention on two elastic spheres suspended on a common axis, of which one rotates and bulges, while the other is at rest and undeformed, it is hard to understand how the spheres "know" which of them rotates and so must bulge.

8   *Maxwell's Ether*

For a time it appeared as though Maxwell's "ether" could be identified with Newton's AS, and so provide an answer to all the above objections. As is well known, in Maxwell's theory there occurs a constant c with the dimensions of a speed, which was originally defined as a ratio between electrostatic and electromagnetic units of charge, and which can be determined by simple laboratory experiments involving charges and currents.   Moreover, Maxwell's theory predicted the propagation of disturbances of the electromagnetic field in vacuum with this speed c—in other words, the existence of electromagnetic waves. The amazing thing was that c coincided precisely with the known vacuum speed of light, which immediately led Maxwell to the realization that light must be an electromagnetic wave phenomenon. To serve as a carrier for such waves, and for electromagnetic "strains" in general, Maxwell resurrected the old idea of a "luminiferous ether." It seemed reasonable to assume that the frame of "still ether" coincided with the frame of the "fixed stars."

Where is Maxwell's Ether?   9

The great success of Maxwell's theory since about 1860 put considerable pressure on experimenters to find direct evidence for the existence of the ether. In particular, they tried to determine the terrestrial "ether drift," i.e., the speed of the earth through the ether, as the earth circles the sun. The best-known of all these experiments is that of Michelson and Morley (1887). They sent a light signal from a source to a mirror and back again, first in the supposed direction of the ether drift and then at right angles to it, attempting to measure a time difference for the two directions by delicate interference methods. The well-known analogy of the swimmer in the river makes the principle of the experiment clear: it takes less time to swim across the river and back than an equal distance downstream and back. Michelson and Morley could detect no time difference at all. Since the earth's orbital speed is 18 miles per second, one could expect the ether drift at *some* time during the year to be at least that much, no matter how the ether streamed past the solar system. Moreover, a drift of this magnitude was well within the capability of the apparatus to detect. Many later and equally ingenious experiments also all failed to find any ether drift whatsoever. The facile explanation that the earth completely "dragged" the ether along with it in its neighborhood could be ruled out because of the observed aberration of starlight. Thus it slowly became apparent that Maxwell's ether was as "useless" in explaining observed phenomena, or predicting new ones, as Kepler's angels or Sciama's demons.

This, of course, left electromagnetic theory with a serious puzzle: no matter how one "chased" a light-wave, one could apparently not alter its speed relative to oneself. Such behavior is totally unlike that of any other wave phenomenon that had ever been known.

10   Lorentz Theory

If Maxwell's ether was a demon invented solely for the purpose of carrying electromagnetic strains, Lorentz (and, in part independently, Fitzgerald and Poincaré) now introduced two secondary demons, whose sole task it was to help the chief demon, ether, to remain unobservable. These demons were the phenomena of length contraction and time dilation. If, when moving with velocity v through the ether, rigid bodies contracted longitudinally and clocks went slow, both by a factor $(1 - v^2/c^2)^{1/2}$, this would so affect every apparatus designed to measure the ether drift as to neutralize exactly all expected effects. As it happens, these *ad hoc* assumptions turned out to be correct in a certain sense, and the phenomena are even observable, as we shall see. But though apparently based on a preferred ether frame, the resulting theory (the "Lorentz theory"—including the so-called Lorentz transformation equations) yielded symmetry, as far as observable predictions went, between all inertial frames, and was from this viewpoint insensitive to which inertial frame was chosen as the ether frame. For from the assumed length contraction and time dilation relative to the ether frame it *follows* that rods and clocks moving at speed v through *any* inertial frame appear, respectively, to be shortened and to go slow *relative to that frame* by the same factor $(1 - v^2/c^2)^{1/2}$. Thus the Lorentz theory could not save Maxwell's ether from the original criticism that it could not be detected, though it pushed the *ad hoc* assumptions one stage further.

The Relativity Principle *11*

At that time of lively debate (1905), Einstein cut the Gordian knot by asserting, in his famous *relativity principle* (RP) that "all inertial frames are totally equivalent for the performance of all physical experiments." Note that this is a generalization to the whole of physics of Newton's purely mechanical relativity principle. At first sight, Einstein's principle appears to be no more than a whole-hearted acceptance of the null-results of all the ether drift experiments. But by ceasing to look for special "explanations" of these results and using them rather as the empirical evidence for a new fundamental principle of nature, Einstein had turned the tables: predictions could be made. Soon a whole new theory based on Einstein's principle (and on the experimental fact that light has the same velocity in all inertial frames) was in existence, and this theory is called special relativity. Its aim is to modify all the laws of physics, where necessary, so as to make them equally valid in all inertial frames. Today, over sixty years later, the enormous success of this theory has made it impossible to doubt the wide validity of its basic premises.

The RP is an overall principle which "explains" the failure of all the ether drift experiments in much the same way as the principle of the conservation of energy "explains" the failure of all attempts to construct a perpetual motion machine. By declaring it necessarily unobservable, the RP abolished Maxwell's ether forever. The phenomena of contracting bodies and slow-going clocks actually reappear in SR, though from quite a different viewpoint. Like all good theories, however, SR did more than illuminate facts already known. It opened up entirely new fields. The situation can be compared to that in astronomy at the time when the intricate geocentric system (corresponding to the Lorentz theory) gave way to the liberating ideas of Copernicus, Galileo, and Newton.

12   Arguments for the RP

Although the weightiest argument today for the principle of relativity is the success of special relativity theory, at least three different types of argument could and can be made for it *ab initio*:

(a) The null results of all the ether drift experiments. Einstein did not even bother to make much of this, as can be seen from the quotation under (b) below. But we do know that he was influenced by the positivists' view that "unobservables" (like the ether) have no place in physics.

(b) The evident "relativity" of Maxwell's theory, if not in spirit, yet in fact. This, to Einstein's mind, carried a great deal of weight. He realized the economy of thought that could be introduced into Maxwell's theory by the RP. Here, in a standard translation, is the beginning of his famous paper (*Annalen der Physik* **17,** 891 (1905)):

> It is known that Maxwell's electrodynamics—as usually understood at the present time—when applied to moving bodies, leads to asymmetries which do not appear to be inherent in the phenomena. Take, for example, the reciprocal electrodynamic action of a magnet and a conductor. The observable phenomenon here depends only on the relative motion of the conductor and the magnet, whereas the customary view draws a sharp distinction between the two cases in which

either the one or the other of these bodies is in motion. For if the magnet is in motion and the conductor at rest, there arises in the neighbourhood of the magnet an electric field with a certain definite energy, producing a current at the places where parts of the conductor are situated. But if the magnet is stationary and the conductor in motion, no electric field arises in the neighbourhood of the magnet. In the conductor, however, we find an electromotive force, to which in itself there is no corresponding energy, but which gives rise—assuming equality of relative motion in the two cases discussed—to electric currents of the same path and intensity as those produced by the electric forces in the former case.

Examples of this sort, together with the unsuccessful attempts to discover any motion of the earth relative to the "light medium," suggest that the phenomena of electrodynamics as well as of mechanics possess no properties corresponding to the idea of absolute rest. They suggest rather that ... the same laws of electrodynamics and optics will be valid for all frames of reference for which the equations of mechanics hold good. We will raise this conjecture (hereafter called the Principle of Relativity) to the status of a postulate ...

(c) The unity of physics. This is an argument of rather more recent origin. It has become increasingly obvious that physics cannot be separated into strictly independent branches; for example, no electromagnetic experiment can be performed without the use of mechanical parts, and no mechanical experiment is independent of the electromagnetic constitution of matter, etc. If there exists a *strict* relativity principle for mechanics, then a large part of electromagnetism must be relativistic also, namely that part which has to do with the constitution of matter. But if part, why not all? In short, if physics is indivisible, either all of it or none of it must satisfy the relativity principle. And since the RP is so strongly evident in mechanics, it is at least a good guess that it is generally valid.

Maxwellian Relativity   *13*

There is an element of irony in the fact that, according to SR, the so-called Lorentz transformations rather than the

Galilean transformations relate *actual measurements* made in inertial frames (as we shall see in Section 27). Lorentz transformations were already known to be those transformations which *formally* leave Maxwell's equations invariant; but their *physical* significance had remained unrecognized. Since Galilean transformations were long thought to relate inertial frames, Maxwell's theory had been regarded as "unrelativistic." Now it turned out to be fully relativistic after all. Newton's theory, on the other hand, which had always contained a relativity principle, conflicts with the Lorentz transformations and had to be modified.

14   *Origins of General Relativity*

While SR completely abolished the ether concept, namely AS in its Maxwellian role, it still provided neither an explanation nor a substitute for AS in its Newtonian role. SR is strongly dependent on the concept of the inertial frames. But *why* these frames constitute a privileged class in nature, serving as a standard of nonacceleration (and also as the arena for the simplest formulation of all physical laws) remained as much of a mystery as before. It was reserved for GR to solve, or at least to shed much light upon, this problem.

It is often said that GR grew out of the failure of the various attempts to modify Newton's gravitational (inverse square) theory so as to fit it satisfactorily into the framework of SR. Certainly, GR is the modern theory of gravitation which has supplanted Newton's—in principle, if not in computational practice. Nevertheless, it is clear that Einstein was led to GR primarily by his philosophic desire to abolish totally the role of absolute space from physics. He would probably not have stopped at a special-relativistic theory of gravitation, however satisfactory, since SR begins by taking the inertial frames for granted. Einstein thus had to go beyond SR. In this task he loyally and repeatedly acknowledged his debt to Mach. It is probably fair to say that Mach, in turn, is indebted to Einstein for honing, elaborating, and immortalizing his ideas.

Mach's Principle   *15*

Mach's ideas on inertia, whose germ was already contained in the writings of Bishop Berkeley, are roughly these: (a) there is no such "thing" as absolute space, or indeed *any* space—except as an abstraction from the totality of distance-relations between matter; (b) a particle's inertia is due to some (unfortunately unspecified) interaction of that particle with all the other masses in the universe; (c) the local standards of nonacceleration are determined by some average of the motions of all the masses in the universe; (d) all that matters in mechanics is the *relative* motion of *all* the masses. Thus Mach wrote: "... it does not matter if we think of the earth as turning round on its axis, or at rest while the fixed stars revolve around it. ... The law of inertia must be so conceived that exactly the same thing results from the second supposition as from the first." It is perhaps significant that even before Einstein, Mach referred to himself and his followers as "relativists."

A spinning elastic sphere bulges at its equator. To the question of how the sphere "knows" that it is spinning and hence must bulge, Newton might have answered that it "felt" the action of absolute space. Mach would have answered that the bulging sphere "felt" the action of the cosmic masses rotating around it. To Newton, rotation with respect to AS produces centrifugal (inertial) forces, which are quite distinct from gravitational forces; to Mach, centrifugal forces *are* gravitational, i.e., caused by the action of mass upon mass.

Einstein coined the term *Mach's principle* for this whole complex of ideas. Of course, with Mach these ideas were still embryonic in that a quantitative theory of the proposed "mass induction" effect was totally lacking. Einstein, at one stage in his progress towards GR, conjectured that Newton's inverse square theory probably differed as much from a complete gravitational theory as a simple electric theory based only on Coulomb's law differed from Maxwell's ultimate theory. Indeed, D. W. Sciama* in 1953 revived and extended an 1872 Maxwell-type gravitational theory of F. Tisserand and found that it includes Mach's principle: inertial forces correspond to the gravitational "radiation field" of the universe, and are proportional to the inverse *first* power of the distance. But, unfortunately, this theory violates relativity on other grounds. Einstein's solution to the problem, GR, turned out to be much more complicated than Maxwell's theory. However, in "first approximation" it reduces to Newton's theory, and in "second approximation" it actually has Maxwellian features. But in what sense GR is truly "Machian" is still a matter of debate. (See Section 92.)

16   *Consequences of Mach's Principle*

It is sometimes held that Mach's principle is physically empty: since we cannot "experiment" with the universe, we cannot test the principle; we can never decide whether it is absolute space or the cosmic masses that determine inertia, and thus the choice is philosophical rather than physical.

Yet this is not so. Even without the help of a detailed theory, Mach's principle leads to certain *testable* non-Newtonian predictions:

(a) The following remark is due to Sciama. It was discovered in 1926 that our galaxy rotates differentially, somewhat like a huge planetary system, with a typical period of 250 million years. Now suppose this rotation could have

*Mon. Nat. Roy. Astr. Soc. **113**, 34 (1953); see also D. W. Sciama, "The Unity of the Universe," New York, Doubleday and Co., Inc., 1959, especially Chaps. 7–9.

been observed in Mach's time, or predicted theoretically as counteracting gravitational collapse. Then Mach could have been led by his principle to postulate the existence of a whole vast extragalactic universe—which was not discovered observationally until much later—simply in order to make the standard of rest in the galaxy come out right. A strict Newtonian, on the other hand, would have seen nothing very strange in the galactic rotation, since, after all, the sun, the earth, the moon, etc., all rotate. At most, he might have felt regret at having to abandon the usual optical identification of AS.

(b) Consider a Foucault pendulum suspended, for the sake of simplicity, from a tripod at the earth's North Pole. It swings in a plane that remains fixed relative to the universe while the earth turns. Now suppose we could remove all the cosmic masses except the earth. According to Newton, the pendulum experiment would not be affected. According to Mach, however, the pendulum would now swing in a plane fixed relative to the earth—which has become the obvious and only standard of nonacceleration. Next let us reintroduce the cosmic masses gradually, until *their* inertia-producing effect predominates again. But, by continuity, it will never predominate totally. The earth will always make *some* contribution to the local "compass of inertia" and thus, however minutely, drag the plane of the Foucault pendulum around in the sense of its rotation. Given sufficiently accurate apparatus, this would be a measurable, non-Newtonian effect. It has recently been suggested that in place of the Foucault pendulum, one could perhaps observe the orbital plane of an artificial satellite in polar orbit.

(c) Consider the following pair of diagrams, representing the system earth-moon-universe, the universe being schematically represented by a massive shell. Figure 2(i) represents the "conventional" view. Figure 2(ii) represents a *relatively* equivalent view, with the moon at rest and the universe revolving. According to Mach, as we have seen,

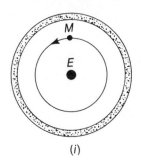 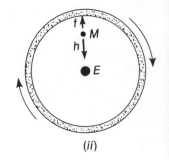

(i)   (ii)

FIGURE 2.

"the law of inertia must be so conceived that exactly the same thing results from the second supposition as from the first." Hence the rotating universe must provide a centrifugal force f to counteract the earth's attraction h. (It is this force, too, which causes the earth's equatorial bulge.) The universe must also provide a Coriolis force which has the cumulative effect of turning the plane of the Foucault pendulum. By a straightforward analogy, we would therefore expect centrifugal and Coriolis forces to arise inside *every* rotating massive shell—another quite non-Newtonian effect.* Furthermore, with reference to Figure 2(i), some force (e.g. a rocket) would be needed to accelerate the earth from rest in a given direction. But this could be reinterpreted as the earth needing a force to stand still inside a universe that accelerates past it. By extension, therefore, we would expect a particle to experience a force whenever masses in its neighborhood are accelerated, the force being in the direction of the acceleration.

(d) Mach's principle even implies interactions between inertia and electromagnetism. Consider, for example, a positively charged, nonconducting sphere which rotates. Each charge on it gives rise to a circular current and thus to a magnetic field. Figures 3(i) and 3(ii) again represent the conventional view and a Mach-equivalent view, re-

---

*This problem was investigated, on the basis of GR, by H. Thirring in *Phys. Zeits.* **19,** 33 (1918), **22,** 29 (1921); and that of (b) above, by H. Thirring and J. Lense in *Phys. Zeits.* **19,** 156 (1918).

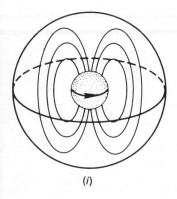 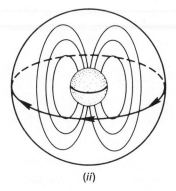

(i)   (ii)

FIGURE 3.

spectively, of the sphere, the universe, and the corresponding magnetic field. By analogy again, a similar nonclassical
effect can be predicted for any massive rotating shell with
stationary charges inside it.*

(e) A single test particle in an otherwise empty universe
would, by Mach's principle, not be expected to have any
appreciable inertia (except "self inertia"). The introduction
of other masses into the universe would gradually bestow
inertia upon the particle. Thus again, by extension, one
would expect any particle's inertia to increase in the presence of large masses. Moreover, one might well expect this
inertia to have directional properties, related to the mass
distribution. (In a Maxwell-type theory, this would certainly be so.) Now to a very high degree of accuracy, inertia is known to be isotropic in our part of the universe.
From this, some people have drawn certain conclusions:
First, since the matter in our *immediate* neighborhood (sun,
planets, etc.) is patently nonisotropic, the overwhelming
part of the induction effect must come from *distant* matter:
a "1/r" law would be consistent with this. And secondly,
the distant matter, i.e., the universe, must be isotropic relative to us. This would add weight to the optically observed
rough isotropy of the universe and speak against the vari-

*An apparently similar but, in fact, quite different problem was discussed, on the
basis of GR, by L. I. Schiff in *Proc. Nat. Acad. Sci.* **25**, 391 (1939).

ous nonisotropic world-models that have been proposed. On the other hand, it can be argued that directional variation, or indeed any variation, of inertia would be *unobservable*, since every apparatus designed to measure it would itself be so affected as to completely mask the effect. Such would certainly be the case if Einstein's strong equivalence principle is true. (See Section 19.)

Even allowing this last disclaimer, examples (a)–(d) should make it amply clear that Mach's principle is certainly not without physical content. On the other hand, Mach's principle is so far still without a single experimental verification. (Some order-of-magnitude calculations suggest that the effects discussed above are too minute for present-day apparatus to detect; see, for example, exercise 1-6.) In spite of its aesthetic appeal, one should therefore keep an open mind about the principle. In particular, Mach's way to resolve the objections against absolute space, namely abolishing space altogether, may be too radical. The main objection against absolute space, that it acts but cannot be acted upon, can also be met while retaining the separate existence of space, but allowing it to interact with matter: this is actually what happens in GR. Strangely enough, though, and as we mentioned before, the logical status of GR vis-a-vis Mach's principle has still not been totally clarified. (See Section 92.)

17   Cosmology

Mach's principle suggests that *the whole universe matters locally*. It will therefore be useful even at this early stage to review briefly the main features of the universe as they are known today. Our galaxy contains about 10^{11} stars— which account for most of the objects in the night sky that are visible to the naked eye. Beyond our galaxy there are other more or less similar galaxies, shaped and spaced roughly like dimes three feet apart. The "known" part of the universe, which stretches to a radius of about 10^9 light-years, contains about 10^{11} such galaxies. They recede from each other in such a way that, had the presently observed recession been uniform in time, the observable universe would have been a dense ball some 10^{10} years ago. However, there are good reasons for believing that the recession has *not* been uniform in time. These facts necessitate some revision of our original definition of inertial frames.

As a very simplified possible model of the universe, consider an infinite array of galaxies, spaced more or less uniformly throughout space, and mutually receding, much like an array of knots in an infinite rubber sponge that is being stretched equally in all directions. The pull of gravity would slow the expansion, and perhaps ultimately reverse it. Our model satisfies the so-called *cosmological principle*, according to which all galaxies stand in the same relation to the whole universe. This principle is adopted, partly for aesthetic but mainly for simplistic reasons, by practically all modern cosmologies. It excludes, for example, a finite "island" universe immersed in infinite space, since that contains atypical "outermost" galaxies.

Now, how could we determine infinitely extended Newtonian inertial frames in this universe? If *our* galaxy were at rest in one such inertial frame, would not each other galaxy also be at rest in one such frame, by the cosmological principle or simply by symmetry? Yet those other inertial frames would *not move uniformly* relative to ours! Moreover, where in *our* inertial frame do free particles obey Newton's first law? At most, in the neighborhood of our own galaxy. Far out among the distant galaxies a test particle would be affected by the same considerable gravitational acceleration that pulls all galaxies towards each other and, in particular, towards us. There simply would not be *any* regions "sufficiently removed" from all attracting matter in which free particles followed straight paths relative to us, except in our immediate vicinity. And so, extended inertial frames would not exist.

Mach's principle obviously suggests that under these conditions the center of each galaxy provides a basic *local* standard of nonacceleration, and the lines of sight from this center to the other galaxies (rather than to the stars of the galaxy itself, which may rotate) provide a local standard of nonrotation: in sum, a *local inertial frame.* Inertial frames would no longer be of infinite extent, and they would not all be in uniform relative motion. A frame which is locally inertial would cease to be so at a distance, if the universe expands nonuniformly. Nevertheless, *at each point* there would still be an infinite set of local inertial frames, all in uniform relative motion.

18   *Inertial and Gravitational Mass*

Much the same conclusion was reached by Einstein in his *equivalence principle* (EP) of 1907, though rather more generally and from a different point of view. (The expansion of the universe was unknown then.) Einstein began with a closer look at the concept of "mass." It is not always stressed that at least two quite distinct types of mass enter into Newton's theory of mechanics and gravitation. These are (i) the inertial mass, which occurs as the ratio between force and acceleration in Newton's second law, and (ii) the gravitational mass, which may be regarded as the gravitational analog of electric charge, and which occurs in the equation

$$f = \frac{Gmm'}{r^2} \tag{18.1}$$

for the attractive force between two masses (G being the gravitational constant.)

One can further distinguish between active and passive gravitational mass, namely between that which causes and that which yields to a gravitational field, respectively. Because of the symmetry of equation (18.1) (due to Newton's third law), no essential difference between active and passive gravitational mass exists in Newton's theory. In GR, on the other hand, the concept of passive mass does not arise, only that of active mass—the creator of the field.

It so happens in nature that for *all* particles the inertial and gravitational masses are in the same proportion, and in fact they are usually made equal by a suitable choice of units. (The proportionality was carefully verified by Eötvös, first in 1889, and finally in 1922 to an accuracy of five parts in 10^9; lately Roll, Krotkov, and Dicke improved the accuracy to one part in 10^{11}.) Some people call this the "weak" equivalence principle. A fully equivalent property is that *all* particles experience the same acceleration in a given gravitational field: for the field times the passive mass gives the force, and the force divided by the inertial mass gives the acceleration. Hence the path followed by a particle in space and time is entirely independent of the kind of particle chosen. This path unicity in a gravitational field is usually referred to as *Galileo's principle*, by a slight extension of Galileo's actual findings. (Recall his alleged experiments on the Leaning Tower of Pisa!)

The proportionality of inertial and gravitational mass is really a very remarkable fact. It is totally unexplained in Newton's theory, taken as an axiom, and apparently fortuitous. Newton's theory would work perfectly well without it: it would then resemble a theory of motion of electrically charged particles under an attractive Coulomb law, where particles of the same (inertial) *mass* can carry different *charges*. GR, on the other hand, relies on Galileo's principle as a primary ingredient, and could not do without it. That is why the concept of passive gravitational mass does not arise in GR.

It may be noted that Mach's principle goes some way towards explaining the *identity* of inertial and passive gravitational mass. Consider, for example, the situation illustrated in Figure 2(ii), where at the moon's location the rotating universe provides an inductive field f to counteract the attraction of the earth. Now it is conceivable that induction acts on one kind of "charge," namely inertial mass, and attraction on another, namely gravitational mass. But it is far more natural, once both kinds of mass are recognized as "charge," to think of them as identical. In Figure 2(ii) the universe and the earth then simply combine to produce a zero field at the moon's location, in which *every* particle would remain at rest.

19   *The Equivalence Principle*

In conjunction with Newton's three laws, the "weak" equivalence principle discussed in the last section both implies, and is implied by, another "relativity" embodied in Newton's theory, different from the one discussed in Section 5, *but one which also invites generalization to the whole of physics.* It is this: Consider an elevator cabin which is severed from its supporting cable and allowed to fall freely down a long shaft under the earth's gravitational pull; Newton's theory predicts that mechanics will take *precisely* the same course in this freely falling "laboratory" as in a laboratory that is unaccelerated and far away from all attracting masses, i.e., at rest in a strict inertial frame.

It is easy to see why: For a particle being pushed around arbitrarily, let $\mathbf{f}$ and $\mathbf{f}_G$ be the total and the gravitational force, respectively, relative to the earth (here treated as a Newtonian inertial frame), and m_I and m_G the inertial and gravitational mass. Then $\mathbf{f} = m_I\mathbf{a}$ and $\mathbf{f}_G = m_G\mathbf{g}$, where $\mathbf{a}$ is the acceleration of the particle and $\mathbf{g}$ the acceleration due to the gravitational field. The acceleration of the particle relative to the cabin is $\mathbf{a} - \mathbf{g}$ and thus the force relative to the cabin is $(\mathbf{a} - \mathbf{g})m_I$. This equals the nongravitational force $\mathbf{f} - \mathbf{f}_G$ *if* $m_I = m_G$; hence Newton's second law (including the first) holds in the cabin. And the same is true of the third law.

Einstein, in his EP, assumed once again that the rest of physics goes along with mechanics. He postulated that "all local, freely falling, nonrotating laboratories are fully

equivalent for the performance of all physical experiments."
(The test for nonrotation can be any one of the obvious
mechanical ones, e.g., the walls of the laboratory must be
unstressed during the free fall, or, if made of loosely laid
bricks, they must not come apart.) Justification for the EP
is discussed in Section 20. According to Einstein, then, a
freely falling laboratory, even near a strongly gravitating
mass, is *fully* equivalent to a laboratory floating motion-
lessly relative to the fixed stars out in space. Each such
freely falling, nonrotating laboratory constitutes a *local
inertial frame* (LIF). All LIF's at the same event are necessarily in uniform relative motion, but LIF's far apart may
mutually accelerate. Thus Einstein, by a somewhat different
line of argument, arrived at conclusions similar to those we
reached in Section 17.

The class of uniformly moving LIF's at any event is
clearly the one discussed by SR, which now appears as a
local theory. (In SR one uses different inertial frames to
look at the *same* situation, and thus one never needs widely
separated reference systems.) Before the recognition of the
EP, the RP could only be understood to refer to the infinitely extended Newtonian inertial frames, i.e., to the
frame of the fixed stars and all others in uniform motion
relative to that one. Instinctively one considered only the
parts of these frames in which gravity was essentially absent, i.e., strictly inertial regions in which free particles
really obey Newton's first law. For it is in the inertial
frames that each physical law is supposed to assume maximal simplicity, including, for example, isotropy; and in
regions of the frames in which there is an "overlay of
gravity," as on earth, isotropy could hardly be assumed
a priori even for "nongravitational" physics. (In Section
21 we shall see the justification for this suspicion.) Thus,
strictly speaking, special-relativity physics seemed to apply
in hypothetical interstellar laboratories only. The EP
changed all that. It both widened and narrowed the RP:
it brought many more frames within its scope, but it limited

their extent; it made all regions equally accessible to SR, but it made SR a local theory. In the future when we speak of the RP, we shall implicitly identify it with the EP.

As a consequence of the equivalence principle, not only can we *eliminate* gravity by free fall, we can also *create* it by acceleration. Consider, for example, a rocket sitting on its pad. This should be indistinguishable, as a physics laboratory, from a rocket that just hovers over its pad. The latter, in turn, should be indistinguishable from any other rocket that moves with acceleration *g* through its LIF, e.g., one in outer space, since all LIF's are equivalent. And this proves our assertion.

Of course, gravity can only be fully eliminated from a rigid laboratory by free fall if the field is parallel. In all other cases the tolerable extent in space *and* time of a LIF depends on the accuracy desired. For example, if an elevator cabin were allowed to fall to the center of the earth, two free particles initially at rest in opposite corners of the floor would gradually approach each other and finally meet at the center. Similarly, two free particles initially at rest in the cabin, one above the other, would gradually separate. Nevertheless, such particle pairs can be treated as being mutually at rest to any desired accuracy *provided* we suitably limit the dimensions of the cabin and the duration of the experiment.

Situations can be imagined where the EP apparently conflicts with Mach's principle. For example, if two identical spheres spin at identical rates in their respective LIF's, one (say, *A*) in tenuous outer space and the other (B) near a heavy mass, should not *B* bulge more, since by Mach's principle its inertia might be expected to be greater? And would not this contradict the EP? There is a way out: time actually runs more slowly near heavy masses (itself a consequence of the EP, as we shall see in Section 70), and thus *A* will *see B* rotate more slowly than itself. But since it sees *B* bulge as much as itself, it concludes that *B* has more inertia. (This argument even tells us by how *much* the inertia increases: since a bulge is proportional to inertia times angular velocity squared, inertia increases by the square of the "time dilation" factor.) Similar arguments can be made in all other cases of apparent conflict.

The RP *denies* the existence of a preferred standard of rest; yet such a standard exists *de facto* everywhere locally in the universe, namely, that which is essentially determined by the local set of galaxies. And although, in accordance with the RP, no known law of physics assumes a special form in that particular frame, logically we could not be surprised if one did (as Bondi has pointed out). And similarly, in a cabin freely hurtling towards the earth, there is obviously a *de facto* preferred direction. Nevertheless, in accordance with the EP, all the known laws of physics appear to be isotropic within the cabin.

The Semi-Strong Equivalence Principle   *20*

Einstein's EP is sometimes called the "strong" EP to distinguish it from its restriction to Newtonian mechanics, known as the "weak" EP. There is also a "semi-strong" (or "local") EP: it asserts the full equivalence of all non-rotating free laboratories *locally*, and this implies a *local* SR everywhere, with its own numerical content. But it envisages the possibility of different numerical contents (speed of light, gravitational "constant," fine structure "constant," etc.) at different regions and times in the universe. The "real" laws whose local approximations are recognized in the various local SR's would presumably involve also the derivatives of these variable "constants." But in this connection it must be said that *every* law of physics could always be generalized and made more complicated while still remaining within all theoretical and observational bounds, and no progress in physics can be made without simplicity assumptions. Complications should therefore not be countenanced except for very good reasons. It is true, however, that all the arguments usually advanced for the EP, *except simplicity*, are in fact arguments only for the semi-strong version:

(a) As for the RP before, one can appeal to the unity of physics, according to which all physics should share the transformation properties of mechanics.

(b) Often cited are the successful experimental checks on two direct predictions made on the basis of the EP (see Section 21).

(c) GR is still the most satisfactory modern theory of gravitation, and GR incorporates the EP. [GR is based on the *strong* EP. As we shall see later, the EP allows GR to be built up from all the local SR's in a certain way—much like a curved surface can be built up, approximately, from a lot of plane elements. But GR can be generalized fairly easily to accommodate the semi-strong EP, if necessary. Such a generalization has been made, for example, by Pascual Jordan, who believes that certain geological facts indicate a secular variation in the "constant" of gravitation.]

It must be said in fairness that the *empirical* evidence for the (strong or semi-strong) EP is very poor. The checks mentioned under (b) above concern two aspects of light propagation, and it can be maintained that what they really test is only the *weak* EP, once we grant the corpuscular nature of light (photons). Nor can the success of GR in reproducing the well-established classical gravitational results be considered specific evidence for the EP, since Newton's theory, of course, does the same without it. Best evidence is provided by the few tested "post-Newtonian" results of GR, but even these can be duplicated by theories denying the EP. The appeal of the EP is thus mainly theoretical. But that is nevertheless so strong that most experts accept it.

21   Consequences of the Equivalence Principle

The two above-mentioned predictions of the EP, even in its local version, are these: First, the EP implies that light bends in a gravitational field, much as though it were made up of particles traveling at speed c. For consider a freely falling cabin, say in an elevator shaft on earth. Consider a flash of light emitted in the cabin at right angles to its motion. By the EP this flash travels along a straight line inside the cabin, but since the latter accelerates while the flash travels uniformly, the light path must in fact be curved parabolically relative to the earth, just like the path of a projectile. This is really a very remarkable argument, since from the mere fact that light travels at finite speed one deduces that "light has weight." Actually, Einstein's ultimate interpretation was not so much that this is a new property of light, but rather a new property of space in the presence of mass, namely curvature.

Secondly, the EP implies that light traveling down a gravitational field suffers a blueshift. For consider now a vertical ray of light entering the cabin's ceiling at the moment when the cabin is dropped. By the EP, an observer A on the cabin's floor, observing the ray just as he passes a stationary observer B outside, observes no Doppler shift between ceiling and floor. But by the time A observes the ray, the cabin is already moving, and, relative to A, B moves *into* the light waves. Since A sees no Doppler shift, B, observing the same light, must see a blueshift. This proves our assertion. Conversely, light traveling *against* a gravitational field suffers a redshift. (The same result can be obtained from the photon theory by appeal to Planck's relation—cf. Section 69.)

The gravitational Doppler shift has actually been observed by Pound and Rebka (1960), and with improved accuracy by Pound and Snider (1964), in highly sensitive experiments which involved sending light down a 70-foot tower at Harvard. It had previously been observed astronomically in the light from a very dense star, following a suggestion of Einstein. The gravitational bending of light has not yet been observed on earth, and astronomically it is somewhat complicated by the need to "patch" many LIF's carefully together (for which the GR field equations are needed). But it is also regarded as verified, by observations of the apparent position of stars near the sun during a total eclipse of the latter.

These results show not only the predictive strength of the EP, but also the danger in regarding gravitational regions of *Newtonian* inertial frames as strictly inertial (e.g., isotropic, homogeneous) for "nongravitational" phenomena. They reinforce our conviction that gravity cannot be divorced from the rest of physics—as we have already found reason to suspect in (d) of Section 16.

2

Einsteinian
Kinematics

In this chapter we begin to develop the consequences of Einstein's "first postulate," the relativity principle (RP)— a principle of venerable standing in mechanics, now newly extended to all of physics. Einstein chose to ignite it with a spark from electromagnetic theory: his "second postulate," according to which light travels rectilinearly with constant speed c in vacuum in every inertial frame. After the blaze, the old relativity principle showed its new mathematical core: the Lorentz transformation (LT). Previously "common sense" had shown that the core "must" be the Galilean transformation (GT).

For if we assume perfect symmetry between inertial frames in accordance with the RP, and tacitly accept *Newton's* "second postulate" of an absolute time covering all inertial frames, then inevitably we find the GT as that transformation which relates *actually measured* Cartesian coordinates in two different inertial frames. But if, instead, we insist against all "common sense" on accommodating Einstein's law of light propagation in all inertial frames, then inevitably the LT must relate the coordinates. It is of course evident that this law of light propagation cannot be reconciled with the GT: for that implies the classical velocity addition law according to which a light signal traveling with velocity c in a frame S has anything *but* the same velocity in a second frame moving collinearly with the signal relative to S.

Theoretically, Einstein's second postulate can be regarded as a corollary of extending Maxwell's equations to all inertial frames. Such extension is strongly suggested by the Michelson-Morley and similar experiments, in conjunction with the usual evidence for Maxwell's theory in our own frame. Apart from Maxwell's theory, the second postulate is reducible to the finiteness of the velocity of light and its independence of the velocity of the source; for its invariant speed then follows from the RP (light from *stationary* sources must have the same velocity in all frames) and its rectilinear propagation from isotropy. The finiteness of its velocity was already established by Roemer in 1675. The source-independence of that velocity was apparently established by de Sitter's analysis of double star systems (1913), but that particular argument has lately been challenged by Fox (1962) who believes that double stars may be enveloped in gas clouds which would re-emit their light anyway with equal velocity (by Ewald and Oseen's "extinction theorem"). Direct laboratory evidence against Ritz's hypothesis (source-dependence of the velocity of light) had to wait until 1964—see Section 38.

The physics based on Einstein's two postulates is called special relativity (SR). The second postulate, however, has served its purpose as soon as the LT's are derived. The first postulate can then be re-expressed mathematically: for a physical law to be valid in *all* inertial frames, its formal mathematical statement in *one* inertial frame must transform into itself under a LT. Hence, according to the first postulate, the new laws must be "Lorentz-invariant." SR, then, is Lorentz-invariant physics. Newton's mechanics, for example, is Galileo-invariant but not Lorentz-invariant, and thus it is inconsistent with SR. It is the task of SR to review *all* existing laws of physics, and to subject them to the test of the RP with the help of the LT's. Any law found to be lacking must be modified accordingly. These modifications, though highly significant in many modern applications, are negligible in most classical circumstances, which explains why they were not discovered earlier.

We shall show at the end of this chapter that the RP by itself (together with certain "reasonable" assumptions) is consistent with only two possible transformations and no others: the GT and the LT. Hence one can replace Einstein's second postulate by *any* phenomenon—and today we know many—which is peculiar to SR, i.e., consistent with the RP but not with the GT. The resulting theory, in every case, must be SR.

Apart from leading to new laws, SR leads to a useful technique of problem solving, namely the possibility of switching inertial reference frames. This often simplifies the problem; for although the laws are the same, the configuration of the problem may be simpler, its symmetry enhanced, its unknowns fewer, etc., in a judiciously chosen inertial frame.

If we accept the equivalence principle, then SR is necessarily a local and approximate theory, since it makes statements about classes of strict inertial frames, and since these are necessarily local and approximate. We must insist on *strict* inertial frames, since we wish to assume perfect isotropy and homogeneity for such frames. For example, we wish to make such assumptions as that light travels rectilinearly in all directions, or that a source moving at given velocity shows the same Doppler shift no matter in what direction it recedes from us. As we have seen in Section 21, these would not be safe assumptions in an extended Newtonian inertial frame. It is in the strict inertial frames—and the EP tells us how to find them in practice—that we assume the laws of physics to hold in their simplest form. These laws are idealizations of those observed to hold in our terrestrial laboratories, which of course are *not* strictly inertial.

The reader may now ask: if Newton's theory is incompatible with SR, and SR is concerned with inertial frames, and inertial frames are defined by Newton's first law, is there not something wrong somewhere? The answer is no: Newton's *first* law *is* compatible with SR, and is in fact accepted by SR. Nevertheless, as an economy, Newton's first law can be replaced by the law of light propagation in singling out the inertial frames among all other rigid frames.

23   *On the Nature of Physical Laws*

This may be a convenient point at which to make a comment on the "truth" of physical laws. According to modern thought, even the best of physical laws do not assert an absolute truth, but rather an approximation to the truth. A physical theory, being an amalgam of invention, definitions, and laws, is regarded as a *model* for a certain part of nature, asserting not so much what nature *is*, but rather what it *is like*. Agreement with experiment is the most obvious requirement on the truth of such a theory. However, no amount of experimental agreement can ever "prove" a theory, partly because no experiment (unless it involves counting only) can ever be infinitely accurate, and partly because we can evidently not test all relevant instances. Experimental disagreement, on the other hand, does not necessarily lead to the rejection of a physical theory, unless an equally simple one can be found to replace it. Such disagreement may simply lead to a narrowing of the known "domain of sufficient validity" of the model. We need only think of Newton's laws of particle mechanics, which today are known to fail in the case of very fast moving particles, or Newton's gravitational theory, which today is known to fail in the finer details of planetary orbit theory. The "truer" relativistic laws are also mathematically more complicated, and so Newton's laws continue to be used whenever their known accuracy suffices.

Although SR is today one of the most firmly established branches of physics, spectacularly verified in literally millions of experiments, it is well to keep an open mind even here. To orders of accuracy so far unattained or unimagined, some law of SR may one day be found to fail— for example, along the lines mentioned at the end of Section 19. We shall not go wrong if we remember that every theory is only a model, with perhaps four prime desiderata: simplicity, internal consistency, compatibility with other scientific concepts of the day, and good experimental "fit." There is also a secondary desideratum, stressed by Popper and Bondi, and that is the possibility of experimental disproof. Theories should not stagnate in complacency: the better a theory, the more forecasts it will make by which it can be disproved.

An Archetypal Relativistic Argument   24

With the following brief example we shall try to illustrate the flavor and the power of many of the relativistic arguments to follow. To make it simple and transparent, we consider a Newtonian example; an Einsteinian version of the same problem will be given later. (See Section 55.) We wish to prove the result, familiar to billiard players, that if a stationary and perfectly elastic sphere is struck by another similar one, then the diverging paths of the two spheres after collision will subtend a right angle. If the incident sphere travels at velocity $2\mathbf{v}$, say, relative to the table, let us transfer ourselves to an inertial frame traveling in the same direction with velocity $\mathbf{v}$. In this frame the two spheres approach each other symmetrically with velocities $\pm\mathbf{v}$ (see Figure 4(i)), and the result of the collision is clear: by momentum conservation, or simply by symmetry, the rebound velocities must be equal and opposite (±**u,** say), and by energy conservation they must be numerically equal to **v** (i.e., $u = v$). With this information, we can revert to the frame of the table, by

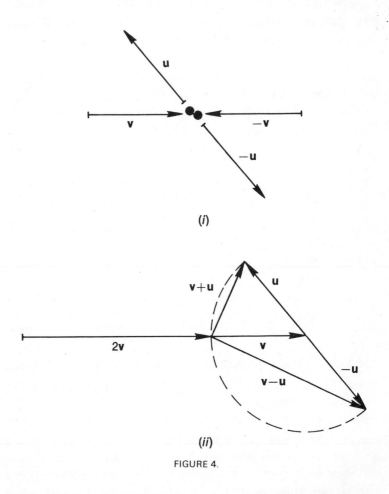

(*i*)

(*ii*)

FIGURE 4.

adding **v** to all the velocities in Figure 4(i), thus arriving at Figure 4(ii). Here the rebound velocities are evidently **v** ± **u,** and the simple expedient of drawing a semicircle centered at the tip of the arrow representing **v** makes the desired result self-evident, by elementary geometry.

It was Einstein's recognition of the fact that arguments of a similar nature were apparently possible also in electromagnetism that significantly influenced his progress towards SR. We have already quoted (in Section 12) the beginning of his 1905 paper, where he discusses the apparent relativity of electromagnetic induction. As late as 1952 (in a letter to a scientific congress), we find him writing: "What led me more or less directly to the special theory of relativity was the conviction that the electromagnetic force acting on a [charged] body in motion in a magnetic field was nothing else but an electric field [in the body's rest frame]."

The Relativity of Simultaneity   *25*

An immediate consequence of the adoption of the *two* postulates of SR is that simultaneity can no longer be absolute. It took a genius like Einstein to face this consequence with equanimity and to realize that our classical and deep-seated concept of absolute time was dispensable.

We shall here adopt the following practical definition of simultaneity: two events $\mathcal{P}$ and $\mathcal{Q}$ occurring at points P and Q of an inertial frame S are simultaneous in S if and only if light emitted at $\mathcal{P}$ and $\mathcal{Q}$ arrives simultaneously at the midpoint M of the segment PQ in S. This definition is implied by the law of light propagation and it avoids all mention of clocks, which at this stage would be an unnecessary complication. Now suppose the above situation obtains, and $\mathcal{P}$ and $\mathcal{Q}$ are simultaneous in S. Let S' be a second inertial frame moving in the direction PQ, let P' and Q' be the fixed points in S' at which $\mathcal{P}$ and $\mathcal{Q}$ occur, and let M' be the midpoint of $P'Q'$ in S'. Figures 5(i) and (ii) are "snapshots" made in S, showing the relative configurations of the various points (i) when the events $\mathcal{P}$ and $\mathcal{Q}$ occur, and (ii) when the light signals emitted at those events meet at M. (For convenience, these snapshots are "dissected": in reality all marked points are collinear.) Now inevitably,

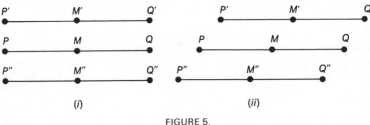

FIGURE 5.

due to the finite speed of light, S' has moved relative to S between (i) and (ii), and the two light signals do *not* meet at M' but to the left of it. With sound signals in an atmosphere at rest relative to S, this result would surprise no one: S is in a privileged position relative to the atmosphere, and in S alone can one use this method for testing synchrony; an observer in S', in which a "wind" blows, would not dream of using sound signals for synchrony. With light, however, the situation is different: no "ether wind" blows in *any* frame. To *all* inertial observers light behaves isotropically, having speed c in all directions. Hence, from the above experiment, an observer in S' has every right to conclude that $\mathcal{Q}$ happened *before* $\mathcal{P}$, since the signals meet closer to P' than to Q'. Similarly, in a frame S'' moving oppositely relative to S, $\mathcal{Q}$ happened *after* $\mathcal{P}$ at some points Q'' and P''. And no one frame can claim authority over the others: within each, each is the ultimate authority. Thus, simultaneity is relative. (And so is the sequence before–after, at least for certain pairs of events.)

This argument immediately invalidates the Galilean time transformation, $t' = t$. But, in fact, the Galilean space transformations are tainted by the same argument. For if $\mathcal{Q}$ happens before $\mathcal{P}$ in S', then the right-hand ends of the two line segments $P'Q'$ and $P''Q''$ meet before the left-hand ends; and thus, relative to S', $P''Q''$ is considered shorter than $P'Q'$. Relative to S'', of course, the opposite is true. Thus, longitudinally moving line segments apparently contract. The present argument also implies that moving clocks go slow. For suppose a clock fixed at P' is compared with the (mutually synchronized) clocks at P'' and Q'' as it passes them. In S'' the elapsed time is

$$\frac{P''Q''}{(\text{velocity of } S' \text{ relative to } S'')}.$$

In S' the elapsed time must be *less*, since the distance covered by P' is considered to be less, but the relative velocity is considered to be the same (by symmetry). Hence the clock at P' must indicate a lesser elapsed time, i.e., it will "go slow" relative to S''.

The Coordinate Lattice 26

Before we actually consider *transformations* of coordinates, it will be well to clarify how coordinates are measured in a single inertial frame. The most obvious way, of course, would be to make distance measurements with rigid scales. But rigid scales are of ill repute in relativity: justly, perhaps, because from the atomic viewpoint they are complicated structures and it may seem more fundamental and even more practical to use clocks (atoms) and light signals (photons) instead. Yet it must be remembered that without the existence of *some* rigid standard of length the constancy of the speed of light would become a mere convention. Another, less cogent, objection often made to the use of rigid scales is that, when accelerated in certain ways, they cannot *remain* rigid, according to relativistic kinematics; but it is perfectly logical to assume that when the acceleration ceases such scales return to their original shape, and if so, their use as distance indicators in inertial frames is above suspicion.

Be this as it may, we shall assume that the observer at the origin of an inertial frame possesses a standard clock, and that he measures the distance to any particle by bouncing a light signal off it and multiplying the elapsed time by $\frac{1}{2}c$. Angle measurements with a theodolite will then furnish the relevant (x, y, z). We may place free test particles at rest at all the "lattice points" ($\pm m$, $\pm n$, $\pm p$), m, n and p being integers, which may be made arbitrarily close by a suitable choice of units. These particles will *remain* at rest, since, by supposition, we are in a *strict* inertial frame. They may conveniently be thought to carry standard clocks, all replicas of the master clock at the origin. These clocks can be synchronized by a single light signal emitted at the origin at time t_0: when this signal is received at any lattice clock, that clock is set to read $t_0 + r/c$, r being its predetermined distance from the origin. On the *classical* theory it is clear that this process would satisfactorily synchronize all the clocks in the "ether frame" so that any two clocks indicate the same time at simultaneous events, according to the definition of simultaneity of the last section. But none of the relevant classical laws is affected by relativity, except that *each* inertial frame is now as good as the ether frame. Hence the process is a valid one for clock synchronization in any inertial frame. Once this is achieved, i.e., once the "lattice" is set up and is spatially and temporally calibrated, we can discard theodolites and light signals: the coordinates of all events can now be read off locally—i.e., directly where the events occur—by suitable auxiliary observers. Of course, any two lattice clocks could also be permanently connected with a rigid scale, if such scales are contemplated.

It is well to realize that other "signals," e.g., cannon balls, can be used *just* as well as light signals to calibrate and synchronize the coordinate lattice (although they could not be used, any more than can sound signals, to clinch the argument summarized in Figure 5). One need merely require that the observer at the origin shoot standard projectiles from standard guns in all directions at time t_0, say. The speed u of the projectiles may be taken to be an arbitrary number, whereby one merely fixes the unit of distance. (Alternatively, the muzzle velocity can be measured at the origin, or even calculated theoretically.) Angle measurements are to be made of the direction of the gun barrels.

When a projectile from the origin passes an auxiliary observer, he is to shoot back a similar one from a similar gun. If that gets to the origin at time t, the auxiliary observer was at distance $\frac{1}{2}u(t - t_0)$ and his clock should have read $\frac{1}{2}(t + t_0)$ when he received the "control signal." All this, of course, presupposes Newton's first law.

The Lorentz Transformation   27

Now consider two *arbitrary* inertial frames S and S' in which Cartesian coordinate lattices have been set up. We wish to find the relation between the S-coordinates (x, y, z, t) and the S'-coordinates (x', y', z', t') corresponding to an arbitrary event. First, this relation must be linear— as is, for example, the GT. This follows most directly (though not trivially) from the definition of inertial frames: only under a linear transformation can the linear equations of motion of free particles in S go over into linear equations of motion also in S'. Actually, this requirement by itself only implies that the transformations are necessarily projective, i.e., that the S'-coordinates are ratios of linear functions of the S-coordinates, all with the same denominator. However, if we reject, for physical reasons, the existence of finite events in S which have infinite coordinates in S', then the denominator must be constant, and thus the transformation linear.* Because of this linearity, in particular, any fixed values of x', y', z' imply unique constant values of $dx/dt, dy/dt, dz/dt$. Thus each inertial frame is in uniform translatory motion relative to every other.

Linearity also implies that the axes of S' remain parallel to themselves relative to S, and that, as in the classical theory, one can choose the coordinates in S and S' in the

---

*Another argument for linearity can be made from the constancy of the speed of light—see RSR, page 17—and yet another from the "homogeneity of space and time," together with the uniform motion of one inertial frame relative to another, if that has been independently established—see RSR, page 21.

"standard configuration" described in Section 3. (This is really obvious, but see, for example, RSR, page 17.) Assume this done. Then the coordinate planes $y = 0$ and $y' = 0$ coincide permanently. Thus $y = 0$ must imply $y' = 0$, whence we can set

$$y' = Ay, \qquad (27.1)$$

where A is a constant (linearity!) possibly depending on v, the velocity of S' relative to S. By reversing the directions of the x and z axes in both S and S', we can reverse the roles of S and S' (presupposing isotropy), without affecting (27.1). But then, by symmetry, we also have

$$y = Ay',$$

whence $A = \pm 1$. The negative value can at once be dismissed, since $v \to 0$ must lead to $y \sim y'$ continuously. The argument for z is similar, and so we arrive at

$$y' = y, \quad z' = z, \qquad (27.2)$$

the two "trivial" members of the transformation.

Next we evidently must have

$$x' = \gamma(x - vt), \qquad (27.3)$$

where γ is a constant (again possibly depending on v), since $x = vt$ must imply $x' = 0$. Similarly,

$$x = \gamma'(x' + vt'), \qquad (27.4)$$

γ' being another such constant. Let us again reverse the directions of the x and z axes in S and S'. Then, replacing x and x' by their negatives in (27.3), we have

$$x' = \gamma(x + vt).$$

But also, by the reversal of roles, we find from (27.4) that

$$x' = \gamma'(x + vt),$$

whence

$$\gamma = \gamma'. \qquad (27.5)$$

Evidently γ must be positive, since, by supposition, the x axes of S and S' coincide, together with their directions.

Now, by the "second postulate" (constancy of the speed of light), we know that $x = ct$ must imply $x' = ct'$, and vice versa. Substituting these expressions in (27.3) and (27.4) and using (27.5), we get

$$ct' = \gamma t(c - v), \quad ct = \gamma t'(c + v).$$

Multiplying these equations together, and canceling tt', yields

$$\gamma = \gamma(v) = \frac{1}{(1 - v^2/c^2)^{1/2}}. \qquad (27.6)$$

(As we have seen above, we need the *positive* root here.) This particular function of v is the famous "Lorentz factor" which plays an important role in the theory. Eliminating x' between (27.3) and (27.4), we now finally obtain

$$t' = \gamma(t - vx/c^2).$$

Thus, collecting our results, we have found the *standard* Lorentz transformation equations

$$x' = \gamma(x - vt), \quad y' = y, \quad z' = z, \quad t' = \gamma(t - vx/c^2). \qquad (27.7)$$

If a law of physics is invariant under these transformations, *and* under spatial rotations, spatial translations, and time translations, then it is invariant between *any* two inertial coordinate systems. For it is easily seen that the general transformation between two inertial frames, whose coordinates are standard but not mutually in standard configuration, consists of the following: (1) a space rotation and translation (to make the x axis of S coincide with the line of motion of the S' origin); (2) a time translation (to make the origins coincide at $t = 0$); (3) a standard LT; and finally, two more transformations of type (1) and (2) to arrive at the coordinates of S'. The resultant transformation is called a *general* LT, or a *Poincaré transformation*. Since each link in this chain of transformations is linear, so is the resultant.

Properties of the Lorentz Transformation   28

We proceed to list some of the more important properties of the standard LT:

(i) Direct algebraic solution of (27.7) for x, y, z, t gives

$$x = \gamma(x' + vt'), \quad y = y', \quad z = z', \quad t = \gamma(t' + vx'/c^2),$$
$$(28.1)$$

and thus the inverse of (27.7) is a LT with parameter $-v$ instead of v, as indeed one would expect from symmetry considerations. The resultant of two LT's, with parameters v_1 and v_2, respectively, is also found to be of type (27.7), with parameter $v = (v_1 + v_2)/(1 + v_1 v_2/c^2)$. (The direct verification of this is a little tedious, but an easy way of seeing it will be given in Section 29.) These two facts imply that the LT's constitute, technically speaking, a "group." As a consequence of them, all coordinate systems related to a given system by LT's are also related to each other by LT's. It is this property of the transformations he discovered that should perhaps have made Lorentz doubt the preeminence of the ether frame. In SR, of course, the group property is vital for the self-consistency of the theory. It can be shown that the general LT's defined at the end of the last section also constitute a group.

(ii) If Δx, Δy, etc., denote the finite coordinate differences $x_2 - x_1, y_2 - y_1$, etc., corresponding to two events E_1 and E_2, then by substituting the coordinates of E_1 and E_2 successively into (27.7), and subtracting, we get the first of the following transformations,

$$\Delta x' = \gamma(\Delta x - v\Delta t), \quad \Delta y' = \Delta y, \quad \Delta z' = \Delta z,$$
$$\Delta t' = \gamma(\Delta t - v\Delta x/c^2); \quad (28.2)$$

$$\Delta x = \gamma(\Delta x' + v\Delta t'), \quad \Delta y = \Delta y', \quad \Delta z = \Delta z',$$
$$\Delta t = \gamma(\Delta t' + v\Delta x'/c^2). \quad (28.3)$$

The second follows similarly from (28.1), or simply by symmetry. If, instead of forming differences, we take differentials in (27.7) and (28.1), we obtain equations identical with the above but in the differentials. Thus the finite coordinate differences, as well as the differentials, satisfy the same transformation equations as the coordinates themselves, as is the case, of course, in all linear homogeneous transformations.

(iii) For $v \neq 0$ the Lorentz factor γ is always greater than unity, though not much so when v is small. For example, as long as $v/c < 1/7$ (at which speed the earth is circled in one second), γ is less than 1.01; when $v/c = \sqrt{3}/2 = .866$, $\gamma = 2$; and when $v/c = .99 \ldots 995$ (2n nines), γ is approximately 10^n. Thus, as comparison of (27.7) with (3.1) shows, the GT approximates well to the LT when v is small. Alternatively, if we formally let $c \rightarrow \infty$, the LT goes over into the GT.

(iv) The appearance of the space coordinate x in the transformation of the time is the mathematical expression of the relativity of simultaneity. It implies that two events with the same t do not necessarily have the same t'.

It has been pointed out by M. v. Laue that a cylinder rotating uniformly about the x' axis in the frame S' will seem *twisted* when observed in the usual second frame S, in which it not only rotates but also travels forward. This can be seen in many ways, but in particular as a simple illustration of the relativity of simultaneity. Think of the cylinder as made up of a lot of circular slices, each slice by its rotation serving as a clock. All these clocks are synchronized in S' by having arbitrary but parallel radii designated as clock "hands." In S the clocks are *not* synchronous, hence the hands are not parallel, hence the cylinder is twisted! (If the angular speed of the cylinder in S' is ω, we find from equation (27.7) (iv), on putting $t = 0$ and $x = 1$, that in S the twist per unit length is $\gamma\omega v/c^2$.)

(v) *Any* effect whose speed in vacuum is finite and invariant could have been used to derive the LT's, as light was used above. Since only *one* transformation can be valid, it follows that all such effects must propagate at the speed of light. In particular, in contrast to their various speeds in translucent media, electromagnetic waves of all frequencies must travel at exactly speed c in vacuum.

(vi) When $v = c$, γ becomes infinite, and $v > c$ leads to imaginary values of γ. This shows that the relative velocity between two inertial frames cannot exceed the speed of light, since real coordinates in one frame must correspond to real coordinates in any other frame.

Indeed, we can show that the speed of particles, and more generally, of all physical "communication," is limited by c, *if* we insist on the invariance of causality. For consider any process whatever, whereby an event $\mathcal{P}$ causes an event $\mathcal{Q}$ (or, whereby information is sent from $\mathcal{P}$ to $\mathcal{Q}$) at a "superlight" speed $U > c$ relative to some frame S. Choose coordinates in S so that these events both occur on the x axis, and let their time and distance separations be $\Delta t > 0$ and $\Delta x > 0$. Then in the usual second frame S', we have, from (28.2),

$$\Delta t' = \gamma\left(\Delta t - \frac{v \Delta x}{c^2}\right) = \gamma \Delta t\left(1 - \frac{v U}{c^2}\right). \qquad (28.4)$$

For sufficiently great $v < c$, we would then have $\Delta t' < 0$. Hence there would exist inertial frames in which $\mathcal{Q}$ precedes $\mathcal{P}$, i.e., in which cause and effect are reversed, or in which information flows from receiver to transmitter.

Among other embarassments, this would allow us to know our future. For if a signal can be sent from a point P to a point Q (in a frame S') so as to reach Q *before* it left P, then, by symmetry, the signal can be returned at once from Q to P, reaching P before it left Q, and consequently before the original signal left P. A man at P can therefore have foreknowledge of events at himself, and could deliberately foil them, which leads to grave contradictions. On the other hand, superlight signals that carry *no* information (e.g., the sweep of a searchlight spot on high clouds) are possible and harmless. (See Section 30.) Also possible are mutual particle or signal velocities up to $2c$ in any frame. For example, the mutual velocity of two photons traveling in opposite directions along a common line is precisely $2c$. (See also exercise 2-16.)

We may note, finally, that the speed limit c *does* guarantee invariance of causality. For if two events happen on a line making an angle θ with the x axis in S (thus not restricting their generality relative to S and S'), and are connectible in S by a signal with speed $u \leq c$, we see on replacing U by

$u \cos \theta$ in (28.4), that for all v between $\pm c$, Δt and $\Delta t'$ have the same sign.

Alternative Form of the Lorentz Transformation   29

For certain purposes, it is convenient to cast the LT (27.7) into the following form:

$$x' = x \cosh \phi - ct \sinh \phi, \quad y' = y, \quad z' = z,$$
$$ct' = -x \sinh \phi + ct \cosh \phi, \qquad (29.1)$$

where

$$\tanh \phi = v/c. \qquad (29.2)$$

This immediately yields the important identity (obtainable also directly from (27.7))

$$c^2 t'^2 - x'^2 - y'^2 - z'^2 = c^2 t^2 - x^2 - y^2 - z^2, \qquad (29.3)$$

or, more generally,

$$\Delta s^2 = c^2 \Delta t'^2 - \Delta x'^2 - \Delta y'^2 - \Delta z'^2$$
$$= c^2 \Delta t^2 - \Delta x^2 - \Delta y^2 - \Delta z^2, \qquad (29.4)$$

where again $\Delta t'$, etc., stand for the finite coordinate differences $t_2' - t_1'$, etc., corresponding to two arbitrary events E_1 and E_2, and Δs^2 is *defined* by (29.4). It is called the squared *interval* between the events E_1 and E_2, and may be positive, zero, or negative.

In particular, (29.4) shows that *any* signal traveling at speed c in S transforms into a similar signal in S', and vice versa, since the characteristic of such a signal is the vanishing of either of the quadratic forms in (29.4). It is important to have checked this, since it is required by the second postulate, and since in order to obtain the LT, we needed to assume it only for signals in the x direction.

By adding and subtracting the x, t equations in (29.1), we obtain yet another useful form of the LT:

$$x' + ct' = e^{-\phi}(x + ct), \quad y' = y, \quad z' = z$$
$$x' - ct' = e^{\phi}(x - ct), \qquad (29.5)$$

where

$$e^{2\phi} = (1 + v/c)/(1 - v/c). \tag{29.6}$$

This form of the equations makes it algebraically obvious that the inverse of a LT is a LT, and that the resultant of two LT's is another LT. Evidently, if the "hyperbolic" parameter of the first LT is ϕ_1, and that of the second is ϕ_2, that of the resultant is $\phi_1 + \phi_2$. The corresponding relation between the "velocity" parameters of these transformations then follows at once from (29.2), if we recall the identity $\tanh(\phi_1 + \phi_2) = (\tanh \phi_1 + \tanh \phi_2)/(1 + \tanh \phi_1 \tanh \phi_2)$:

$$v = (v_1 + v_2)/(1 + v_1 v_2/c^2). \tag{29.7}$$

This, of course, must be the velocity at which the third frame moves relative to the first, and thus it represents the "relativistic sum" of the (collinear) velocities v_1 and v_2.

This may be as good a moment as any to make a remark of very general usefulness. In working a SR problem or calculation, especially for the first time, one can always omit the c's, i.e. one can work in units in which $c = 1$. The c's can easily be inserted later, either throughout the work or in the answer only, by simple dimensional arguments. E.g., had we worked towards (29.7) without the c's, it would be quite obvious where to put a c^2, since by use of c alone the dimensions must be made to balance.

30   *Graphical Representation of the Lorentz Transformation*

What chiefly distinguishes the LT (27.7) (or (29.1)) from the GT is the fact that space and time coordinates *both* transform; indeed, they transform quite similarly, as becomes especially obvious if we choose units in which $c = 1$, as we now shall. The x and t coordinates "get mixed," rather like the x and y coordinates do when we apply a rotation of axes in the Cartesian x, y plane. The standard LT can in fact be regarded as a "pseudo-rotation" in the x, t plane (preserving the value of $t^2 - x^2$ instead of $t^2 + x^2$). Figure 6

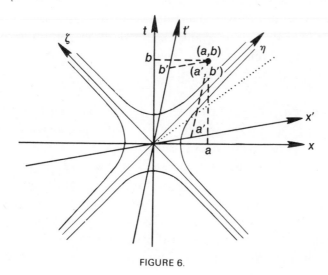

FIGURE 6.

illustrates this. The x, t system is somewhat favored in being assigned orthogonal axes, but this has no intrinsic significance. By (27.7), the t' axis ($x' = 0$) has equation $x = vt$, and the x' axis ($t' = 0$) has equation $t = vx$; i.e., they subtend equal angles $\tan^{-1} v$ with the t and x axes, respectively. For calibrating the primed axes, it is convenient to draw the hyperbolae $t^2 - x^2 = \pm 1$, since they coincide with $t'^2 - x'^2 = \pm 1$. Hence they cut all the axes at the corresponding unit time or unit distance from the origin. The diagram shows how to read off the coordinates (a, b), (a', b') of a given event with respect to either frame. Incidentally, observe from (29.5) that a LT corresponds to a stretching and shrinking, respectively, of the $\pm 45°$ axes of $\eta = (t + x)/\sqrt{2}$ and $\zeta = (t - x)/\sqrt{2}$, by a factor e^ϕ.

Such "Minkowski diagrams" can be extremely helpful and illuminating in certain types of relativistic problems. For example, one can often use them to get a rough preliminary idea of the answer. But one should beware of trying to use them for *everything*, for their utility is limited. Analytic or algebraic arguments are generally much more powerful.

As a simple example on the use of the diagram, we shall

look at a noninformative superlight signal such as may occur in reality. For example, if a slanting guillotine blade falls past a level block, the intersection point of blade and block travels at an arbitrarily large speed if the slant is small enough; or, a searchlight spot can be made to travel over high clouds at arbitrarily large speeds by simply rotating the searchlight fast enough. In Figure 6, such a signal along the (material) x axis of S is shown as a dotted line, deliberately, to suggest that it be considered as a sequence of events rather than as a moving object. Since the x' and t' axes may cut at any angle between 0° and 180°, there is a frame S' in which the signal has infinite velocity (i.e. coincides with the x' axis in the diagram) and others in which it moves in the opposite spatial direction. If the signal were informative, it would have to be regarded in this latter case as traveling with unchanged spatial sense into the past. The interested reader may wish to figure out (though not from the diagram) why in S' the signals can travel backwards (with superlight speed) whereas the guillotine blade still drops *down* and the searchlight is still rotated *forwards*. (See exercise 2–21.)

31   *World-Picture and World-Map*

In relativity, it is important to distinguish between what an observer *sees* and what he knows *ex post facto*. What he actually or potentially sees at any one instant is called his *world-picture* at that instant. This is a practically not very important and theoretically quite complicated concept, since what is seen at any one instant is a composite of events that occurred progressively earlier as they occurred further and further away. (Only in cosmology does the world-picture assume importance; there it is our prime datum.) A much more useful concept is the *world-map*. This, as the name implies, may be thought of as a mapping of events into an observer's instantaneous space $t = t_0$: a kind of three-dimensional snapshot exposed everywhere simultaneously. It can be most conveniently thought of as being made by auxiliary observers at the "lattice points" of a given inertial frame—each mapping *his* neighborhood at a predetermined instant $t = t_0$.

When we loosely say "the length of an object in S," or "a snapshot taken in S," or "a moving cylinder seems twisted," etc., we invariably think of the world-map, unless the contrary is stated explicitly. The world-map is generally what matters. These remarks are relevant in the next section, where we show that moving bodies shrink. The shrinkage refers to the world-map. What the eye actually sees is rather different, and not very significant, except that in this case some of the facts of vision are rather amusing, as will be seen in Section 41.

Length Contraction   *32*

Consider two inertial frames S and S' in standard configuration. In S' let a rigid rod of length $\Delta x'$ be placed at rest along the x' axis. We wish to find its length in S, relative to which it moves with velocity v. To measure its length in *any* inertial frame (other than S'), its end-points must be observed simultaneously *in that frame*. Thus, setting $\Delta t = 0$ in (28.2)(i), we have $\Delta x' = \gamma \Delta x$, or, writing for Δx, $\Delta x'$ the less specific symbols L, L_0, respectively,

$$L = \frac{L_0}{\gamma} = \left(1 - \frac{v^2}{c^2}\right)^{1/2} L_0. \qquad (32.1)$$

This shows, quite generally, that *the length of a body in the direction of its motion with uniform velocity v is reduced by a factor* $(1 - v^2/c^2)^{1/2}$.

Evidently the greatest length is ascribed to a uniformly moving body in its *rest frame*, i.e., the frame in which its velocity is *zero*. This length, L_0, is called the *rest length* or *proper length* of the body. On the other hand, measured in a frame in which the body moves with a velocity approaching that of light, its length approaches zero.

The statement following (32.1) happens to be identical with that proposed by Lorentz to explain *ad hoc* the null-results of the ether drift experiments—except that he qualified "uniform velocity v" with the phrase "*relative to the ether.*" According to Lorentz, the mechanism responsible for the contraction was a certain increment in electrical cohesive forces which tightened the atomic structure. In relativity,* on the other hand, the effect is a purely geometric "projection" effect, quite analogous to looking at a *stationary* rod which is not parallel to the plane of the retina. Imparting a uniform velocity in relativity corresponds to making a pseudo-rotation in "spacetime" (see Figure 6). Our eye, though essentially designed to receive two-dimensional impressions, has long been trained to sense, and to make allowance for, a third spatial dimension. We are thus not surprised at the foreshortening of a spatially rotated rod. If the speed of light were small, and significant length contractions could thus arise at "ordinary" speeds, our eyes would also have learned to sense the fourth dimension, namely time. Just as by bringing the eye into a suitable spatial position we can restore the full length of a rotated stationary rod, so by moving the eye along with the moving rod we could undo the relativistic length contraction. The eye would soon learn to look at this effect "geometrically."

By the relativity principle, it is *a priori* evident that if two observers A and B compare yardsticks along their common line of motion, and if A considers B's stick to be shorter than his own, then B considers A's stick to be the shorter. The projection analogy makes this unsurprising: a corresponding situation occurs when two relatively stationary observers hold their yardsticks at the same angle relative to their line of sight. The symmetry of length contraction is particularly well illustrated by the example of Section 25, Figure 5. We have already remarked on how fortuitous

*The following remarks to the end of the present paragraph are intended to be suggestive only, and no very accurate understanding is called for at this stage.

this symmetry must seem on the basis of the Lorentz theory where it can only be discovered by calculation, since the *cause* of length contraction resides in the preferred ether frame.

Length Contraction Paradoxes *33*

The relativistic length contraction is no "illusion": it is real in every way. Though no direct experimental verification has yet been attempted, there is no question that in principle it could be done. Consider the admittedly unrealistic situation of a man carrying horizontally a 20-foot pole and wanting to get it into a 10-foot garage. He will run at speed $v = .866c$ to make $\gamma = 2$, so that his pole contracts to 10 feet. It will be well to insist on having a sufficiently massive block of concrete at the back of the garage, so that there is no question of whether the pole finally stops in the inertial frame of the garage, or vice versa. Thus the man runs with his (now contracted) pole into the garage and a friend quickly closes the door. In principle we do not doubt the feasibility of this experiment, i.e., the reality of length contraction. When the pole stops in the rest frame of the garage, it is, in fact, being "rotated in spacetime" and will tend to assume, if it can, its original length relative to the garage. Thus, if it survived the impact, it must now either bend, or burst the door.

At this point a "paradox" might occur to the reader: what about the symmetry of the phenomenon? Relative to the runner, won't the garage be only 5 feet long? Yes, indeed. Then how can the 20-foot pole get into the 5-foot garage? Very well, let us consider what happens in the rest frame of the pole. The open garage now comes towards the stationary pole. Because of the concrete wall, it keeps on going even after the impact, taking the front end of the pole with it. But the back end of the pole is still at rest: it cannot yet "know" that the front end has been struck, because of the finite speed of propagation of *all* signals. Even if the "signal" (in this case the elastic shock wave) travels along the pole with the speed of light, that signal has 20 feet to travel against the garage front's 15 feet, before reaching the back end of the pole. This race would be a dead heat if v were .75c. But v is .866c! So the pole *more* than just gets in. (It could even get into a garage whose length was as little as 5.4 feet at rest and thus 2.7 feet in motion: the garage front would then have to travel 17.3 feet against the shock wave's 20 feet, requiring speeds in the ratio 17.3 to 20, i.e., .865 to 1 for a dead heat.)

There is one important moral to this story: whatever result we get by correct reasoning in any one frame, must be true; in particular, it must be true when viewed from any other frame. As long as the physical laws we are using are Lorentz-invariant, there *must* be an explanation of the result in every other frame, although it may be quite a different explanation from that in the first frame. Recall Einstein's "hunch" that the force experienced by an electric charge when moving through a magnetic field is equivalent to a simple electric force in the rest frame of the charge.

Consider, as another example, a "rigid" rod of rest length L sliding over a hole of diameter $\frac{1}{2}L$ on a smooth table. When its Lorentz factor is 10, the length of the rod is $\frac{1}{5}$ of the diameter of the hole, and in passing over the hole, it will fall into it under the action of gravity* (at least slightly: enough to be stopped). This *must* be true also in the frame of the rod—in which however, the diameter of the hole is only $\frac{1}{20}L$! The only way in which this can happen is that the front of the "rigid" rod *bends* into the hole. Moreover, even after the front end strikes the far edge of the hole, the back end keeps coming in (not yet "knowing" that the front end has been stopped), as it must, since it does so in the first description.

---

*We are here violating our resolve to work in *strict* inertial frames only! The conscientious reader may replace the force of gravity acting down the hole by a sandblast from the top—the result will be the same. For a full discussion of this paradox, see W. Rindler, *Am. J. Phys.* **29**, 365 (1961).

Indeed, "rigidity" is an impossible requirement in relativity. A rod pushed at one end cannot start to move at the other end at once, since that would allow us to send a "signal" at infinite speed. A body being acted on by various forces at various points simultaneously will yield to *each* force initially as though all the others were absent; for at each point it takes a finite time for the effects of the other forces to arrive. Hence, in relativity, a body has infinitely many degrees of freedom. Again, a body which appears rigid in one inertial frame need not appear rigid in another: the rod falling into the hole may keep its precise shape in the frame of the table (at least, until it hits), while in its own original rest frame it bends. For reasons similar to those preventing the existence of rigid bodies in relativity, incompressible fluids are equally impossible.

Time Dilation 34

Let us again consider two inertial frames S and S' in standard configuration. Let a standard clock be fixed in S' and consider two events at that clock at which it indicates times t_1' and t_2' differing by T_0. We inquire what time interval T is ascribed to these events in S. From (28.3)(iv) we see at once, since $\Delta x' = 0$, that

$$T = \gamma T_0 = \frac{T_0}{(1 - v^2/c^2)^{1/2}}. \qquad (34.1)$$

We can deduce from this quite generally that *a clock moving uniformly with velocity v through an inertial frame S goes slow by a factor* $(1 - v^2/c^2)^{1/2}$ *relative to the stationary clocks in S*. Clearly, then, the fastest rate is ascribed to a clock in its rest frame, and this is called its *proper rate*. On the other hand, the rate of a clock moving with a velocity approaching that of light would be close to zero.

If an *ideal* clock moves *nonuniformly* through an inertial frame, we shall *assume* that acceleration as such has no effect on the rate of the clock, i.e., that its instantaneous rate depends only on its instantaneous speed v according to the above rule. Unfortunately, there is no way of *proving* this. Various effects of acceleration on a clock would be consistent with SR. Our assumption is one of simplicity—or it can be regarded as a definition of an "ideal" clock. We shall call it the *clock hypothesis*. That certain natural clocks (namely, vibrating atoms) very accurately conform to it has been recently demonstrated in the so-called thermal Doppler effect experiments. (See Section 40 below.) It may be noted that for the nonuniform longitudinal motion of an *infinitesimal* rod a similar assumption is usually made, namely that the relation between its length and proper length depends only on its instantaneous velocity v according to formula (32.1). This we shall call the *length hypothesis*.

Time dilation, like length contraction, must *a priori* be symmetric: if one observer considers the clocks of a second observer to run slow, the second must also consider the clocks of the first to run slow. We can see in detail how this is possible by considering a specific example. Suppose that synchronized standard clocks $A, B, C, \ldots$ and $A', B', C', \ldots$ are fixed at certain equal intervals along the x axes of two frames S and S' in standard configuration. An auxiliary observer in a frame S'', relative to which S and S' have equal and opposite velocities, makes "snapshots" of these two sets of clocks at convenient time intervals. In each such snapshot, the clocks of S and S' will, of course, be all seen to indicate different times, since simultaneity is relative. Figure 7* shows three such snapshots. The clocks in the diagram indicate seconds. As can be seen, A' reads 4 seconds ahead of A in (a), only 2 seconds ahead of C in (b), and equal with E in (c). Thus A' loses steadily relative to the clocks in S. Similarly, E loses relative to the clocks in S', and indeed all clocks in the diagram lose at the same

*Taken from W. Rindler, "Special Relativity," Edinburgh and London, Oliver and Boyd, 1966, by permission of the publishers. Note that the roles of the frames S and S'' of Figure 5 are reversed in Figure 7.

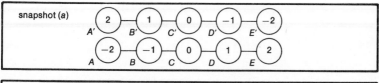

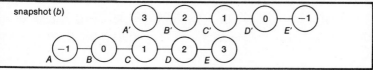

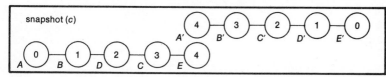

FIGURE 7.

rate relative to the clocks of the other frame. The interested reader can easily work out the relative velocity between S and S' and the spacing of the clocks in the situation illustrated by Figure 7. Only one set of values fits. (See exercise 2-18.)

Time dilation, like length contraction, is *real*. And this *has* been confirmed experimentally. For example, certain mesons (muons) reaching us from the top of the atmosphere in cosmic rays are so short-lived that, even had they traveled with the speed of light, their travel time in the absence of time dilation would exceed their lifetime by factors of the order of 10. That these particles do, nevertheless, reach us intact is due to the fact that their very high velocities "keep them young," as it were (Rossi and Hall, 1941). Equivalent experiments on pi meson decay at rest and in motion in the laboratory have yielded similar results (Durbin, Loar, and Havens, 1952). It may be objected that mesons are not clocks—but the time dilation argument of course applies to *any* temporal change or development.

Another striking instance of time dilation is provided by "relativistic focusing" of electrically charged particles, which plays a role in the operation of high-energy particle accelerators. Any stationary cluster of electrons (or protons) tends to expand at a characteristic rate because of mutual electrostatic repulsion. But electrons in a fast-moving beam are observed to spread at a much slower rate. If we regard the stationary cluster as a kind of clock, we have here an almost visible manifestation of the slowing down of a moving clock. Yet another such manifestation, the so-called transverse Doppler effect, is discussed in Section 40.

35   The Twin Paradox

Like length contraction, so also time dilation can lead to an apparent paradox when viewed by two different observers. In fact this paradox, the so-called twin or clock paradox, is the oldest of all the relativistic paradoxes. It is quite easily resolved, but its extraordinary emotional appeal keeps debate alive as generation after generation goes through the cycle of first being perplexed, then elated at understanding (sometimes mistakenly), and then immediately rushing into print as though no one had understood before. The articles that have been published on this one topic are practically uncountable, while their useful common denominator would fill a few pages at most. But while no one can get very excited about pushing long poles into short garages and the like, the prospect of going on a fast trip through space and coming back a few years later to find the earth aged by a few thousand years—this modern *elixir vitae*—cannot fail to stir the imagination.

As we have seen, a standard clock A moving in any way through the synchronized standard lattice clocks of an inertial frame loses steadily relative to those clocks. Consequently, if A is taken on a complete round-trip through an inertial frame, let us say from the origin O back to O, it will read slow compared with the clock B that has remained at O. If, of two twins, one travels with A while the other stays with B, the B-twin will be older than the A-twin when they meet again, for time dilation applies to life processes as well as to clocks.

Now the paradox is this: cannot A (we shall identify clocks with persons) say with equal right that *he* remained where he was, while B went on a round-trip, and that, consequently, B should be the younger when they meet? The answer, of course, is no, and this resolves the paradox: B has remained at rest in a single inertial frame, while A, in the simplest case of a uniform to-and-fro motion, must at least be accelerated briefly out of B's frame into another, decelerated again briefly to turn around, and finally decelerated to stop at B. These accelerations (positive and negative) are *felt* by A, who can therefore be under no illusion that it was he who remained at rest. Of course, the first and last of these accelerations are nonessential, since age comparisons can be made "in passing," but the middle one is unavoidable.

Still, it may be argued in the above to-and-fro case that there *is* symmetry between A and B for "most of the time," namely during the times of A's free fall. The three asymmetric accelerations can be confined to arbitrarily short periods (as measured by B—they are even shorter as measured by A). How is it, then, that a large asymmetric effect can build up, and, moreover, one that is proportional to the symmetric parts of the motion? But the situation is no more strange than that of two drivers α and β going from point O to P to Q (which lie in a straight line), β going directly, while α deviates from P to a point R off the line, and thence to Q. They behave quite similarly except that α turns his steering wheel briefly at P and again at R. Yet when they get to Q, their odometers may indicate a large difference!

In one way, the twins' eventual age difference can be seen to arise during A's initial acceleration away from B. During this period, however brief, if his γ factor gets to be 2, say, A finds he has accomplished more than half his outward journey! For he has transferred himself to a frame in which the distance between the earth and his celestial target is halved (length contraction!), and this halving is real to him in every possible way. Thus he accomplishes his outward trip in about half the time which B ascribes to it, and the same is true of his return trip.

In another way, the eventual age difference can be seen to arise during a certain period after A's turning-round point, namely between then and the time that B *sees* A turn round. For suppose A makes a flying start and compares ages with B "in passing." Then A and B are totally symmetric until A turns round. At that point, A *immediately* sees B's clock tick faster, since he is now traveling *into* B's signals; B, on the other hand, cannot see A's clock tick faster until he sees A turn round. From then on, the situation is again symmetric to the end. But A has seen slow ticks for half the time and fast ticks for the other half, while B has seen slow ticks for *more* than half the time. Hence B sees altogether *fewer* ticks than does A. And this, of course, is as it should be, since A's clock has ticked fewer times by time dilation.

Arguments of this nature are perhaps instructive or amusing, but not essential. They simply illustrate the self-consistency of the theory and embroider the lack of symmetry between twin A and twin B. But the paradox is disposed of as soon as the asymmetry is pointed out. Sciama has astutely remarked that the twin paradox has the same status as Newton's experiment with the two buckets of water—one, rotating, suspended below the other, at rest. If these were the whole content of the universe, it would be odd that the water surface in the one should be curved and that in the other flat. But inertial frames cannot be ignored, and relative to the inertial frames there is no symmetry between the buckets, and no symmetry between the twins, either.

It should be noted, finally, that the clock paradox is entirely independent of the clock hypothesis. Whatever the effects of the accelerations as such may be on the moving clock or organism, these effects can be dwarfed by simply extending the periods of free fall. Authors who assert that the clock paradox can only be discussed by GR, since SR cannot *prove* what happens during the accelerations, gravely miss the point for two reasons: (a) because of the possible dwarfing just mentioned, and (b) because GR has to posit the clock hypothesis just like SR (unless the turning round of twin A is accomplished purely by gravitation, e.g., by the close skirting of a star).

Velocity Transformation   *36*

Consider, once more, two frames S and S' in standard configuration.   Let **u** be the vector velocity of a particle in S. We wish to find its velocity **u'** in S'. If the particle moves uniformly, we have

$$\mathbf{u} = (u_1, u_2, u_3) = (\Delta x/\Delta t, \Delta y/\Delta t, \Delta z/\Delta t) \tag{36.1}$$
$$\mathbf{u'} = (u_1', u_2', u_3') = (\Delta x'/\Delta t', \Delta y'/\Delta t', \Delta z'/\Delta t'), \tag{36.2}$$

where the increments refer to any two events at the particle. Substitution from (28.3) in (36.2) and comparison with (36.1) immediately yields the velocity transformation formulae:

$$u_1' = \frac{u_1 - v}{1 - u_1 v/c^2}, \quad u_2' = \frac{u_2}{\gamma(1 - u_1 v/c^2)},$$

$$u_3' = \frac{u_3}{\gamma(1 - u_1 v/c^2)}. \tag{36.3}$$

These formulae, of course, apply equally well to sub- and superlight velocities, and it would be quite proper to use them to transform, for example, the speed of the searchlight spot of Section 30.

We can pass to the inverse relations without going through the same work again, simply by interchanging primed and unprimed symbols and replacing v by $-v$. (For if we replace unprimed by primed, and primed by doubly primed symbols, we evidently get a transformation from S' to a frame S'' which moves with velocity v relative to S'; replacing v by $-v$ then makes S'' into S.) Thus,

$$u_1 = \frac{u_1' + v}{1 + u_1'v/c^2}, \quad u_2 = \frac{u_2'}{\gamma(1 + u_1'v/c^2)},$$

$$u_3 = \frac{u_3'}{\gamma(1 + u_1'v/c^2)}. \tag{36.4}$$

For nonuniform velocities, (36.1) and (36.2) hold in the limit, and (36.3) and (36.4) are equally true.

Equations (36.4) can be interpreted, alternatively, as giving the "resultant" $\mathbf{u} = (u_1, u_2, u_3)$ of the two velocities $\mathbf{v} = (v, 0, 0)$ and $\mathbf{u}' = (u_1', u_2', u_3')$, and they take the place of the classical formula $\mathbf{u} = \mathbf{v} + \mathbf{u}'$. In this role they are referred to as the *relativistic velocity addition formulae*. For any such addition to be meaningful, of course, the axes of S and S' must be equally oriented, though not necessarily in standard configuration. It is perhaps worth remarking that the relativistic addition of $\mathbf{u}'$ to $\mathbf{v}$ is *not* the same as that of $\mathbf{v}$ to $\mathbf{u}'$—though, in fact, the magnitudes are the same in both cases. For example, if $\mathbf{v} = (v, 0, 0)$ and $\mathbf{u}' = (0, u', 0)$, it is easily seen that $\mathbf{v} \dotplus \mathbf{u}' = (v, u'/\gamma(v), 0)$ while $\mathbf{u}' \dotplus \mathbf{v} = (v/\gamma(u'), u', 0)$, where "$\dotplus$" denotes "relativistic sum." That the magnitudes of $\mathbf{u}' \dotplus \mathbf{v}$ and $\mathbf{v} \dotplus \mathbf{u}'$ are always equal follows from (36.5) below (since $u_1'v = \mathbf{u}' \cdot \mathbf{v}$).

A straightforward computation yields from (36.4) the following relation between the magnitudes $u = (u_1^2 + u_2^2 + u_3^2)^{1/2}$ and $u' = (u_1'^2 + u_2'^2 + u_3'^2)^{1/2}$ of corresponding velocities in S and S':

$$c^2 - u^2 = \frac{c^2(c^2 - u'^2)(c^2 - v^2)}{(c^2 + u_1'v)^2}. \tag{36.5}$$

If $u' < c$ and $v < c$, the right member is positive whence $u < c$. Hence the resultant of two velocities less than c is always a velocity less than c. This shows that, however many velocity increments (less than c) a particle receives in its instantaneous rest frame, it can never attain the velocity of light relative to a given inertial frame. Thus the velocity of light plays the role in relativity of an infinite velocity, inasmuch as no "sum" of lesser velocities can ever equal it. More generally, (36.5) shows that if $v < c$ (as is the case for any two inertial frames) $u \lesseqgtr c$ implies $u' \lesseqgtr c$, respectively, and vice versa.

Rewriting (36.5) we have

$$\frac{1 - u'^2/c^2}{1 - u^2/c^2} = \frac{(1 + u_1'v/c^2)^2}{1 - v^2/c^2},$$

which, on taking square roots, yields the first of the following two useful relations,

$$\frac{\gamma(u)}{\gamma(u')} = \gamma(v)\left(1 + \frac{u_1'v}{c^2}\right), \quad \frac{\gamma(u')}{\gamma(u)} = \gamma(v)\left(1 - \frac{u_1 v}{c^2}\right); \quad (36.6)$$

the second results again from the generally valid process of interchanging primed and unprimed symbols and replacing v by $-v$.

Proper Acceleration **37**

A useful concept in the study of nonuniform motion is that of *proper acceleration*. This is defined as the acceleration of a particle relative to its instantaneous rest frame. We here restrict ourselves to a discussion of one-dimensional motion, say along the x axis of S. Let S' (in standard configuration with S) be the instantaneous rest frame of a particle moving with velocity u, so that $u' = 0$ and $u = v$ momentarily, but v is constant whereas u and u' are not. Then, from (36.4)(i), we find after some calculation,

$$du = \gamma^{-2}(u)du'. \quad (37.1)$$

If α denotes the proper acceleration, we have $du' = \alpha dt'$; and, by time dilation, $dt' = dt/\gamma(u)$. Thus $du = \alpha dt/\gamma^3(u)$, i.e.,

$$\alpha = \left(1 - \frac{u^2}{c^2}\right)^{-3/2} \frac{du}{dt} = \frac{d}{dt}[\gamma(u)u]. \quad (37.2)$$

This gives the transformation of the acceleration from the rest frame to an arbitrary frame, and we note that acceleration is *not* invariant under a LT.

If α is constant, we can integrate (37.2) at once with respect to t (choosing $t = 0$ when $u = 0$), solve for u, integrate once more and, by suitably adjusting the constant of integration, obtain the following equation of motion:

$$x^2 - c^2 t^2 = c^4/\alpha^2. \qquad (37.3)$$

Thus, for obvious reasons, rectilinear motion with constant proper acceleration is called "hyperbolic" motion (see Figure 8). (Note, incidentally, that $\alpha = \infty$ implies $x = \pm ct$; hence the proper acceleration of a photon can be taken to be infinite.) Consider next the equation

$$x^2 - c^2 t^2 = X^2, \qquad (37.4)$$

for various values of the parameter X. For each fixed X it represents a particle moving with constant proper acceleration c^2/X. Altogether it represents, as we shall show, the equations of motion of all points of a rod "moving rigidly" in the x direction.

[By the rigid motion of a body one understands a motion during which every small volume element of the body shrinks always in the direction of its motion in proportion to its instantaneous Lorentz factor relative to a given inertial frame. Or, in other words, every small volume element appears to preserve its dimensions to a comoving observer, and thus no elastic stresses are set up. A body so moving cannot start to rotate, since circumferences of circles described by points of the body would have to shrink, while their radii would have to remain constant, which is impossible. In general, therefore, the motion of one point of a rigidly moving body determines that of all others.]

Going back to equation (37.4), we can find the velocity u and the corresponding γ factor of a particle moving such that $X = $ constant:

$$u = \frac{dx}{dt} = \frac{c^2 t}{x}, \quad \gamma(u) = \frac{x}{X}. \qquad (37.5)$$

Now consider the motion of two such particles, whose parameters X differ by dX; at any fixed time t we have, again from (37.4) and then from (37.5),

$$dx = \frac{X dX}{x} = \frac{dX}{\gamma(u)}. \qquad (37.6)$$

Hence at every instant t = constant the two particles are separated by a coordinate distance dx inversely proportional to their γ factor, and consequently they "move rigidly"; moreover, dX is recognized as their *proper* separation. Since this applies to any two neighboring particles in the aggregate represented by (37.4), that whole aggregate "moves rigidly," like an unstressed rigid rod.   Figure 8 shows the position of such a rod at various instants t = constant. Units are chosen to make c = 1.   The rod cannot be

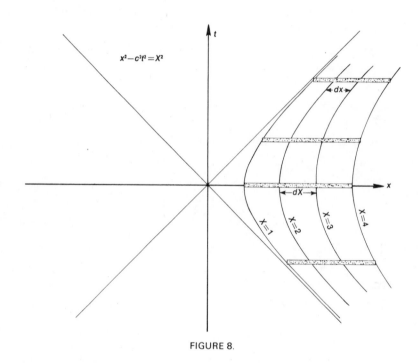

FIGURE 8.

extended to negative values of X, since the asymptotes in the diagram represent photon paths; if continued right up to $X = 0$, the rod "ends in a photon."

It is interesting to observe that, according to the equivalence principle, an observer traveling with this rod at some fixed X_0 can be under the illusion that he is in a static gravitational field of strength c^2/X_0.   A whole bundle of such rods, say of the length of a skyscraper, can give comoving observers the illusion of living in a rigid skyscraper immersed in a parallel and static gravitational field whose strength, however, falls off inversely as distance. A *uniform* gravitational field can *not* be constructed by this method.

38   *Special Relativity Without the Second Postulate*

We shall now investigate the full implications of the relativity principle by itself, without the "second postulate," i.e., without assuming the invariance of the speed of light. We shall, however, demand Euclidicity, isotropy, and the invariance of causality. We recall that in Section 27 we went as far as equation (27.5) and the fact that $\gamma > 0$, without the second postulate, appealing merely to the Euclidicity and isotropy of inertial frames. We were careful to point out that for calibrating the coordinate lattice, light signals were dispensable. Let us now return to equations (27.1) through (27.5). Elimination of x' between (27.3) and (27.4) gives

$$t' = \gamma\left(t - \frac{\gamma^2 - 1}{\gamma^2 v} x\right) = \gamma\left(t - \frac{v}{V^2} x\right), \qquad (38.1)$$

where we have simply written V^2 for $v^2\gamma^2/(\gamma^2 - 1)$, i.e.,

$$0 < \gamma = (1 - v^2/V^2)^{-1/2}. \qquad (38.2)$$

Equation (38.1), together with our previous equations

$$x' = \gamma(x - vt), \quad y' = y, \quad z' = z, \qquad (38.3)$$

constitute the complete transformation, and this is as far as we can go from the relativity principle. Without further assumptions, γ can be any positive number. The choice $\gamma = 1$ (i.e., $V^2 = \infty$) gives the Galilean transformation, and reference to (38.1) shows this to be the only case in which simultaneity is absolute between S and S' (i.e., $t' = t$). The choice $\gamma > 1$ gives a Lorentz-type transformation with $V^2 > 0$ in place of the usual c^2: we shall call this a (V^2) − LT. The choice $\gamma < 1$ gives a $(-V^2)$ − LT.

This last transformation can be written (neglecting the "trivial" members of (38.3)) in the form

$$x' = x \cos \phi - Vt \sin \phi$$
$$Vt' = x \sin \phi + Vt \cos \phi, \qquad (38.4)$$

where $\tan \phi = v/V$. This can be interpreted as an ordinary rotation about an angle $\phi \, (-\frac{1}{2}\pi < \phi < \frac{1}{2}\pi)$ in the plane of x and Vt. Now if the transformation between any *one* pair of frames with relative velocity v is of type (38.4) (together, of course, with the trivial members of (38.3)), then the same transformation must relate *all* pairs of frames having *that particular* relative velocity v. But it is evident that the resultant of n such transformations applied in succession will be of the same form, with parameter $n\phi$ instead of ϕ. For suitable values of n, this parameter will lie between $\frac{1}{2}\pi$ and $\frac{3}{2}\pi$; but then in the resultant time transformation, t has a negative coefficient which implies, for example, that for events at the spatial origin of S, the temporal order in S' is reversed. Hence Lorentz transformations with negative "lightsquare" must be ruled out if causality is to be invariant.

Thus we are left with LT's having arbitrary positive "lightsquare" V^2, and GT's. The latter are really particular cases of the former (corresponding to $V^2 = \infty$) *and in this paragraph we shall regard them as such.* We can now show that if *any* two inertial frames are related by a $(V^2) - $ LT, all inertial frames are related by a $(V^2) - $ LT with the *same* V^2. For suppose frame S' is in standard configuration with frame S at relative velocity v, and related to it by a $(V^2) - $ LT. Now consider *any* other frame S'' in standard configuration with S' at relative velocity u. Suppose S' and S'' are related by a $(U^2) - $ LT. Then

$$x' = \gamma(x - vt), \qquad t' = \gamma(t - vx/V^2), \qquad (38.5)$$
$$x'' = \gamma'(x' - ut'), \qquad t'' = \gamma'(t' - ux'/U^2), \qquad (38.6)$$

where γ and γ' are the Lorentz factors corresponding to V and U, respectively. If we substitute from (38.5) into (38.6), we find the transformation between S and S'':

$$x'' = \gamma\gamma'\left(1 + \frac{uv}{V^2}\right)\left(x - \frac{u+v}{1+uv/V^2}\,t\right)$$

$$t'' = \gamma\gamma'\left(1 + \frac{uv}{U^2}\right)\left(t - \frac{u/U^2 + v/V^2}{1+uv/U^2}\,x\right). \tag{38.7}$$

Now this is not *any* kind of LT unless $U^2 = V^2$. But it must be a LT! Hence $U^2 = V^2$, and thus the transformation between S' and S'' is a $(V^2) - $ LT. Now if *one* pair of frames at relative velocity u is related by a $(V^2) - $ LT, *all* pairs at relative velocity u must be so related. But u was arbitrary; hence *all* pairs of frames are related by $(V^2) - $ LT's, if one is.

Thus the RP by itself (together with Euclidicity, isotropy, and invariance of causality) necessarily implies either that all inertial frames are related by GT's ($V^2 = \infty$), or that all are related by LT's with the same positive V^2. The role of a "second postulate" in relativity is now clear: it merely has to isolate one or the other of these transformation groups. *Any* second postulate consistent with the RP but not with the GT isolates the LT group. However, to determine the value of the invariant V^2 the postulate must be quantitative. For example, a statement like "simultaneity is not absolute," while implying *a* Lorentz group, fails to determine V^2. On the other hand, the statement "at speed $3c/5$ there is a time dilation by a factor $5/4$," not only implies *a* Lorentz group, but *the* Lorentz group (with $V^2 = c^2$). We shall see later that the relativistic mass increase, or the famous formula $E = mc^2$, and others, could all equally well serve as second postulates.

This renders less crucial the question of whether the speed of light is really independent of the speed of the source (which, in conjunction with the relativity principle, is equivalent to the invariance of the speed of light). This question was not finally settled directly and experimentally beyond all doubt until 1964, when Alväger, Farley, Kjellman, and Wallin observed decay radiation from rapidly moving π^0 mesons in the laboratory. Before that, it had been the subject of recurrent debate, since many people believed it to be one of the two pillars on which the whole of relativity is built.

We may note an alternative and somewhat more physical approach to the problem of the present section: Either there exists an upper limit to all signal speeds or not. If yes, that limiting speed, say c, must transform into itself, and we derive the LT as in Section 27. If not, synchronize the clocks in all inertial frames with cannon balls, and then show that *all* events with $t > 0$ can be causally dependent on the origin-event $x = y = z = t = 0$. Hence they must occur *after* that event in all frames. Hence $t = 0$ transforms into $t' = 0$ and this leads directly to the GT.

[Early deductions of the LT without the postulate of light propagation were given by W. v. Ignatowsky in *Physik. Zeitschr.* **11,** 972 (1910) and by L. A. Pars in *Phil. Mag.* **42,** 249 (1921). However, like numerous others that followed, these have gone largely unnoticed.]

3

Einsteinian Optics

39 *The Drag Effect*

Relativity provided an ideally simple solution to a problem that had considerably exercised the ingenuity of theoreticians before. The question is, to what extent a flowing liquid will "drag" light along with it. Flowing air, of course, drags sound along totally, but the optical situation is different: on the basis of an ether theory, it would be conceivable that there is no drag at all, since light is a disturbance of the ether and not of the liquid. Yet experiments indicated that there *was* a drag: the liquid seemed to force the ether along with it, but only partially. If the speed of light in the liquid *at rest* is u', and the liquid is set to move with velocity v, then the speed of light relative to the outside was found to be of the form

$$u = u' + kv, \quad k = 1 - 1/n^2, \qquad (39.1)$$

where k is the "drag coefficient," a number between zero and one indicating what fraction of its own velocity the liquid imparts to the ether within, and *n* is the refractive index c/u' of the liquid. Fifty years before Einstein, Fresnel succeeded in giving a plausible ether-based explanation of this. From the point of view of special relativity, however, the result (39.1) is nothing but the relativistic velocity addition formula! The light travels relative to the liquid with velocity u', and the liquid travels relative to the observer with velocity v, and therefore (see Section 36),

$$u = u' \dotplus v = \frac{u' + v}{1 + u'v/c^2} = \frac{(c/n) + v}{1 + v/cn} \approx \frac{c}{n} + v\left(1 - \frac{1}{n^2}\right),$$

(39.2)

when first-order terms only are retained. Einstein already gave the velocity addition formula in his 1905 paper but, strangely, it took two more years before Laue made this beautiful application of it.

The Doppler Effect *40*

Even on pre-relativistic theory, if I watch a clock moving away from me, it will *appear* to go more slowly than a standard clock at rest. For when it indicates "two," say, it is further away than when it indicated "one," and light from it then takes longer to reach me in addition to having been emitted one unit of time later. If instead of a clock I watch a receding vibrating atom, then for the same reason the frequency that I observe will be smaller than that of the atom at rest, or, in other words, the spectrum of the atom will be redshifted. The reverse happens when these "clocks" approach, rather than recede. Similar effects exist for sound waves in air; all are named after the Austrian physicist Doppler.

Relativity merely added a small but significant correction to the optical Doppler effect: the receding clock will appear to go even more slowly, and the receding atom will be even more redshifted, because of the time dilation of the moving clock or atom.

Let a "source" travel arbitrarily in an inertial frame S, and let it instantaneously have a velocity u, with radial component u_r relative to the origin-observer O. Then in the time Δt_0 which a comoving observer C measures between the emission of successive "wavecrests" (or ticks of a clock), the source has increased its distance from O by $\Delta t_0 \gamma(u) u_r$ (time dilation!). Consequently, the times between wavecrests as observed by O and C are $\Delta t_0 \gamma(u) + \Delta t_0 \gamma(u) u_r/c$ and Δt_0, respectively. The ratio of these times gives the Doppler shift

$$D = \frac{\lambda}{\lambda_0} = \frac{1 + u_r/c}{(1 - u^2/c^2)^{1/2}} = 1 + \frac{u_r}{c} + \frac{1}{2}\frac{u^2}{c^2} + O\left(\frac{u^3}{c^3}\right), \quad (40.1)$$

λ_0 being the proper wavelength (as observed by C) and λ that observed by O. (The pre-relativistic formula simply had the Lorentz factor missing, but it was considered valid only in the ether frame. In other frames the formula, and its derivation, were more complicated.) Our series expansion separates the "pure" Doppler effect $1 + u_r/c$ from the contribution $\frac{1}{2}u^2/c^2$ of time dilation, to the order shown.

In relativity there is a Doppler shift even for a purely transversely moving source, due, of course, *entirely* to time dilation. This gives us yet another way of verifying the existence in nature of time dilation, e.g., with rotor experiments. Consider a large disc, rotating at uniform angular velocity ω, and having two standard clocks C_1 and C_2 affixed at two arbitrary points, at distances r_1 and r_2 from the center, respectively. By time dilation (and appeal to the clock hypothesis), the rates of these clocks will be slowed by factors $\gamma(\omega r_1)$ and $\gamma(\omega r_2)$, respectively. Hence if they are speeded up by these factors prior to attachment, they will keep in step with the outside clocks. Suppose this is done. Then, by the stationary nature of the situation, an observer moving with C_1 and looking at C_2 will *see* C_2 neither gain nor lose relative to C_1. Hence wavecrests emitted at C_2 at proper time intervals $1/\gamma(\omega r_2)$ are received at C_1 at proper time intervals $1/\gamma(\omega r_1)$. Consequently, the

Doppler shift in the light from C_2 to C_1 must be

$$D = \frac{\gamma(\omega r_2)}{\gamma(\omega r_1)}. \qquad (40.2)$$

[To reproduce this result in its full generality *directly* from (40.1) would not be quite trivial: the receiving observer is only momentarily at rest in an inertial frame S at the time of reception; it would be necessary to find the velocity of the source relative to this frame, at the time of emission.]

The most obvious experiment would be to place the source at the rim and the receiver at the center of the disc; in practice, however, the exact opposite was done (thus essentially measuring the time dilation of the receiver rather than of the source) by Hay, Schiffer, Cranshaw, and Engelstaff in 1960, using Mössbauer resonance. Agreement with the theoretical predictions was obtained to within an expected experimental error of a few percent. This, incidentally, furnished some validation of the clock hypothesis, for the "clock" at the receiver was clearly accelerated (up to about $6 \times 10^4 \, g$, in fact), and at least no measurable effect of this acceleration could be detected.

Prior to the rotor experiments, it was difficult to ensure exact transverseness in the motion of the sources (e.g., fast-moving hydrogen ions). The slightest radial component would swamp the transverse effect. Ives and Stilwell (in 1938) cleverly used a to-and-fro motion whereby the first-order Doppler effect cancelled out, and thus they were able to verify the contribution of time dilation to considerable accuracy.

A similar canceling of the first-order contribution occurs in the so-called "thermal" Doppler effect. Radioactive nuclei bound in a hot crystal move thermally in a rapid and random way. Because of this randomness, their first-order Doppler effects average out, but not the second-order effect due to their mean square velocities. These velocities were calculated and the Doppler shift was observed, once again by use of Mössbauer resonance (in 1960, by Rebka and

Pound). Again the agreement with theory was excellent, to within an expected experimental error of about ten percent. One by-product of this experiment was an impressive validation of the clock hypothesis: in spite of accelerations up to $10^{16} g$ (!), these nuclear "clocks" were slowed simply by the velocity factor $(1 - v^2/c^2)^{1/2}$.

For reference purposes, we cast (40.1) into two alternative forms: one that applies when the motion of the source is purely radial,

$$D = \frac{\lambda}{\lambda_0} = \left(\frac{1 + u/c}{1 - u/c}\right)^{1/2}; \qquad (40.3)$$

and another,

$$D = \frac{\lambda}{\lambda'} = \frac{1 + (v/c)\cos\alpha}{(1 - v^2/c^2)^{1/2}}, \qquad (40.4)$$

that applies when a ray of unspecified origin, making an angle α with the x axis in S, is observed both in S and in the usual second frame S'. To obtain this latter formula, we assume (without loss of generality) that the ray was emitted by a source at rest in S', and then simply write λ', v, and $v\cos\alpha$ for λ_0, u, and u_r in (40.1).

41   *Aberration and the Visual Appearance of Moving Objects*

If I drive into the rain, it seems to come at my car obliquely. For similar reasons, if two observers measure the angle which an incoming ray of light makes with their relative line of motion, their measurements will generally not agree. This phenomenon is called aberration, and of course it was well known before relativity. Nevertheless, as in the case of the Doppler effect, the relativistic formula contains a correction, and, moreover, applies to all pairs of frames, whereas the pre-relativistic formula was simple only if one of the frames was the ether frame.

Aberration implies, for example, that as the earth travels along its orbit, the apparent directions of the fixed stars trace out small ellipses in the course of each year (with major axes of about 41 seconds of arc). Aberration also causes certain distortions in the visual appearance of extended moving objects. For, from the viewpoint of the rest frame of the object, as the observer moves into the pattern of rays from the object, rays from its different points are unequally aberrated. Alternatively, from the viewpoint of the observer's rest frame, the light from different parts of the moving object takes different times to reach his eye, and thus it was emitted at different past times. The more distant points of the object consequently appear displaced relative to the nearest point, in the direction opposite to the motion. It is in connection with the visual appearance of moving objects that the relativistic formulae are genuinely amusing.

To obtain the basic aberration formulae, consider a light signal coming towards the momentarily coincident origins O and O' of the usual two frames S and S', respectively, and making angles α and α' with the x-axes in these frames. The velocity transformation formula (36.3)(i) can evidently be applied to this signal, with $u_1 = -c\cos\alpha$ and $u_1' = -c\cos\alpha'$, yielding

$$\cos\alpha' = \frac{\cos\alpha + v/c}{1 + (v/c)\cos\alpha}. \qquad (41.1)$$

Similarly, from (36.3)(ii) we obtain the alternative formula (assuming temporarily, without loss of generality, that the signal lies in the x, y plane)

$$\sin\alpha' = \frac{\sin\alpha}{\gamma[1 + (v/c)\cos\alpha]}. \qquad (41.2)$$

However, the most interesting version of the aberration formula is obtained by substituting from (41.1) and (41.2) into the trigonometric identity

$$\tan\tfrac{1}{2}\alpha' = \sin\alpha'/(1 + \cos\alpha'),$$

which gives

$$\tan\tfrac{1}{2}\alpha' = \left(\frac{c - v}{c + v}\right)^{1/2}\tan\tfrac{1}{2}\alpha. \qquad (41.3)$$

By use of this formula, and a little geometry, we can at once predict the visual appearance of any extended moving object. Following an ingenious argument of R. Penrose, let us draw a sphere of unit diameter around each observer's space-origin (see Figure 9), cutting the negative and positive x axis at points P and Q, respectively. All that an observer sees at any instant can be mapped onto this sphere (his "sky"). Let it further be mapped from this sphere onto the tangent plane at Q (his "screen") by stereographic projection from P. We recall that the angle subtended by an arc

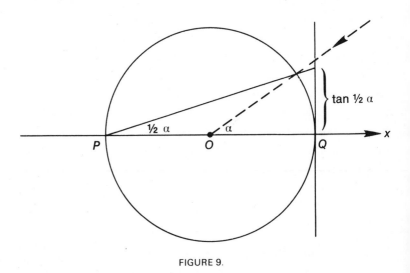

FIGURE 9.

of a circle at the circumference is half of the angle subtended at the center, and we have accordingly labeled the diagram (for a single incident ray). Thus the significance of (41.3) is seen to be precisely this: whatever two momentarily coincident observers see, the views on their "screens" are identical except for scale!

Now consider, for example, a solid sphere Z at rest somewhere in the frame of an inertial observer O'. He sees a circular outline of Z in his sky, and a circular outline also on his screen (for under stereographic projection, circles on the sphere correspond to circles or straight lines on the plane). Relative to the usual second observer O, of course, Z moves. Nevertheless, by our theory, his screen image will differ from that of O' only in size, and thus it will also be circular; consequently, his "sky" image of Z must be circular also. This shows that a moving sphere presents a circular outline to *all* observers *in spite* of length contraction! (Or rather: *because* of length contraction; for without length contraction the outline would be distorted.) By the same argument, moving straight lines (rods) will, in general, have the appearance of circular arcs, and flying saucers or fast-moving bicycle wheels are liable to look boomerang-shaped.

Another interesting though less realistic way of studying the visual appearance of moving objects is by use of what we may call "supersnapshots." These are life-size snapshots made by receiving *parallel* light from an object and catching it directly on a photographic plate placed at right angles to the rays. One could, for example, make a supersnapshot of the *outline* of an object by arranging to have the sun behind it and letting it cast its shadow onto a plate. Moreover, what the eye sees (or the ordinary camera shoots) of a *small and distant* object approximates quite closely to a supersnapshot. Now, the beautiful result (due to Terrell) is this: all supersnapshots that can be made of an object at a certain place and time by observers in any state of uniform motion are identical. In particular, they are all identical to the supersnapshot that can be made in the rest frame of the object!

To prove this result, let us consider two photons P and Q traveling abreast along parallel straight paths a distance Δr apart, relative to some frame S. Let us consider two arbitrary events $\mathcal{P}$ and $\mathcal{Q}$ at P and Q, respectively. If $\mathcal{Q}$ occurs a time Δt after $\mathcal{P}$, then the space separation between $\mathcal{P}$ and $\mathcal{Q}$ is evidently $\sqrt{\Delta r^2 + c^2 \Delta t^2}$, and thus, by (29.4), the squared interval between $\mathcal{P}$ and $\mathcal{Q}$ is $-\Delta r^2$, independently of their time separation. But if, instead of traveling abreast, Q leads P by a distance Δl, then the space separation between $\mathcal{P}$ and $\mathcal{Q}$ would be $\sqrt{\Delta r^2 + (c\Delta t + \Delta l)^2}$, and the squared interval would *not* be independent of Δt. Now, since squared interval is an invariant (and since parallel rays transform into parallel rays), it follows that two photons traveling abreast along parallel paths a distance Δr apart in one frame do precisely the same in all other frames! But a supersnapshot results from catching an array of photons traveling abreast along parallel paths. By our present result, these photons travel abreast along parallel lines with the same space separation in *all* inertial frames, and thus the equality of supersnapshots is established.

Suppose, for example, the origin-observer O in S sees at $t = 0$ a small object, apparently on his y axis ($\alpha = 90°$). Suppose this object is at rest in the usual second frame S'. The origin-observer O' in S' will see the object at an angle $\alpha' < 90°$, given by (41.3). If the object is a cube with its edges parallel to the coordinate axes of S and S', O' of course sees the cube not face-on but rotated. The surprising fact is that O, who might have expected to see a contracted cube face-on, also sees an uncontracted rotated cube!

What is even more surprising is that it took something like fifty years from the advent of special relativity before these simple facts of vision were discovered (apart from the basic aberration formula, which, together with the Doppler formula, already appear in Einstein's 1905 paper). The interested reader may wish to think of various other situations, but we shall not pursue these matters further, since their intrinsic significance appears to be limited. Unlike the Doppler effect and the drag effect, aberration has not so far led to experiments with the express purpose of testing special relativity. On the other hand, it *does* provide another good example of the effectiveness of relativity theory. Before relativity, it was complicated to obtain an aberration formula for two frames like S and S' with an "ether wind" blowing through S in an arbitrary direction—even if one assumed, as we have done so far, the corpuscular (photon) nature of light. On the basis of a wave theory of light, the Galilean transformation gave no aberration of the wave normal at all, and one had to introduce the concept of "rays," whose direction need not coincide with the wave normals. In relativity, the wave analysis is as straight-forward as the corpuscular analysis of the problem (see exercise 3-9). Thus it is wrong to think that relativity always "complicates things." In optics it is certainly quite the other way round.

4

Spacetime and
Four-Vectors

42   Spacetime

Einstein taught us to regard *events* as the basic data of
physics. He showed us the fundamental significance of
inertial frames and inertial observers. It was he who found
that every inertial observer has his own subjectively valid
time, and, correspondingly, his own "instantaneous three-
spaces" consisting of all events (x, y, z, t) with fixed time
coordinate. But it was the mathematician Minkowski (in
1908) who taught us to think of the totality of events in the
world as the "points" of an absolute four-dimensional
manifold called "spacetime." Different inertial observers
draw different sections through spacetime as their "instants." In fact, each inertial observer, using his standard
x, y, z, and t, coordinatizes all of spacetime, just as a choice
of x and y axes coordinatizes the Euclidean plane. Figure 6
represents spacetime with two dimensions suppressed, but
that suffices to illustrate how two observers make different

instantaneous sections (for example, the x and x' axes) and how they have different time axes. Certain lines in spacetime correspond to the history of material particles, and are aptly called "particle worldlines." They are straight if the particles are free. Extended bodies have "worldtubes" in spacetime.

Of course, in Newtonian physics, governed by the Galilean transformation, one can define spacetime just as well and use it to carry various graphical representations. Here all observers agree on how to slice spacetime into instants, but they still have different time axes (these being the worldlines of their origins). Free particles still have straight worldlines, and extended bodies have worldtubes.

But in the relativistic case, spacetime is very much *more* than a convenient scheme for drawing graphs. It is a four-dimensional *metric* space. Analogously to "distance," we can define an "interval"

$$\Delta s = (c^2 \Delta t^2 - \Delta x^2 - \Delta y^2 - \Delta z^2)^{1/2} \qquad (42.1)$$

for any two of its points. And this is *absolute*, i.e., it has the same value when evaluated by *any* inertial observer using standard coordinates, since it is invariant under a standard Lorentz transformation (see equation (29.4)) and also under translation and rotation of spatial axes and under translation of time (which preserve $\Delta x^2 + \Delta y^2 + \Delta z^2$ and Δt^2 separately). As Minkowski demonstrated, the existence of the "metric" (42.1) of spacetime has a significant mathematical consequence: it leads to a vector calculus ("four-vectors") beautifully adapted to the needs of special relativity. Moreover, spacetime with this metric provides us with a new *absolute* background for our intuitive thought about the physical world, a background that seemed lost forever with the abolition of absolute space and absolute time. Minkowski was so struck by his discovery that he exclaimed: "Henceforth space by itself, and time by itself, are doomed to fade away into mere shadows, and only a kind of union of the two will preserve an independent reality." And again: "In my opinion physical laws might find their most perfect expression as the mutual relations between worldlines." (In the study of general relativity we shall see how prophetic this statement was.) Minkowski may well be regarded as the father of the "fourth dimension."

No corresponding development is possible in Galilean spacetime, where there is only an absolute "temporal distance" Δt between events. The spatial distance $(\Delta x^2 + \Delta y^2 + \Delta z^2)^{1/2}$ depends on the observer, and no Galileo-invariant "metric" involving all of $\Delta x, \Delta y, \Delta z, \Delta t$ exists. Consequently, Galilean spacetime is nonmetric, and Galilean four-vectors are "unnormed," and thus not very useful. (But see Section 52.)

We may discuss here briefly the physical significance of Δs, or better, of Δs^2, though we shall have occasion to return to this point more than once. Evidently $\Delta s^2 = 0$ for two given events $\mathcal{P}$ and $\mathcal{Q}$ if and only if these events are connectible by a light signal. When $\Delta s^2 > 0$, then, in any inertial frame, $\Delta r^2/\Delta t^2 < c^2$ (where $\Delta r^2 = \Delta x^2 + \Delta y^2 + \Delta z^2$) and thus an observer moving with uniform velocity less than c can be sent from one of the events to the other; in *his* rest frame $\Delta r = 0$ and $\Delta s = c\Delta t$. Thus when $\Delta s^2 > 0$, Δs represents c times the time separation between $\mathcal{P}$ and $\mathcal{Q}$ measured in an inertial frame in which $\mathcal{P}$ and $\mathcal{Q}$ occur at the same point. Similarly, if $\Delta s^2 < 0$, then $(-\Delta s^2)^{1/2}$ is the space separation between $\mathcal{P}$ and $\mathcal{Q}$ measured in an inertial frame in which they are simultaneous, and such a frame always exists. The first part of our assertion is obvious, and the second is proved if we can find a rod of rest length $(-\Delta s^2)^{1/2}$ moving at some uniform speed $v < c$ in an arbitrary inertial frame along the line joining $\mathcal{P}$ and $\mathcal{Q}$ such that $\mathcal{P}$ and $\mathcal{Q}$ occur at opposite ends of the rod. For this we need (by length contraction in the rod frame) $\Delta r^2/(-\Delta s^2) = 1 - v^2/c^2$; but since $\Delta s^2 < 0$ implies $-\Delta s^2 \geq \Delta r^2 > 0$, there exists a $v < c$ to satisfy this condition, and our assertion is proved.

Three-Vectors *43*

Before introducing four-vectors, it will be well to review the
salient features of three-vectors, i.e., of "ordinary" vectors.
Anyone who has done three-dimensional geometry or mechanics will be aware of the power of the vector calculus.
Just what *is* that power? First, of course, there is power
simply in abbreviation. A comparison of Newton's second
law in scalar and in vector form makes this clear:

$$\left.\begin{array}{l} f_1 = ma_1 \\ f_2 = ma_2 \\ f_3 = ma_3 \end{array}\right\} \ \mathbf{f} = m\mathbf{a}.$$

This is only a very mild example. In looking through older
books on physics or geometry, one often wonders how anyone could have seen the underlying physical reality through
the triple maze of coordinate-dependent scalar equations.
Yet abbreviation, though in itself often profoundly fruitful,
is only one aspect of the matter. The other is the abolition
of the coordinate-dependence just mentioned: vectors are
absolute.

In studying three-dimensional Euclidean analytic geometry, each "observer" can set up his standard coordinates
(right-handed orthogonal Cartesians) at any point and in
any orientation. Does this mean that there are as many
spaces as there are coordinate systems? No: underlying all
subjective "observations" there is a single space with *absolute* elements and properties, i.e., those on which all observers agree, such as specific points, specific straight lines,
distances between specific points and lines, angles between
lines, etc. Vector calculus treats these absolutes in a co-
ordinate-free way that makes their absoluteness evident.
All relations expressed vectorially, such as $\mathbf{a} = \mathbf{b} + \mathbf{c}$, or
$\mathbf{a} \cdot \mathbf{b} = c$, are necessarily absolute.

A (Cartesian) vector $\mathbf{a}$ can be defined as a number triple
(a_1, a_2, a_3) relative to any given Cartesian coordinate system, and the various vector operations can be defined via

these "components"; e.g., $\mathbf{b} + \mathbf{c} = (b_1 + c_1, b_2 + c_2, b_3 + c_3)$, or $\mathbf{a} \cdot \mathbf{b} = a_1 b_1 + a_2 b_2 + a_3 b_3$. But they can be interpreted absolutely, e.g., $\mathbf{a}$ as a directed line segment, $\mathbf{b} + \mathbf{c}$ by the parallelogram law, etc. Only operations having absolute significance are admissible. To check a vector equation, an observer could proceed *directly* by measuring absolutes like lengths and angles, but he would then really be a "superobserver." The observers we have in mind simply possess a standard coordinate lattice, and in fact they can be identified with such a lattice. Thus they could only read off components of all relevant vectors. To check a relation like $\mathbf{a} = \mathbf{b} + \mathbf{c}$, they would each obtain a set of three scalar equations $a_i = b_i + c_i$ ($i = 1, 2, 3$) which differ from observer to observer; but either all sets are false, or all are true. A vector (component) equation which is true in one coordinate system is true in all: this is the most salient feature of the vector calculus. Speaking technically, vector (component) equations are form-invariant under the rotations about the origin and the translations of axes which relate the different "observers" in Euclidean geometry and which in fact constitute the "relativity group" of Euclidean geometry.

The prototype of a three-vector is the displacement vector $\Delta\mathbf{r} = (\Delta x, \Delta y, \Delta z)$. Under a translation of axes its components remain unchanged, and under a rotation about the origin they suffer the same (linear, homogeneous) transformation as the coordinates themselves (compare (28.2)), say

$$\begin{aligned}
\Delta x' &= \alpha_{11}\Delta x + \alpha_{12}\Delta y + \alpha_{13}\Delta z \\
\Delta y' &= \alpha_{21}\Delta x + \alpha_{22}\Delta y + \alpha_{23}\Delta z \qquad (43.1) \\
\Delta z' &= \alpha_{31}\Delta x + \alpha_{32}\Delta y + \alpha_{33}\Delta z,
\end{aligned}$$

where the α's are certain functions of the angles of the rotation. *Any set of three components (a_1, a_2, a_3) which undergo exactly the same transformation (43.1) as $(\Delta x, \Delta y, \Delta z)$ under the contemplated changes of coordinates is said to constitute a three-vector.* This shows at once that if the components of two three-vectors are equal in one coordinate system, they are equal in all coordinate systems: for both sets of new components are the same linear combination of the old components. If $\mathbf{a} = (a_1, a_2, a_3)$ and $\mathbf{b} = (b_1, b_2, b_3)$ separately transform like $(\Delta x, \Delta y, \Delta z)$, then so does $\mathbf{a} + \mathbf{b} = (a_1 + b_1, a_2 + b_2, a_3 + b_3)$, because of the linearity of (43.1): hence sums of vectors are vectors. Similarly, if k is a *scalar* (or *invariant*), i.e. a number measured equally by all observers, then $k\mathbf{a}$ defined as (ka_1, ka_2, ka_3) is a vector. If (x, y, z) is the current point of a curve in space, and $\Delta l = (\Delta x^2 + \Delta y^2 + \Delta z^2)^{1/2}$ is the length of a chord (a scalar), we find on dividing (43.1) by Δl and letting $\Delta l \to 0$, that the "unit tangent"

$$\mathbf{t} = \frac{d\mathbf{r}}{dl} = \left(\frac{dx}{dl}, \frac{dy}{dl}, \frac{dz}{dl} \right) \qquad (43.2)$$

is a vector. Going from geometry to Newtonian mechanics now, if a particle moves along this curve, the time interval Δt between two events at the particle is a scalar. Dividing (43.1) by Δt and letting $\Delta t \to 0$, we see that the velocity $\mathbf{u} = d\mathbf{r}/dt$ is also a vector. (The position "vector" $\mathbf{r} = (x, y, z)$, however, is a vector *only* under rotations about the origin, not under translations.) One easily sees from (43.1) that the derivative of any vector with respect to a scalar (defined by differentiating its components) is also a vector. Thus the acceleration $\mathbf{a} = d\mathbf{u}/dt$ is a vector. Multiplying $\mathbf{u}$ and $\mathbf{a}$ by the mass m (a scalar) yields two more vectors, the momentum $\mathbf{p} = m\mathbf{u}$ and the force $\mathbf{f} = m\mathbf{a}$. Note how all the basic vectors of mechanics arise by the application of vector operations to the one prototype $(\Delta x, \Delta y, \Delta z)$.

Associated with each three-vector $\mathbf{a} = (a_1, a_2, a_3)$ there is a very important positive scalar, the norm or magnitude, written $|\mathbf{a}|$ or simply a, and defined by

$$a^2 = a_1^2 + a_2^2 + a_3^2, \quad a \geq 0. \qquad (43.3)$$

That this is invariant follows easily from the invariance of the squared norm $\Delta x^2 + \Delta y^2 + \Delta z^2$ of the prototype vector; i.e., it follows from the invariant metric of Euclidean space. If $\mathbf{a}$ and $\mathbf{b}$ are vectors, then $\mathbf{a} + \mathbf{b}$ is a vector, whose norm must be invariant; but

$$|\mathbf{a} + \mathbf{b}|^2 = (a_1 + b_1)^2 + (a_2 + b_2)^2 + (a_3 + b_3)^2$$
$$= a^2 + b^2 + 2(a_1 b_1 + a_2 b_2 + a_3 b_3),$$

and since a^2 and b^2 are invariant, it follows that the "scalar product"

$$\mathbf{a} \cdot \mathbf{b} = a_1 b_1 + a_2 b_2 + a_3 b_3 \qquad (43.4)$$

is invariant, i.e., coordinate-independent. If this were our first encounter with vectors, we would now look for the absolute (coordinate-independent) significance of $\mathbf{a} \cdot \mathbf{b}$, which *a priori* must exist; and by going to a specific coordinate system, we would soon discover it. The product $\mathbf{a} \cdot \mathbf{b}$, incidentally, as defined by (43.4), is easily seen to obey the Leibniz differentiation rule, $d(\mathbf{a} \cdot \mathbf{b}) = d\mathbf{a} \cdot \mathbf{b} + \mathbf{a} \cdot d\mathbf{b}$.

44   Four-Vectors

We are now ready to develop four-vectors by an almost direct analogy with three-vectors. And it is easy to guess what we are going to get: we shall get a vector calculus whose equations are form-invariant under *general* Lorentz transformations (see the final paragraph of Section 27), i.e., whose equations have precisely the property required by the relativity principle of all physical laws! This often enables us to recognize by its *form* alone whether a given or proposed law is Lorentz-invariant, and so assists greatly in the construction of relativistic physics. However, let it be said at once that not *all* Lorentz-invariant laws are expressible as relations between four-vectors; some require "four-tensors." (But none require more: even the so-called "spinor laws" are expressible tensorially.) We shall touch briefly on four-tensors in Section 45.

The prototype of a four-vector is the displacement four-vector $\Delta \mathbf{R} = (\Delta x, \Delta y, \Delta z, \Delta t)$ *between two events.* * The ad-

---

*Other authors (e.g. RSR) take as the prototype $(\Delta x, \Delta y, \Delta z, c\Delta t)$, whose advantage is that in the resulting calculus all components of a four-vector (or four-tensor) always have equal physical dimensions.

missible coordinate systems are the "standard" coordinates of inertial observers, and hence the relevant transformations are the general Lorentz transformations (compounded of translations, rotations about the origin, and standard LT's). These give rise to the four-dimensional analog of (43.1). We shall consistently use lower case boldface letters to denote three-vectors, and boldface capitals to denote four-vectors. Under spatial and temporal translations, the components of $\Delta \mathbf{R}$ (and thus of *any* four-vector) are unchanged; under spatial rotations about the origin, the first three components of $\Delta \mathbf{R}$ (and thus of *any* four-vector) transform like a three-vector, while the last component is unchanged; and under a standard LT, the components of a four-vector transform precisely as in (28.2). [The entity $\mathbf{R} = (x, y, z, t)$ is a four-vector *only* under homogeneous general LT's, i.e., those that leave $x = y = z = t = 0$ unchanged.] Sums and scalar multiples of four-vectors are defined by analogy with three-vectors, and are recognized as four-vectors.

An important scalar under general LT's is the squared interval Δs^2 or, in differential form, ds^2. However, it is often convenient to work instead with the corresponding *proper time* interval $d\tau$, defined by

$$d\tau^2 = \frac{ds^2}{c^2} = dt^2 - \frac{dx^2 + dy^2 + dz^2}{c^2}. \qquad (44.1)$$

This gets its name from the fact that, for a moving particle, $d\tau$ coincides with the dt that is measured by a clock attached to the particle; for in its instantaneous rest frame the particle satisfies $dx = dy = dz = 0$. We shall not be surprised, therefore, to find $d\tau$ appearing in many relativistic formulae where in the classical analog there is a dt. For example, if (x, y, z, t) are the coordinates of a moving particle, we find by dividing the four-dimensional analog of (43.1) by $\Delta\tau$ and letting $\Delta\tau \to 0$, that

$$\mathbf{U} = \frac{d\mathbf{R}}{d\tau} = \left(\frac{dx}{d\tau}, \frac{dy}{d\tau}, \frac{dz}{d\tau}, \frac{dt}{d\tau} \right) \qquad (44.2)$$

is a four-vector. This is called the *four-velocity* of the particle. It really is the analog of (43.2), and $\mathbf{U}$ can be regarded as the tangent vector of the worldline of the particle in spacetime. Now from (44.1),

$$\frac{d\tau^2}{dt^2} = 1 - \frac{dx^2 + dy^2 + dz^2}{c^2 dt^2} = 1 - \frac{u^2}{c^2},$$

u being the speed of the particle, whence

$$\frac{dt}{d\tau} = \gamma(u). \tag{44.3}$$

Since $dx/d\tau = (dx/dt)(dt/d\tau) = u_1 \gamma(u)$, etc., we see that

$$\mathbf{U} = \gamma(u)(u_1, u_2, u_3, 1) = \gamma(u)(\mathbf{u}, 1). \tag{44.4}$$

We shall often recognize in the first three components of a four-vector the components of a familiar three-vector (or a multiple thereof), and in such cases we adopt the notation exemplified by (44.4).

As in three-vector theory, scalar derivatives of four-vectors (defined by differentiating the components) are themselves four-vectors. Thus, in particular,

$$\mathbf{A} = \frac{d\mathbf{U}}{d\tau} = \frac{d^2\mathbf{R}}{d\tau^2} \tag{44.5}$$

is a four-vector, called the *four-acceleration*. Its relation to the three-acceleration $\mathbf{a}$ is not quite as simple as that of $\mathbf{U}$ to $\mathbf{u}$; by (44.3), we have

$$\mathbf{A} = \gamma \frac{d\mathbf{U}}{dt} = \gamma \frac{d}{dt}(\gamma\mathbf{u}, \gamma), \tag{44.6}$$

and it is easily seen from this that the components of $\mathbf{A}$ *in the rest frame* of the particle ($u = 0$) are given by

$$\mathbf{A} = (\mathbf{a}, 0), \tag{44.7}$$

since the derivative of γ contains a factor u.

The norm or magnitude $|\mathbf{V}|$ or V of a four-vector $\mathbf{V} = (V_1, V_2, V_3, V_4)$ is defined by

$$V^2 = -V_1^2 - V_2^2 - V_3^2 + c^2 V_4^2, \tag{44.8}$$

and its invariance follows from the invariance of the

squared norm $-\Delta x^2 - \Delta y^2 - \Delta z^2 + c^2 \Delta t^2$ of the prototype vector. Precisely as in (43.4) we deduce from the invariance of $|\mathbf{V}|$, $|\mathbf{W}|$ and $|\mathbf{V} + \mathbf{W}|$ that the *scalar product* $\mathbf{V} \cdot \mathbf{W}$, defined by

$$\mathbf{V} \cdot \mathbf{W} = -V_1 W_1 - V_2 W_2 - V_3 W_3 + c^2 V_4 W_4, \qquad (44.9)$$

is invariant. For example, by looking at $\mathbf{U}$ and $\mathbf{A}$ in the rest frame, it is clear from (44.4) and (44.7) that

$$\mathbf{U} \cdot \mathbf{A} = 0 \qquad\qquad (44.10)$$

there; but since this is an invariant, it must therefore vanish in all frames. Thus the four-velocity is "orthogonal" to the four-acceleration. If $\mathbf{A}, \mathbf{B}, \mathbf{C}$ are arbitrary four-vectors, one easily verifies at once from the definitions that

$$\mathbf{A} \cdot \mathbf{A} = A^2, \quad (\mathbf{A} + \mathbf{B}) \cdot \mathbf{C} = \mathbf{A} \cdot \mathbf{C} + \mathbf{B} \cdot \mathbf{C}.$$

We next inquire into the absolute significance of the scalar product. We do not expect this to be purely geometric, but rather kinematic, since LT's are essentially concerned with motion. Let $\mathbf{U}$ and $\mathbf{V}$ be the four-velocities of two particles, and let us look at $\mathbf{U} \cdot \mathbf{V}$ in the rest frame of the first, relative to which the second has velocity v, say; then, by (44.4) and (44.9),

$$\mathbf{U} \cdot \mathbf{V} = c^2 \gamma(v). \qquad\qquad (44.11)$$

Thus $\mathbf{U} \cdot \mathbf{V}$ is c^2 times the Lorentz factor of the *relative* velocity of the corresponding particles. Of course, four-velocities are not *arbitrary* four-vectors, if only because their norms are always c (put $\mathbf{U} = \mathbf{V}$ in (44.11)). But we shall not need an absolute interpretation in other cases. The norm of the four-acceleration is apparent from (44.7):

$$A^2 = -a_0^2, \qquad\qquad (44.12)$$

where a_0 is the norm of the proper three-acceleration. As in the case of $\mathbf{a} \cdot \mathbf{b}$, it can be seen at once from (44.9) that $\mathbf{V} \cdot \mathbf{W}$ obeys Leibniz's rule,

$$d(\mathbf{V} \cdot \mathbf{W}) = d\mathbf{V} \cdot \mathbf{W} + \mathbf{V} \cdot d\mathbf{W}. \qquad (44.13)$$

As an example, we may differentiate the equation $\mathbf{U} \cdot \mathbf{U} = c^2$, and so obtain (44.10) again.

45   *Four-Tensors*

The typical transformation scheme (43.1) as applied to a three-vector **a** may be written in abbreviated form as

$$a_i' = \sum_{j=1}^{3} \alpha_{ij} a_j, \tag{45.1}$$

while the analogous transformation for a four-vector **A** may be written

$$A'^{\mu} = \sum_{\nu=1}^{4} \alpha_{\nu}^{\mu} A^{\nu}. \tag{45.2}$$

Greek indices are traditional here; and so is the use of both upper and lower indices: there is a certain convention which tells us which to use, but we need not go into this now. For three-vectors the convention does not distinguish between upper and lower indices, and so we can place them where we wish.

Just as four-*vectors* are defined by the behavior of their components under general LT's, so also are four-*tensors*. But the latter have more components than just four. For example, a four-tensor of *rank* 2 has 4^2 components $A^{\mu\nu}$, which obey the transformation rule

$$A'^{\mu\nu} = \sum_{\sigma,\tau=1}^{4} \alpha_{\sigma}^{\mu} \alpha_{\tau}^{\nu} A^{\sigma\tau}, \tag{45.3}$$

where the α's are the same as in (45.2). In general, a four-tensor of rank n has 4^n components, which are written with n indices, and they transform analogously to (45.3). Four-vectors, then, are simply four-tensors of rank 1. Many of their basic properties are typical for all four-tensors. E.g., four-tensor (component) equations are form-invariant under general LT's; and sums, scalar multiples, and scalar derivatives of four-tensors (defined by the corresponding operations on their components) are clearly four-tensors. One obvious way to construct a second-rank tensor is to form the "outer" (or "tensor") product $A^{\mu}B^{\nu}$ of two vectors **A** and **B** (sometimes written **A** $\otimes$ **B**). Certain combinations of the components of four-tensors, corresponding to the scalar product $\mathbf{A} \cdot \mathbf{B}$ of four-vectors, also play an important role in the theory, but we shall not pursue this subject further here. (The interested reader may consult RSR for details. Tensor theory is taken up again in Section 72, though from a more general point of view.)

The Null Cone   46

There is one particular in which the analogy between Euclidean three-space and spacetime (and between three-vectors and four-vectors) breaks down. Whereas the metric $\Delta x^2 + \Delta y^2 + \Delta z^2$ of three-space is always positive, the metric of spacetime can be positive, zero, or negative. (And so, correspondingly, can the squared norm of four-vectors.) From this it follows that spacetime is not isotropic, i.e., not all displacements away from a given event $\mathcal{P}$ are equivalent. Rather, they fall into three distinct classes according to the sign of their squared norm. Displacements with $\Delta s^2 > 0$ are separated from displacements with $\Delta s^2 < 0$ by those with $\Delta s^2 = 0$. These last, as we have noted before, correspond to events connectible with $\mathcal{P}$ by a light signal and evidently satisfy the equation

$$c^2 \Delta t^2 = \Delta x^2 + \Delta y^2 + \Delta z^2. \qquad (46.1)$$

Under suppression of one spatial dimension, say the z dimension, this equation represents a right circular cone (see Figure 10) on a set of axes Δx, Δy, $c\Delta t$ corresponding to any one particular observer. Nevertheless, this cone, called the *null cone* or *light cone* at $\mathcal{P}$, is absolute (i.e., independent of any particular observer), and so is the separation of events into three classes relative to $\mathcal{P}$. In full spacetime, the null cone at $\mathcal{P}$, regarded as a set of events, is the history of a spherical light front π which converges onto the event and diverges again away from it. In Figure 10, π is reduced to a circle collapsing to and expanding from the event $\mathcal{P}$, with the passage of time. Events whose displacement relative to

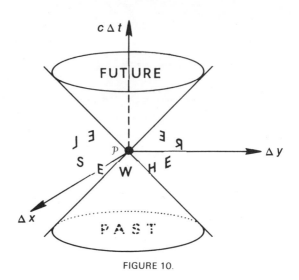

FIGURE 10.

$\mathcal{P}$ have positive squared norm lie inside the cone, i.e., where the time axis is, whereas those with negative squared norm lie outside. In full spacetime the former occur at points *within* the collapsing or expanding light sphere π. Thus, all events that can be attended by a particle present at $\mathcal{P}$ lie inside the cone. Conversely, all vector displacements from $\mathcal{P}$ into the cone correspond to possible particle worldlines through $\mathcal{P}$, hence to possible inertial observers, and hence to possible t axes in spacetime; they are therefore called *timelike*. No particle can be present both at $\mathcal{P}$ and at an event outside the cone. Corresponding displacements are called *spacelike*. And for obvious reasons, displacements from $\mathcal{P}$ along the cone are called *lightlike* or *null*. According as their squared norm is positive, zero, or negative, we shall classify *all* four-vectors as timelike, null, or spacelike. Thus, for example, the four-velocity $\mathbf{U}$ is timelike, while the four-acceleration $\mathbf{A}$ is spacelike. Note that a four-vector can be null without being zero, i.e., without having all its components zero.

We have already seen (at the end of Section 28) that all observers agree on the time sequence of two events which are connectible in any frame by a signal with speed $\leq c$. Consequently, the events on and within the upper sheet of the null cone are regarded by *all* observers as occurring *after* $\mathcal{P}$, and they are said to constitute the *absolute future* of $\mathcal{P}$. Similarly, the events on and within the lower sheet of the cone constitute the *absolute past* of $\mathcal{P}$. Events in the remaining region form the "elsewhere." Since no inertial observer can be present at $\mathcal{P}$ and one of the latter events, they can never be considered to happen at the same place as $\mathcal{P}$; hence the name. The time separation between $\mathcal{P}$ and an event in the "elsewhere," as measured by various inertial observers, varies all the way from minus to plus infinity (see equation (28.4)).

The Minkowski diagram shown in Figure 6 is nothing but a null cone diagram like that shown in Figure 10 with yet another spatial dimension suppressed. Thus Figure 10 may be regarded as a three-dimensional Minkowski diagram, and may be used, like Figure 6, to illustrate or solve SR problems.

The null cones at each event imprint a "grain" onto spacetime, which has no analog in isotropic Euclidean space, but is somewhat reminiscent of crystal structure. Light travels along the grain, and particle worldlines have to be within the null cone at each of their points.

It should be clear from our discussion that, given *any* timelike vector **V,** we can find coordinates in spacetime to make its first three components vanish: we need merely choose the t axis parallel to **V.** Similarly, given any spacelike vector **W,** we can make its last three components vanish by choosing the x axis parallel to **W.** For a null vector (and indeed, for any vector) we can make two of the spatial components vanish, simply by a rotation of the spatial axes. (See also exercise 4-7.) These simplifications are sometimes very useful.

An Example: Wave Motion   *47*

As a good example of the power of four-vectors, we shall here investigate the transformation properties of plane waves. Consider a series of plane "disturbances" or "wave-crests," of an unspecified nature, a wavelength λ apart, and progressing in a unit direction $\mathbf{n} = (l, m, n)$ at speed w relative to a frame S. A plane in S with normal $\mathbf{n}$ and at distance p from a point $P_0(x_0, y_0, z_0)$ is given by

$$l(x - x_0) + m(y - y_0) + n(z - z_0) = p.$$

If this propagates with speed w, the equation is

$$l\Delta x + m\Delta y + n\Delta z = w\Delta t,$$

where Δt measures time from when the plane crosses P_0, and $\Delta x = x - x_0$, etc. A whole set of such traveling planes, at distances λ apart, has the same equation with $N\lambda$ added to the right-hand side, N being any integer. And this can be written as

$$\mathbf{L} \cdot \Delta \mathbf{R} = N, (N \text{ any integer}), \qquad (47.1)$$

where

$$\mathbf{L} = \frac{1}{\lambda}\left(\mathbf{n}, \frac{w}{c^2}\right) = \nu\left(\frac{\mathbf{n}}{w}, \frac{1}{c^2}\right), \qquad (47.2)$$

$\nu = w/\lambda$ being the frequency. Conversely, any equation of form (47.1) will be recognized as representing a moving set of equidistant planes, with λ, $\mathbf{n}$, and w determined by (47.2). We have written $\mathbf{L}$ *like* a four-vector, though we do not yet know that it is one. Suppose, however, we transform (47.1) directly to an arbitrary second frame S': since the components of $\Delta \mathbf{R}$ undergo a general LT, i.e., a linear homogeneous transformation, we shall get on the left a linear homogeneous polynomial in $\Delta x'$, $\Delta y'$, $\Delta z'$, $\Delta t'$, and on the right N as before:

$$\mathbf{L}' \cdot \Delta \mathbf{R}' = N,$$

where $\Delta \mathbf{R}'$ stands for $(\Delta x', \ldots, \Delta t')$ and $\mathbf{L}'$ stands for the coefficients of these components. On the other hand, by the invariance of the scalar product, it is certainly true that

$$\mathbf{T}' \cdot \Delta \mathbf{R}' = N,$$

where $\mathbf{T}'$ stands for the vector transforms into S' of the components of $\mathbf{L}$. Hence, by subtraction,

$$(\mathbf{L}' - \mathbf{T}') \cdot \Delta \mathbf{R}' = 0. \qquad (47.3)$$

We can certainly find four linearly independent vectors $\Delta \mathbf{R}'$ corresponding to events on the planes, and thus satisfying (47.3) (e.g., of the form $(a,0,0,0)$, $(0,b,0,0)$, $(0,0,c,0)$, $(0,0,0,d)$). But this implies that $(\mathbf{L}' - \mathbf{T}') = 0$, i.e., $\mathbf{L}' = \mathbf{T}'$, or, in words, that the components of $\mathbf{L}$ *do* transform as vector components. Hence $\mathbf{L}$ *is* a vector. It is called the *frequency four-vector*.

Now consider the usual two frames S and S' in standard configuration, and in S a train of plane waves with frequency ν and velocity w in a direction $\mathbf{n} = -(\cos \alpha, \sin \alpha, 0)$. The components of the frequency vector in S are given by

$$\mathbf{L} = \left(\frac{-\nu \cos \alpha}{w}, \frac{-\nu \sin \alpha}{w}, 0, \frac{\nu}{c^2} \right). \qquad (47.4)$$

Transforming these components by the scheme (28.2), we find for the components in S':

$$\frac{\nu' \cos \alpha'}{w'} = \frac{\gamma \nu (\cos \alpha + vw/c^2)}{w}, \qquad (47.5)$$

$$\frac{\nu' \sin \alpha'}{w'} = \frac{\nu \sin \alpha}{w}, \qquad (47.6)$$

$$\nu' = \nu \gamma \left(1 + \frac{v}{w} \cos \alpha \right). \qquad (47.7)$$

The last equation expresses the Doppler effect for waves of all velocities, and, in particular, for light waves ($w = c$). In the latter case, it is seen to be equivalent to our previous formula (40.4).

From (47.5) and (47.6), we obtain the general wave aberration formula

$$\tan \alpha' = \frac{\sin \alpha}{\gamma (\cos \alpha + vw/c^2)}. \qquad (47.8)$$

In the particular case when $w = c$, this is seen to be equivalent to our previous formulae (41.1) and (41.2)—in fact, it corresponds to their quotient.

Finally, to get the transformation of w, we *could* eliminate the irrelevant quantities from (47.5) through (47.7), yet it is simpler to make use of the invariance of $|\mathbf{L}|^2$. Writing this down in S and S', we obtain

$$\nu^2 \left(1 - \frac{c^2}{w^2}\right) = \nu'^2 \left(1 - \frac{c^2}{w'^2}\right), \tag{47.9}$$

whence, by use of (47.7),

$$1 - \frac{c^2}{w'^2} = \frac{(1 - c^2/w^2)(1 - v^2/c^2)}{(1 + v \cos \alpha/w)^2}. \tag{47.10}$$

This formula is *not* analogous to (36.5). The reason is that a particle riding the crest of a wave in the direction of the wave normal in one frame does not, in general, do so in another frame: there it rides the crest of the wave also, but not in the normal direction. The one exception is when $w = c$.

5

Relativistic Particle Mechanics

Domain of Sufficient Validity of Newton's Laws · 48

Newton's mechanics is not Lorentz-invariant. According to the program of special relativity, therefore, a new mechanics had to be constructed, which is generally known as "relativistic" mechanics. This is not really a good name, since, as we have seen, Newton's mechanics, too, is relativistic, but under the "wrong" (Galilean) transformation group. Still, Newton's theory has excellently served astronomy (e.g., in foretelling eclipses and planetary motions in general), it has been used as the basic theory in the incredibly delicate operations of sending probes to Moon and Venus, and it has proved itself reliable in countless terrestrial applications. Thus it cannot be *entirely* wrong. Before the twentieth century, in fact, only a single case of irreducible failure was known, namely the excessive advance of the perihelion of the planet Mercury (by about 43 seconds of arc per century). Since the advent of modern

particle accelerators, however, vast discrepancies with Newton's laws have been uncovered, whereas the new mechanics
consistently gave correct descriptions.* This new mechanics overlaps with the old in a large domain of applications
(dealing with motions that are slow compared with the
speed of light) and, in fact, it delineates the domain of sufficient validity of the old mechanics as a function of the desired accuracy. Roughly speaking, the old mechanics is in
error to the extent that the γ-factors of the various motions
involved exceed unity. But within its acceptable domain,
Newton's theory will undoubtedly continue to be used for
reasons of technical convenience. It simply must not be
stretched unduly, as for example, by applying it to the action of a constant force on a particle to the stage where
the velocity approaches or exceeds c.

49   *Why Gravity Does Not Fit into Special Relativity*

In this chapter we shall restrict ourselves to the mechanics
of mass points *in the absence of gravity.* We shall construct
a new collision mechanics within special relativity. Several
attempts have been made to construct also new theories of
gravitation within special relativity, but this can only be
done at the heavy cost of abandoning the equivalence principle. For, by its very nature, the EP excludes gravity from
SR: it allows SR to be done in the vicinity of gravitating
matter, but only in those local inertial frames in which the
gravity cannot be felt.

No single "rigid" frame containing a "mass point" like
the sun could itself be inertial if we accept the EP and the
uniform relative motion of inertial frames. For all the local
inertial frames around the sun accelerate towards the sun,
and no motion of the large frame could eliminate *all* these
accelerations. Yet, in order to discuss gravity within SR,

---

*Of course, Newton's mechanics has undergone *two* "corrections," one due to
relativity and one to quantum mechanics. We are here concerned exclusively with
the former.

one *must* have inertial frames large enough to contain mass points and their fields. The only way out is to go back to Newton's extended inertial frames; to regard gravity as an "overlay" that does not systematically affect the rest of physics; and to apply SR to these extended frames.

But this would imply a definite break with the EP: not in the local frames but in the extended frames would the relativistic laws of physics hold. Thus, presumably, light would travel rectilinearly *not* in the freely falling elevator cabin, but outside. This, of course, leads to testable predictions, and, as we have seen, the evidence here favors the EP. Other difficulties concern the very setting up of "standard" coordinates: *if* gravity bends light, we no longer have straight signals to help us synchronize clocks, for example, in an extended frame. If, in particular, the gravitational field is nonstationary, synchronization by signaling methods then becomes impossible. One could still fall back on another synchronization method that is above suspicion in ordinary SR, namely, the infinitely slow transport of standard clocks. (For the total time lag suffered by such a clock over a given distance in an inertial frame tends to zero with its velocity.) However, one would have to assume that the gravitational field has no effect on the clock rate. And this is in contradiction with the gravitational red shift phenomenon—itself a consequence of the EP, but well established empirically by now.

For reasons such as these, and others, Einstein was driven to construct a theory of gravitation (general relativity) which lies outside SR, without, however, contradicting it: rather, it generalizes it. We shall discuss general relativity in Chapter VII. For the moment, we restrict our discussion to problems in which the gravitational forces are negligible.

Shortcut to Relativistic Mechanics *50*

Though the result is always the same, there are many different ways of deriving, or justifying, the new mechanics. One very quick way is to assume that there will still exist a law of momentum conservation, the momentum **p** being defined as inertial mass times velocity:

$$\mathbf{p} = m\mathbf{v}. \qquad (50.1)$$

Consider a very slight glancing collision of two equal spherical particles A and A', at rest, respectively, in the two usual inertial frames S and S', before collision. By symmetry, these spheres after collision will have equal and opposite transverse velocity components (at right angles to the x axes) in their respective frames, say of magnitude u. By (36.4)(ii), the transverse velocity of A' relative to S will therefore be $\sim u/\gamma(v)$. Transverse momentum conservation in S then implies

$$Mu \approx \frac{M'u}{\gamma(v)}, \qquad (50.2)$$

where M and M' are the post-collision masses of A and A', respectively, in S. Now let $u \rightarrow 0$, i.e., consider ever more glancing collisions. Then $M \rightarrow m_0$, the "rest mass" of one particle, and $M' \rightarrow m$, the mass at velocity v of an identical particle. Proceeding to the limit in (50.2), we get

$$m = \gamma(v)m_0. \qquad (50.3)$$

This conclusion is inevitable *if* momentum is conserved. (For consistency, however, it still remains to be shown that *with* this definition of mass, momentum conservation in all collisions is indeed a Lorentz-invariant requirement.) Note that, according to (50.3), the inertial mass of a particle increases with v from a minimum m_0 at $v = 0$ to infinity as $v \rightarrow c$. We should not be too surprised at this, since there must be *some* process in nature to prevent particles from being accelerated beyond the speed of light.

For accelerating particles, incidentally, we shall have to adopt a hypothesis (the *mass hypothesis*—analogous to our previous clock and length hypotheses), namely that the mass depends only on the instantaneous velocity according to (50.3), and *not* on the acceleration.

Equation (50.3) contains the germ of the famous mass-energy equivalence discovered by Einstein. For, expanding (50.3) by the binomial theorem we find, to second order,

$$m = m_0 \left(1 - \frac{v^2}{c^2}\right)^{-1/2} \approx m_0 + \frac{\frac{1}{2}m_0 v^2}{c^2}. \tag{50.4}$$

This shows that the mass of a particle, in a frame in which it moves, exceeds its rest mass by $1/c^2$ times its kinetic energy (assuming the approximate validity of the Newtonian expression for the latter). Consequently, energy appears to *contribute* to the mass in a way that would be consistent with Einstein's postulate of a general mass-energy equivalence according to the formula

$$E = mc^2. \tag{50.5}$$

Note that the inertial mass m of a particle is *defined* by momentum conservation, i.e., as that quantity which would be calculated if, for example, a particle A were made to collide with a standard particle at rest, and the masses of A before and after collision were calculated from momentum conservation and from the observed velocities. If (50.5) is valid, then the conservation of energy is equivalent to the conservation of inertial mass. (However, for consistency, we shall still have to show that with this formula for the energy, energy conservation in *all* collisions is a Lorentz-invariant requirement.)

Apart from the question of consistency, we now have the laws of relativistic collision mechanics in a nutshell: Newton's first law (already accepted previously), plus conservation of momentum and energy, with momentum and energy defined by (50.1), (50.3), and (50.5).

Formal Approach to Relativistic Mechanics   *51*

A second approach to the new mechanics is formal, and consists essentially in *guessing* the right form of the relativistic laws, aided by four-vector theory. However, as in most such cases, we have at the back of our minds some concrete results or conjectures. In the present case, we have the tentative results of the preceding section, plus the fact that Newton's laws cannot be entirely wrong.

Let us define for each particle a scalar, characteristic of its internal state: the rest mass (or proper mass) m_0. This is to be regarded as identical with the Newtonian mass which the particle manifests in slow-motion experiments. We then define for each particle, analogously to Newton's momentum $m_0\mathbf{u}$, a four-momentum

$$\mathbf{P} = m_0\mathbf{U} = m_0\gamma(u)(\mathbf{u}, 1) = (\mathbf{p}, m), \qquad (51.1)$$

where $\mathbf{U}$ is the four-velocity (44.4) of the particle, and $\mathbf{p}$ and m are defined by this equation, i.e.,

$$m = \gamma(u)m_0, \qquad (51.2)$$
$$\mathbf{p} = m\mathbf{u}. \qquad (51.3)$$

We call these quantities the *relativistic (inertial) mass* and the *relativistic momentum*, respectively. (For the moment we shall assume $u < c$ and $m_0 \neq 0$. But, as will be shown in detail in Section 59, it is possible to include in the theory also particles of zero rest mass m_0 moving at speed c—e.g., photons—which nevertheless have finite m and $\mathbf{p}$. Most results about ordinary particles can be extended to zero rest mass particles also.)

In any collision between two particles having four-momenta $\mathbf{P}_1$, $\mathbf{P}_2$ before collision and $\mathbf{P}_3$, $\mathbf{P}_4$ afterwards, the *conservation of four-momentum,*

$$\mathbf{P}_1 + \mathbf{P}_2 = \mathbf{P}_3 + \mathbf{P}_4, \qquad (51.4)$$

is clearly a Lorentz-invariant requirement, and is equivalent, because of (51.1), to the separate conservation equations (suffixes being used as in (51.4))

$$\mathbf{p}_1 + \mathbf{p}_2 = \mathbf{p}_3 + \mathbf{p}_4, \qquad (51.5)$$
$$m_1 + m_2 = m_3 + m_4. \qquad (51.6)$$

(All these equations clearly generalize to collisions in which more than two particles participate, or in which more, or fewer, or other particles emerge than went in.) Moreover, the truth of (51.5) in *all* inertial frames would imply the truth of (51.6) in all frames, and vice versa. [For, quite generally, if a four-vector $\mathbf{V}$ (in our case, $\mathbf{P}_1 + \mathbf{P}_2 - \mathbf{P}_3 - \mathbf{P}_4$) has one particular one of its four components zero in *all* inertial frames, then the whole vector must vanish. To prove this, suppose first that one of the spatial components of $\mathbf{V}$ is always zero, and, without loss of generality, let it be the first. Then if there is a frame in which one of the other spatial components is *nonzero*, apply a rotation to interchange the relevant space axis with the x axis, whereupon the x-component will become nonzero, contrary to hypothesis; if, on the other hand, there exists a frame in which the temporal component of $\mathbf{V}$ is nonzero, a LT (28.2) will produce a nonzero x-component, again contrary to hypothesis. Next, suppose $\mathbf{V}$ always has its temporal component equal to zero. Then if there exists a frame in which a spatial component is nonzero, without loss of generality let it be the first, and apply a LT: now a nonzero fourth component will appear, contrary to hypothesis. This establishes our result.]

Now let us put the various bits together. In the last section we proved that *if* a momentum of the form $m\mathbf{u}$ is conserved, then the mass m must be of the form (51.2), i.e., the momentum must be the "relativistic" momentum as defined above. We have now shown that the conservation of relativistic momentum *and* of relativistic mass together give a possible (Lorentz-invariant) law, and that we cannot have the one without the other. Finally, in the case of slow motion, m reduces to the Newtonian mass m_0 and $\mathbf{p}$ to the Newtonian momentum $m_0\mathbf{u}$; thus if, for a certain collision, there exist frames in which all the motions are slow, the proposed relativistic momentum conservation law (51.5) reduces in such frames to the well-established Newtonian analog, and so does (51.6). In other situations there was no precedent to follow at the time when the new mechanics was first constructed, yet the formalism strongly suggested general adoption of (51.5) as a *postulate*, with its *corollary* (51.6) (or vice versa), i.e., equivalently, the adoption of (51.4). This has been thoroughly borne out by experiment in the sequel.

From (51.1) we obtain two alternative expressions for the norm of **P**,

$$P^2 = c^2 m_0^2 = c^2 m^2 - p^2, \qquad (51.7)$$

from which we deduce the important formula

$$p^2 = c^2(m^2 - m_0^2). \qquad (51.8)$$

The conservation law (51.6) is really quite different from the classical conservation law of mass, which was naturally thought of as the conservation of matter. Equation (51.6) involves velocities, and is therefore much more analogous to the classical conservation of kinetic energy in perfectly elastic collisions, except that it holds in *all* collisions, including nonelastic ones. Thus, even without the considerations of the preceding section, one can be led from the purely formal viewpoint to regard (51.6) as the conservation of total *energy*, and to postulate that the total energy of a particle is a multiple of its inertial mass. That this multiple must be c^2 is then clear from (50.4).

52   *A Note on Galilean Four-Vectors*

In analogy to Minkowskian four-vectors, one can define "Galilean" four-vectors as those that transform like $(\Delta x, \Delta y, \Delta z, \Delta t)$ under a general Galilean transformation (i.e., (3.1) compounded with spatial rotations and spatial and temporal translations). The vanishing of the spatial components of a Galilean four-vector in all inertial frames implies the vanishing also of its temporal component, since a Galilean transformation would otherwise produce a non-zero spatial component in some frame. Evidently, $m_0(\mathbf{u}, 1)$ constitutes a Galilean four-vector (multiply the prototype by the scalar $m_0/\Delta t$ and go to the limit), and thus, as in the relativistic case, the conservation of Newtonian momentum $m_0 \mathbf{u}$ under Galilean transformations implies the conservation of Newtonian mass m_0. But *not* vice versa!

Equivalence of Mass and Energy   *53*

All through relativistic physics there occur indications that mass and energy are equivalent according to the formula

$$E = mc^2. \tag{53.1}$$

We have seen in Section 50 that kinetic energy *contributes* to the total mass of a particle according to this formula (at least, to lowest order). Hence *all* energy has mass, since all energy is convertible into kinetic energy. [Suppose, for example, that a particle's *heat* energy is increased by an amount ΔE. Now use up this extra heat energy to split the particle and drive the pieces apart. The pieces will have a total *kinetic* energy ΔE, which increases their mass by $\Delta E/c^2$. By mass conservation, therefore, this must have been the mass increment due to the heat energy ΔE before the splitting.]

We shall see in Section 57 that the work done on a particle by a relativistic force contributes to its mass according to formula (53.1), rigorously. Further indications appear in Maxwell's theory: for example, Kelvin's energy density $(e^2 + h^2)/8\pi$ and Thomson's momentum density $\mathbf{e} \times \mathbf{h}/4\pi c$ reduce to $e^2/4\pi$ and $e^2/4\pi c$ in the case of radiation (when $\mathbf{e}$ and $\mathbf{h}$ are equal and orthogonal) so that (energy/c^2) × (velocity) = momentum. Even general relativity corroborates this equivalence. (See Section 73, last paragraph but two, and Section 76.) The ultimate reason for all this is that Lorentz-invariance severely restricts all possible conservation laws and that essentially there *can* be only one nondirectional velocity-dependent conserved quantity, namely m (see RSR, Section 27), and one directional one, namely $m\mathbf{u}$ as we have seen; and both or neither are conserved.

The only direct theoretical indications available to Einstein when he proposed $E = mc^2$ were that energy *contributes* to mass (as in our example of the kinetic energy). To equate *all* mass with energy required an act of aesthetic faith, very characteristic of Einstein. For one of the prime attributes of energy is its transmutability, and implicit in (53.1) is the assertion that *all* the mass of a particle can be transmuted into available energy. It would be perfectly consistent with special relativity if the elementary particles were indestructible. Energy would then merely *contribute* to mass and the available energy of a compound particle of mass m would be $c^2(m - q)$, where q is the total rest mass of its constituent elementary particles. In free systems of particles, each of the sums $\Sigma c^2 m$, $\Sigma c^2 q$, $\Sigma c^2(m - q)$ would then be separately conserved, but only the last could justly be called energy. The bold hypothesis (53.1), however, was amply confirmed by later experience, especially by the observation of "pair annihilation" in which an elementary particle and its anti-particle annihilate each other and set free a corresponding amount of radiative energy; also by the spontaneous decay of neutral mesons into photon pairs; and by collisions in which different elementary particles emerge than went in, with different total rest mass.

We shall distinguish between the *kinetic* energy T, which a particle possesses by virtue of its motion,

$$T = c^2(m - m_0), \tag{53.2}$$

and its *internal* energy $c^2 m_0$. For an "ordinary" particle, this internal energy is vast: in each gram of mass there are 9.10^{20} ergs of energy, roughly the energy of the Hiroshima bomb (20 kilotons). A very small part of this energy resides in the thermal motions of the molecules constituting the particle, and can be given up as heat; a part resides in the intermolecular and interatomic cohesion forces, and in the latter form it can sometimes be given up in chemical explosions; another part may reside in excited atoms and escape in the form of radiation; much more resides in nuclear bonds and can also sometimes be set free, as in atomic explosions. But by far the largest part of the energy (about 99%) resides simply in the mass of the ultimate particles, and cannot be further explained. Nevertheless, it too can be liberated under suitable conditions, e.g., when matter and antimatter annihilate each other. Generally, therefore, *rest mass* will not be conserved in relativistic collisions.

We note that, according to Einstein's hypothesis, *every* form of energy has a mass equivalent: (i) Anticipating the fact that all mass exerts and suffers gravity, we shall expect even an electromagnetic field to exert a gravitational attraction, and light to bend under gravity (this we have already deduced by a different line of reasoning). (ii) We shall expect a gravitational field *itself* to gravitate. (iii) The radiation which the sun pours into space is equivalent to more than four million tons of mass per second! Radiation, having mass and velocity, must also have momentum; accordingly, the radiation from the sun is thought to be at least a contributing factor in the observed deflection of the tails of comets away from the sun. (iv) An electric motor (with battery) at one end of a car, driving a heavy flywheel at the other end by means of a belt, transfers energy and thus mass to the flywheel; in obeyance to the law of momentum conservation, the car must therefore move in the opposite direction. (v) Stretched or compressed objects have more mass by virtue of the stored potential energy. (vi) The total mass of the separate components of an atom, held together by nuclear forces, exceeds the mass of the atom, since energy (i.e., mass) would have to be supplied in order to decompose the atom. This is the reason for the well-known "mass defect."

The Center of Momentum Frame   *54*

We have seen in Section 46 that, given any timelike four-vector **V**, there exists a frame S_0 in which its components reduce to $(0, 0, 0, V_4)$. Moreover, the *sign* of the fourth component is invariant, since **V** either "points" into the absolute future ($V_4 > 0$) or into the absolute past ($V_4 < 0$). If **W** is a second timelike vector "isochronous" with **V** (i.e., $V_4 W_4 > 0$), then in S_0 we have

$$| \mathbf{V} + \mathbf{W} |^2 = c^2(V_4 + W_4)^2 - W_1^2 - W_2^2 - W_3^2$$
$$= V^2 + W^2 + 2c^2 V_4 W_4 > 0. \qquad (54.1)$$

Hence the sum of two isochronous timelike vectors is another timelike vector, and clearly isochronous with the summands. By iteration we see that the same is true of any number of timelike isochronous vectors.

Now, by (51.1), all four-momenta of particles with non-zero rest mass are timelike (since $\mathbf{U}$ is) and isochronous (since $m > 0$). Consequently, in a system of such particles subject to no forces except mutual collisions, the total four-momentum $\overline{\mathbf{P}} = \Sigma \mathbf{P}$ is timelike,* and there exists a frame S_0 in which its spatial components vanish. This frame is unique up to a rotation of spatial axes: for, in an arbitrary frame S,

$$\overline{\mathbf{P}} = (\overline{\mathbf{p}}, \overline{m}), \qquad (54.2)$$

(bars denoting sums over all the particles of the system), and the velocity of S_0 relative to S must be

$$\mathbf{u} = \overline{\mathbf{p}}/\overline{m}. \qquad (54.3)$$

In S_0 the total three-momentum of the system vanishes, hence S_0 is sometimes called the CM (center of mass) frame of the system, though "center of momentum" is a better reading. For in contrast to Newton's theory, relativistic mechanics allows no unique point to be designated as *the* center of mass of a system. And it is easy to see why: suppose two identical particles move in opposite directions along parallel lines l_1 and l_2, and suppose l is the line mid-

---

*There is a subtlety involved here: if all observers agreed on which individual $\mathbf{P}$'s make up the sum $\Sigma \mathbf{P}$, then $\Sigma \mathbf{P}$ would *clearly* be a vector. But each forms the sum at one instant in *his* frame, which may result in different $\mathbf{P}$'s making up the $\Sigma \mathbf{P}$ of different observers. A spacetime diagram such as Figure 10 is useful in proving that $\Sigma \mathbf{P}$ is nevertheless a vector, and the suppression of z makes the argument a little more transparent without affecting its validity. A simultaneity of S is given by the horizontal plane π through $\mathscr{P}$, and a simultaneity of S' is given by a tilted plane π' through $\mathscr{P}$. Now the observer in S would get the same result by forming his $\Sigma \mathbf{P}$ over π' instead of π: For as π is tilted into coincidence with π', each $\mathbf{P}$ remains constant except when π moves across a collision; but then the relevant sub-sum of $\Sigma \mathbf{P}$ remains constant. In the end, observers in S and S' are indeed summing the *same* $\mathbf{P}$'s. Hence $\Sigma \mathbf{P}$ is a vector.

way between these. In the rest frame of either particle the other particle is the more massive, and thus the center of mass lies *beyond l*. The center of mass is therefore frame-dependent, though it can be shown quite easily that in any frame it moves with the velocity of S_0.

Let us now consider how one would define the "rest mass" m_0 of a *system* of particles which do not interact except in collisions. By analogy with (51.1), the only sensible definition is that m_0 is $1/c$ times the norm of the total four-momentum. This is certainly what would be recognized as the rest mass of the system if its discrete nature were *not* recognized (as in the case of an "ordinary" particle). From (54.2) and (54.3), we therefore have

$$m_0 = \left(\overline{m}^2 - \frac{\overline{\mathbf{p}}^2}{c^2}\right)^{1/2} = \frac{\overline{m}}{\gamma(u)}, \qquad (54.4)$$

which shows that the rest mass of the system is related to its total mass *as though* it were a single particle with the velocity of its CM frame. It also shows that m_0 equals $\overline{m}$ in the CM frame:

$$m_0 = \overline{m}_{CM}, \qquad (54.5)$$

and that $\overline{m}$ is least in that frame. If the system is elastic, its total *kinetic* energy, $T = c^2(\overline{m} - \overline{m}_0)$, is also least in the CM frame: $T_{CM} = c^2(m_0 - \overline{m}_0)$. We note that the effective rest mass of the system exceeds the rest masses of its parts by the mass equivalent of the kinetic energy of the parts in the CM frame. This is precisely what one would expect.

Relativistic Billiards   55

As a first example on the new mechanics, let us consider the relativistic analog of the collision treated classically in Section 24. The situation in the CM frame is the same, and for the same reasons. Only the transformation to the rest frame of one of the particles (the "lab" frame) is different. We identify the lab and the CM frames with the usual frames S and S', respectively. Without loss of generality, we can write the post-collision velocities in S' as $\pm(u'_1, u'_2, 0)$, with $u'^2_1 + u'^2_2 = v^2$. By (36.4), the corresponding velocities in S are

$$\left(\frac{\pm u'_1 + v}{1 \pm u'_1 v/c^2}, \frac{\pm u'_2}{\gamma(1 \pm u'_1 v/c^2)}, 0\right).$$

Note that the first component is non-negative. Thus, if θ and ϕ denote the magnitudes of the (acute) angles which the emerging particle paths make with the incident particle path,

$$\tan \theta \tan \phi = \left| \frac{u'_2}{\gamma(u'_1 + v)} \cdot \frac{-u'_2}{\gamma(-u'_1 + v)} \right| = \frac{1}{\gamma^2}. \quad (55.1)$$

This shows that in relativity the angle between the emerging particle paths is *less* than 90°. For if it were 90°, we would have $\tan \phi = \cot \theta$ and $\tan \theta \tan \phi = 1$. To express (55.1) in terms of the incident velocity V, say, (which is not $2v$ now), we apply (36.6) to the incident particle (setting $u'_1 = u' = v, u = V$) and easily find $\gamma(V) = 2\gamma^2(v) - 1$, whence

$$\tan \theta \tan \phi = \frac{2}{\gamma(V) + 1}. \quad (55.2)$$

This result is obviously of interest in connection with bubble chamber collision experiments.

56   *p, E Diagrams and Threshold Energies*

In one-dimensional collision problems, two of the momentum components (say, the second and third) vanish identically and then the one-dimensional momentum p and the mass m specify the four-momentum $\mathbf{P}$ completely, being its first and last components. If we work in units in which $c = 1$ (as we now shall), m is also the energy E. It is sometimes useful in such cases to represent four-momenta $(\mathbf{p}, E)$ as vectors in a plane, using the invariance of $E^2 - p^2$, and sometimes also the fact that p and E transform like x and t under a standard Lorentz transformation.

Of course, few relativistically interesting collisions (e.g., of elementary particles) are ever truly one-dimensional. Exceptions are (a) single particles spontaneously decaying into two fragments or the converse, as viewed from the CM frame, and (b) a type of problem where the one-dimensional "limit" is of great interest, namely the problem of threshold energies. Consider, for example, the case of a stationary proton (of rest mass M) being struck by a moving proton, such that not only the two protons but also a meson (of rest mass m), emerge. We shall ignore the electric influence between the particles, which is negligible at the high energies of interest here. The question is, what is the minimum ("threshold") energy of the incident proton for this reaction to be possible? It is *not* simply $M + m$: in other words, it is *not* enough to provide just the energy that will create the required final rest mass. For, by momentum conservation, the end products will move. In all such cases the least expenditure of energy occurs when the end products are *at rest in the* CM *frame.* For in that frame the ratio of the speeds of the original two particles is fixed by the requirement of vanishing total momentum (in the case of zero rest mass particles, whose momentum will be seen to be $h\nu/c$, read "frequency" for "speed"); both their speeds will therefore be least, and thus also their *relative* speed (or frequency), when their energy is least; and this occurs precisely when the end products are at rest. Hence, to find the threshold energy, we simply assume that *all* end products travel in a lump in the direction of the incident particle: and this is now a one-dimensional problem.

The following (see Figure 11) is a graphical solution of the meson problem stated earlier. We have plotted the hyperbola $E^2 - p^2 = M^2$, marked "M": both incident protons have four-momenta with this norm. We have also plotted the hyperbola $E^2 - p^2 = (2M + m)^2$, marked "$2M + m$": the final lump has this norm. The dotted hyperbola "D" is a translation of "M" by M units, and the intersection of "D" with "$2M + m$" gives the four-momentum $\mathbf{P}_3$ of the lump as the sum of the four-momenta

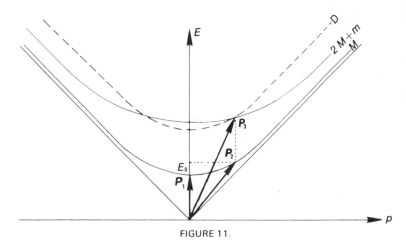

FIGURE 11.

$\mathbf{P}_1$ and $\mathbf{P}_2$ of two protons, one of which is stationary. The energy, E_0, of the other is the required threshold energy.

However, such diagrams should not be overworked; in the present case, for example, a direct algebraic solution is certainly quicker. Simply equating the squared norms of $\mathbf{P}_3$ and $\mathbf{P}_1 + \mathbf{P}_2$ we have, writing u for the threshold velocity and γ for $\gamma(u)$, and remembering that a norm can be evaluated in *any* frame,

$$(2M + m)^2 = M^2(\gamma + 1)^2 - M^2\gamma^2u^2 = 2M^2(\gamma + 1),$$

whence

$$\gamma = 1 + \frac{2m}{M} + \frac{m^2}{2M^2}. \tag{56.1}$$

This formula, incidentally, can easily be adapted to other end products; for example, if it were required to end up with a total of three protons and an antiproton, we need merely replace m by $2M$ to find the corresponding γ.

To see how any four-momentum marked in the diagram changes under the application of a Lorentz transformation with velocity v, we could draw a new set of axes p' and E', equally inclined to the old (analogously to the x' and t' axes in Figure 6), with the new p' axis having slope v. However, we shall not pursue these ideas here.

Three-Force and Four-Force   *57*

Newton's second law can be written in either of the following two forms

$$\mathbf{f} = m_0\mathbf{a}, \quad \mathbf{f} = \frac{d\mathbf{p}}{dt} = \frac{d(m_0\mathbf{u})}{dt},$$

of which the second is the more general, since it applies even in situations where m_0 is not constant, such as rocket motion. By analogy with this second form, we can define the *relativistic (three-) force* $\mathbf{f}$ in terms of the relativistic momentum or mass:

$$\mathbf{f} = \frac{d\mathbf{p}}{dt} = \frac{d(m\mathbf{u})}{dt}. \tag{57.1}$$

This definition has no physical content until other properties of force are specified, and the suitability of the definition will depend on these other properties.

Among them, we have Newton's third law, which asserts the equality of the forces of action and reaction. If an action and its reaction occur at different points (e.g., at opposite ends of a stretched spring), this law cannot be taken over directly into relativity because of the ambiguity of simultaneity.* But if the law refers to the impact of two particles, it is well defined also in relativity. Adopting it *in this case only* (we shall verify its Lorentz-invariance below), Newton's third law in conjunction with (57.1) directly leads to the conservation of relativistic momentum in two-particle collisions, and so supports (57.1). Secondly, (57.1) makes the usual definition of work compatible with Einstein's mass-energy equivalence, as we shall see in equation (57.7). And further support comes from electrodynamics, where (57.1) is consistent with Lorentz's well-established law of force.

First, however, let us define the four-force **F** on a particle

---

*This is what makes the discussion of systems of mutually interacting particles so difficult in relativity.

having four-momentum $\mathbf{P}$ by the relation

$$\mathbf{F} = \frac{d\mathbf{P}}{d\tau},\qquad\qquad(57.2)$$

which ensures the four-vector property of $\mathbf{F}$. From (51.1), (44.3) and (57.1), we then find

$$\mathbf{F} = \gamma(u)\frac{d}{dt}(\mathbf{p}, m) = \gamma(u)\left(\mathbf{f}, \frac{dm}{dt}\right).\qquad(57.3)$$

The appearance of $\gamma(u)\mathbf{f}$ as the spatial part of a four-vector tells us the transformation properties of $\mathbf{f}$. Under a standard LT, for example, the two "trivial" transformation equations are $\gamma(u')f_2' = \gamma(u)f_2$ and $\gamma(u')f_3' = \gamma(u)f_3$. We note that they depend on the speed u of the particle on which $\mathbf{f}$ acts; hence $\mathbf{f}$ is certainly not invariant in special relativity.

We can now check that Newton's third law (for impact) is Lorentz-invariant and therefore acceptable: in some particular frame S let the four-forces exerted by two colliding particles on each other be

$$\mathbf{F}_i = \gamma(u_i)\left(\mathbf{f}_i, \frac{dm_i}{dt}\right),\quad(i = 1, 2);$$

then, since the particles are in contact, $u_1 = u_2$; by energy conservation, $d(m_1 + m_2)/dt = 0$; and, if Newton's third law holds in S, $\mathbf{f}_1 + \mathbf{f}_2 = 0$. Consequently, $\mathbf{F}_1 + \mathbf{F}_2 = 0$. But this is a Lorentz-invariant equation, and so $\mathbf{f}_1 + \mathbf{f}_2 = 0$ in all frames.

Now assume that m_0 remains constant throughout the motion of a given particle. Then from (57.2) and (51.1),

$$\mathbf{F} = m_0\frac{d\mathbf{U}}{d\tau} = m_0\mathbf{A},\qquad\qquad(57.4)$$

whence, by (44.10),

$$\mathbf{F}\cdot\mathbf{U} = 0.\qquad\qquad(57.5)$$

Substituting from (57.3) and (44.4) into this equation, we get

$$\mathbf{f}\cdot\mathbf{u} = c^2\frac{dm}{dt}.\qquad\qquad(57.6)$$

Thus, if we adopt the classical definition of work, we find that the work dW done by a force $\mathbf{f}$ in moving its point of application a distance $d\mathbf{r}$, is given by

$$dW = \mathbf{f} \cdot d\mathbf{r} = \mathbf{f} \cdot \mathbf{u}\, dt = c^2 dm. \qquad (57.7)$$

Here we have another manifestation of the general relation $E = mc^2$.

Substituting from (57.6) into the expanded form of (57.1), we obtain the relation

$$\mathbf{f} = m\mathbf{a} + \frac{dm}{dt}\mathbf{u} = \gamma m_0 \mathbf{a} + \frac{\mathbf{f} \cdot \mathbf{u}}{c^2}\mathbf{u}, \qquad (57.8)$$

which shows that in relativity the acceleration is not, in general, parallel to the force that causes it. There are just two cases when it *is*, namely when $\mathbf{f}$ is either parallel or orthogonal to $\mathbf{u}$; and then we find from (57.8) that

$$f_{\parallel} = \gamma^3 m_0 a_{\parallel}, \quad f_{\perp} = \gamma m_0 a_{\perp}, \qquad (57.9)$$

respectively, in a self-explanatory notation. It appears, therefore, that a moving particle offers different resistances to the same force, according as it is subjected to the force longitudinally or transversely. In this way there arose the (now rather outdated) concepts of "longitudinal" mass $\gamma^3 m_0$, and "transverse" mass γm_0. Since any force can be resolved into longitudinal and transverse components, equations (57.9) provide one method of calculating the resultant acceleration in each case. (Cf. exercise 5-8.)

De Broglie Waves   *58*

In Section 41 we have already used the idea of photons, taking it for granted that light can be described alternatively as particles or as waves. This dualism, and its generalization to particles of nonzero rest mass, originated in quantum mechanics, but its consistency depends on relativistic kinematics and dynamics. Guided by thermodynamic considerations, Planck in 1900 had made the momentous suggestion that radiant energy is *emitted* in definite "quanta" of energy

$$E = h\nu, \qquad (58.1)$$

where ν is the frequency of the radiation and h some universal constant (Planck's constant) whose presently accepted value is 6.626×10^{-27} erg-sec. In 1905 Einstein, crystallizing the observed facts of the photoelectric effect, suggested that not only is radiant energy *emitted* thus, but that it also travels and is absorbed as quanta, which were later called photons. According to Einstein, a photon has energy $h\nu$, momentum $h\nu/c$, and mass $h\nu/c^2$, but rest mass zero. In 1923 de Broglie proposed a further extension of this idea, namely that associated with *any* particle of energy E there are waves of frequency E/h traveling in the same direction; however, as we have seen in Section 47, these waves cannot travel at the same speed as the particle (unless that speed is c), for this would not be a Lorentz-invariant situation. De Broglie found that, for consistency, the speeds u and w of the particle and its associated wave, respectively, must be related by the equation

$$uw = c^2. \qquad (58.2)$$

Let us see why. A particle is fully specified (dynamically) by its four-momentum **P**, and a wave is fully specified (kinematically) by its frequency four-vector **L**. Any invariant association must be expressible as a relation between these four-vectors, and, looking at their fourth components, the relation suggested by Planck's equation (58.1) is

$$\mathbf{P} = h\mathbf{L}, \quad \text{i.e., } m(\mathbf{u}, 1) = h\nu(\mathbf{n}/w, 1/c^2). \qquad (58.3)$$

We shall call this *de Broglie's equation*. Being a four-vector equation, it is a supposition consistent with special relativity. Comparing components, we find:

$$\mathbf{u} \propto \mathbf{n}, \quad mu = \frac{h\nu}{w}, \quad m = \frac{h\nu}{c^2}.$$

The first of these equations locks the direction of motion of the particle to that of the wave-normal; the third is equivalent to (58.1), since $E = mc^2$; and the quotient of the last two is equivalent to (58.2).

For particles of nonzero rest mass, $u < c$ and thus $w > c$. The de Broglie wave speed then has an interesting and simple interpretation. Suppose a whole swarm of identical particles travel along parallel lines and something happens to all of them simultaneously in their rest frame: suppose, for example, they all "flash." Then this *flash* travels at the de Broglie velocity in any frame. To see this, suppose the particles are at rest in the usual frame S', traveling at speed v relative to a frame S; setting $t' = 0$ for the flash, (27.7)(iv) yields $x/t = c^2/v$, and this is evidently the speed of the flash in S. Thus the de Broglie waves can be regarded as "waves of simultaneity."

De Broglie's idea proved to be of fundamental importance in the further development of quantum mechanics. One of its first successes was in explaining the permissible electron orbits in the old Bohr model of the atom, as those containing a whole number of electron waves. A striking empirical verification of electron waves came later, when Davisson and Germer in 1927 observed the phenomenon of electron diffraction. And, of course, the superiority of the electron microscope hinges on de Broglie's principle, according to which electrons allow us to "see" with very much greater resolving power than photons since they have very much smaller wavelength.

Photons. The Compton Effect   59

In the special case of light, (58.2) is satisfied by $u = w = c$ and, from (58.3), we then find for the four-momentum of a photon,

$$\mathbf{P} = \frac{h\nu}{c^2}(c\mathbf{n}, 1). \qquad (59.1)$$

(This follows also from (51.1)(iii) and Einstein's values $h\nu/c^2$, $h\nu/c$ for the mass and momentum of a photon.) Clearly (59.1) is a *null* vector. Photons may be regarded as limiting particles whose rest mass has become zero while their Lorentz factor has become infinite, leaving the product (the inertial mass) $m_0\gamma = m = h\nu/c^2$ finite. In collision problems, photons can be treated like any other particles, and conservation of momentum and energy also applies to particle systems with photons. Systems consisting of photons only may or may not have a CM frame (a single photon certainly does *not*), but any system K containing at least one particle of nonzero rest mass does have a CM frame. For, if subscripts 1 and 2 refer to two arbitrary photons, we have from (59.1) that

$$\mathbf{P}_1 \cdot \mathbf{P}_2 = h^2 c^{-2} \nu_1 \nu_2 (1 - \cos\theta), \qquad (59.2)$$

where θ is the angle between the paths of these photons. Consequently,

$$|\mathbf{P}_1 + \mathbf{P}_2|^2 = 2\mathbf{P}_1 \cdot \mathbf{P}_2 \geq 0,$$

and thus the sum of two photon four-momenta is null or timelike, and evidently it is future-pointing (fourth-component positive) like the summands. On the other hand, the sum of a timelike vector and an isochronous null vector is always an isochronous timelike vector, as can be seen by adapting the argument of equation (54.1). By iteration of these results, it is seen that the total four-momentum of the system K is timelike, and that consequently a CM frame exists, as we asserted. (The reader may find it instructive to rederive, at least heuristically, the above results on sums of isochronous timelike and null vectors by reference to a spacetime diagram like Figure 10.)

As an example, consider a stationary electron of mass m_e being struck by a photon of frequency ν, whereupon the photon is deflected through an angle θ and its frequency is changed to ν' (the *Compton effect*). We wish to relate θ, ν, ν'. Let $\mathbf{P}$ and $\mathbf{P}'$ be the four-momenta of the photon before and after collision, and $\mathbf{Q}$, $\mathbf{Q}'$ those of the electron. Now in any elastic two-particle collision (i.e., one in which the individual rest masses are preserved), the four-momenta $\mathbf{P}'$, $\mathbf{Q}'$ *after* impact are general Lorentz transforms of the four-momenta $\mathbf{P}$, $\mathbf{Q}$ *before* impact, since in the CM frame they are, fairly obviously, just a spatial rotation. Thus, following a pleasant argument of Siemon and Snider,

$P + Q = P' + Q'$ by momentum conservation, whence $P' \cdot (P + Q) = P' \cdot (P' + Q')$. But also $P' \cdot (P' + Q') = P \cdot (P + Q)$ by the permanence of vector equations under general Lorentz transormations. Consequently,

$$P' \cdot (P + Q) = P \cdot (P + Q), \quad \text{i.e.,} \, P \cdot P' = Q \cdot (P - P'),$$

from which we find at once, by reference to (59.2) and (51.1), and canceling a factor h, the desired relation

$$hc^{-2}\nu\nu'(1 - \cos\theta) = m_e(\nu - \nu'). \tag{59.3}$$

In terms of the corresponding wave lengths λ, λ', this may be rewritten in the more standard form

$$\lambda' - \lambda = (2h/cm_e)\sin^2(\theta/2). \tag{59.4}$$

The Matter Tensor of Dust   *60*

After studying the mechanics of particles, it would be natural to turn our attention to the mechanics of continuous media (solids, fluids, and gases). And, indeed, special relativity has brought several interesting modifications to this subject, though these are perhaps of less direct interest to the general physicist than some of the other topics we have discussed. Yet there is one aspect of the relativistic mechanics of continua that is fundamental to the understanding of general relativity and cosmology, and that is the characterization of continua by their "matter tensor." A *particle* is fully characterized by its mass and momentum, which are conveniently exhibited in its four-momentum $P = (\mathbf{p}, m)$. A *continuum*, on the other hand, not only has density and velocity at each point, but also internal stresses, and it turns out that these are as inseparably tied to its density as the momentum of a particle is tied to its mass. In fact, the internal stresses, the momentum density, and the density of a continuum constitute the space-space, space-time and time-time components, respectively, of a second-rank four-tensor $M^{\mu\nu}$. [Most four-tensors split in this way relative to a given frame, just as most four-vectors split into separately meaningful space and time parts. This is due to the fact that spatial rotations and translations form a sub-group of the Lorentz transformations, and that entities invariant under the former are those studied and named in classical physics. But it is also due to the fact that space and time, though interrelated, are simply *not* equivalent.]

The analysis of the general continuum is not quite trivial (see, for example, RSR, Chapter 8), but for our purposes it will suffice to discuss the simplest of all continua, namely dust. Technically, "dust" means a fluid totally without internal stress or pressure. Its *proper* (mass) *density* ρ_0 at any event E is defined as the density measured by an observer O_E at rest relative to the dust at E (assuming a unique velocity can be assigned to it). To get the density relative to an arbitrary frame in which the dust at E has velocity $\mathbf{u} = (u_1, u_2, u_3)$, we must allow for the foreshortening of what is considered a unit volume by O_E and also for the mass increase. Both effects involve a factor $\gamma(u)$, and thus

$$\rho = \rho_0 \gamma^2(u). \tag{60.1}$$

Because of the occurrence of *two* γ factors, the simplest four-tensor containing ρ is of rank 2, namely (see Section 45)

$$M^{\mu\nu} = \rho_0 U^\mu U^\nu, \tag{60.2}$$

where U^μ are the components of the four-velocity $\mathbf{U} = \gamma(\mathbf{u}, 1)$ of the dust. The density ρ is given by the component M^{44}. $M^{\mu\nu}$ is called the *matter tensor*. Its first and most obvious property is symmetry:

$$M^{\mu\nu} = M^{\nu\mu}. \tag{60.3}$$

Its second important property is that, in the absence of external forces, it satisfies the differential equations

$$\sum_{\nu=1}^{4} \partial_\nu M^{\mu\nu} = 0, \tag{60.4}$$

(where the four symbols ∂_ν denote partial differentiation with respect to x, y, z, t, respectively), as we shall now show.

Setting $\mu = 4$ in the left member of (60.4), we get the expression

$$\Sigma \, \partial_\nu M^{4\nu} = \partial_1(\rho u_1) + \partial_2(\rho u_2) + \partial_3(\rho u_3) + \partial_4 \rho, \quad (60.5)$$

whose vanishing constitutes the well-known "equation of continuity." [For consider a small coordinate volume $dV = dx\,dy\,dz$. In time dt a mass $\rho u_1 dt\,dy\,dz$ enters one face perpendicular to the x axis, while a mass

$$\left(\rho u_1 + \frac{\partial(\rho u_1)}{\partial x}\,dx\right)dt\,dy\,dz$$

goes out through the other. Hence the net mass increase due to this pair of faces is $-(\partial(\rho u_1)/\partial x)\,dV\,dt$; the total increase per unit time and unit volume is $-\sum_{i=1}^{3}\partial_i(\rho u_i)$, therefore, and this must equal $\partial \rho/\partial t$.] Next, setting $\mu = i$ ($i = 1, 2, 3$) in the left member of (60.4), we get

$$\Sigma\,\partial_\nu M^{i\nu} = \partial_1(\rho u_i u_1) + \partial_2(\rho u_i u_2) + \partial_3(\rho u_i u_3) + \partial_4(\rho u_i)$$
$$= u_i\{\partial_1(\rho u_1) + \partial_2(\rho u_2) + \partial_3(\rho u_3) + \partial_4 \rho\}$$
$$+ \rho\{u_1\partial_1 u_i + u_2\partial_2 u_i + u_3\partial_3 u_i + \partial_4 u_i\}. \quad (60.6)$$

The first brace vanishes, as we have shown above; the second brace vanishes because of the dynamics, being equal to the i-component of the acceleration. [For if the velocity field of the dust is given by $\mathbf{u} = \mathbf{u}(x, y, z, t)$, and an element of dust follows the path $x = x(t)$, $y = y(t)$, $z = z(t)$, then its acceleration is given by

$$\frac{d\mathbf{u}}{dt} = \frac{\partial \mathbf{u}}{\partial x}\frac{dx}{dt} + \frac{\partial \mathbf{u}}{\partial y}\frac{dy}{dt} + \frac{\partial \mathbf{u}}{\partial z}\frac{dz}{dt} + \frac{\partial \mathbf{u}}{\partial t}.\Big]$$

Equation (60.4) is thus established. The occurrence in the dust case of the density as the time-time component of a tensor makes it likely that this is a general state of affairs. And indeed it can be shown that *all* continua are characterized by matter tensors $M^{\mu\nu}$ which, though more complicated than (60.2), nevertheless have the properties (60.3) and (60.4). Moreover, in order to uphold the general ideas of conservation of momentum and energy when a charged fluid interacts with an electromagnetic field, it is necessary also to ascribe to such *fields* a "matter" tensor $E^{\mu\nu}$ with the same general properties. (Its components are fairly simple combinations of the electric and magnetic field strengths.)

6

Relativity and Electrodynamics

61 *Transformation of the Field Vectors*

This chapter is deliberately not called "relativistic" electrodynamics, because there really has never been a "nonrelativistic" precursor. Maxwell's theory has always been relativistic in Einstein's sense, though no one before Einstein
realized this. To be precise, the *formal* transformations (of
the coordinates *and* of the electric and magnetic field vectors) leaving Maxwell's equations invariant had already
been found by Lorentz (and this was the origin of the
"Lorentz transformations"), but it simply was not understood that these transformations had a *physical* significance,
namely that they related actual measurements in different
inertial frames. Since the physically relevant coordinate
transformation was thought to be the Galilean transformation, Maxwell's theory was in fact thought to be strictly
true only in *one* inertial frame—that of still ether.

Thus, special relativity found here a theory whose laws

needed no amendment.* Nevertheless, recognizing the relativity of Maxwell's theory made a considerable difference to one's understanding of it, and also to the techniques of problem solving in it.

We shall first derive the transformation equations of the electric and magnetic field vectors, **e** and **h**. These vectors can be defined by their effect on a moving charge: the three-force **f** on a charge q moving with velocity **u** is given by

$$\mathbf{f} = q\left(\mathbf{e} + \frac{\mathbf{u} \times \mathbf{h}}{c}\right). \tag{61.1}$$

This is the usual Lorentz force law, written in electrostatic units, except that we shall understand **f** to mean the relativistic force as defined in (57.1). Of course this equation can serve as definition of **e** and **h** only if the velocity dependence of q is known. In Maxwell's theory q is, in fact, velocity-independent, and this agrees well with even the most modern experiments. We shall further assume that the action of the electromagnetic field on a charged test particle leaves its rest mass invariant. Then we can deduce the transformation properties of **e** and **h** from the known transformation properties of **f**. As we have seen in (57.3) and (57.6), **f** enters into the components of a four-vector **F** (the four-force) thus:

$$\mathbf{F} = \gamma(u)\left(\mathbf{f}, \frac{\mathbf{f} \cdot \mathbf{u}}{c^2}\right), \tag{61.2}$$

where **u** is the velocity of the particle on which **f** acts. Substituting (61.1) into (61.2), we get

$$\mathbf{F} = q\gamma(u)\left(\mathbf{e} + \frac{\mathbf{u} \times \mathbf{h}}{c}, \frac{\mathbf{e} \cdot \mathbf{u}}{c^2}\right), \tag{61.3}$$

and we suppose that the various quantities are measured in a definite inertial frame S. Now let us consider the components of this same four-vector in the usual second frame

---

*This is true, at least, of Maxwell's theory in vacuum. On the other hand, Minkowski's extension of that theory to the inside of "ponderable" media (1908) was a purely relativistic development.

S'. We are interested only in **e** and **h,** and we shall clearly not restrict the generality of this field by specializing the velocity of the test charge. Let this charge, therefore, be at rest in S', so that $\mathbf{u} = (v, 0, 0)$ and $\gamma = \gamma(v)$. Then in S' we have

$$\mathbf{F'} = q(\mathbf{e'}, 0), \qquad (61.4)$$

and since the four components of **F** and **F'** must be related as the corresponding coordinates in (27.7), we find

$$e_1' = \gamma\left(\gamma e_1 - \frac{v^2\gamma e_1}{c^2}\right) = e_1, \qquad (61.5)$$

$$e_2' = \gamma\left(e_2 - \frac{v}{c}h_3\right), \qquad (61.6)$$

$$e_3' = \gamma\left(e_3 + \frac{v}{c}h_2\right). \qquad (61.7)$$

To get the transforms of the h's, we remember that from any transformation formula between S and S' we can always get another (the inverse) by interchanging primed and unprimed quantities and replacing v by $-v$ (see Section 36). Let us do this to equation (61.7), and then eliminate e_3' from the resulting pair. This yields at once (if we note that $\gamma^2 - 1 = \gamma^2 v^2/c^2$) the equation

$$h_2' = \gamma\left(h_2 + \frac{v}{c}e_3\right), \qquad (61.8)$$

and, similarly, (61.6) yields

$$h_3' = \gamma\left(h_3 - \frac{v}{c}e_2\right). \qquad (61.9)$$

We still lack the transformation of h_1. Let us give the charge in S' an *infinitesimal* y'-velocity w, with corresponding y-velocity $w/\gamma(v)$ in S. Then, instead of (61.4), we now have

$$\mathbf{F'} = q\left(\mathbf{e'} + \frac{\mathbf{w} \times \mathbf{h'}}{c}, \frac{\mathbf{e'} \cdot \mathbf{w}}{c^2}\right), \qquad (61.10)$$

where $\mathbf{w} = (0, w, 0)$, and in (61.3) $\mathbf{u}$ is now $(v, w/\gamma, 0)$. Equating the z-components of (61.3) and (61.10) in accordance with (27.7), we then find

$$e_3' - wh_1'/c = \gamma(e_3 + vh_2/c - wh_1/\gamma c),$$

whence, by reference to (61.7), $h_1' = h_1$. (The transformation for the x-component of (61.10) would reproduce (61.9); and similarly we could reobtain (61.8).) Collecting our results, we have therefore found

$$e_1' = e_1, \quad e_2' = \gamma(e_2 - vh_3/c), \quad e_3' = \gamma(e_3 + vh_2/c), \quad (61.11)$$
$$h_1' = h_1, \quad h_2' = \gamma(h_2 + ve_3/c), \quad h_3' = \gamma(h_3 - ve_2/c). \quad (61.12)$$

For consistency we would still have to check that, *with* these transformations, the Lorentz four-force (61.3) is indeed a four-vector.

The interested reader can now verify that, because of equations (61.11) and (61.12), the components of **e** and **h** actually form a second-rank contravariant four-tensor, according to our definition of Section 45, in the following way:

$$A^{\mu\nu} = \begin{pmatrix} 0 & h_3 & -h_2 & -e_1/c \\ -h_3 & 0 & h_1 & -e_2/c \\ h_2 & -h_1 & 0 & -e_3/c \\ e_1/c & e_2/c & e_3/c & 0 \end{pmatrix}. \quad (61.13)$$

For this reason, the most convenient mathematical apparatus for theoretical electrodynamics is the calculus of four-tensors, which we have not developed. By its use one can write the usual four Maxwell equations as two tensor equations involving the field tensor $A^{\mu\nu}$ and then their invariance under Lorentz transformations becomes self-evident. (See RSR, Section 42.) This invariance we can also establish laboriously by direct use of (61.11) and (61.12), without, however, gaining any conceptual insights. Again, by tensor methods one can quite easily verify that the Lorentz four-force is indeed a four-vector, being q/c times the "inner product" of $A^{\mu\nu}$ and U^{μ}.

Still, for many applications, equations (61.11) and (61.12) and the four-vector calculus serve quite well. For example, it is not hard to verify by direct use of these equations that the following expressions are invariant under general Lorentz transformations:

$$\text{(i) } \mathbf{h}^2 - \mathbf{e}^2, \quad \text{(ii) } \mathbf{e} \cdot \mathbf{h}. \qquad (61.14)$$

They are evidently invariant under spatial rotation and translation (by their three-vector form) and trivially so under time translation; only their invariance under a standard Lorentz transformation need be checked. It is less clear, from our present viewpoint, that these are essentially the *only* invariants of the field, whereas from the tensor theory this is easily seen.

One thing that is illustrated well by equations (61.11) and (61.12) is the intermingling of $\mathbf{e}$ and $\mathbf{h}$ under a Lorentz transformation. For example, a "pure" $\mathbf{e}$ field, or a "pure" $\mathbf{h}$ field, in one frame, has *both* $\mathbf{e}$ and $\mathbf{h}$ components in another frame. (As Einstein had rightly presumed, the magnetic force deflecting a moving charge—even if there is no electric field, as around a current-carrying wire—is felt as an electric force in the rest frame of the charge.) Of course, pure $\mathbf{e}$ or $\mathbf{h}$ fields are untypical: the general electromagnetic field cannot be transformed into one of these by going to a suitable frame, for that would imply the vanishing of the invariant $\mathbf{e} \cdot \mathbf{h}$.

On the other hand, our present analysis shows that *any* three-force $\mathbf{e}$ (whether of electrostatic origin or not) which in one frame S is independent of the velocity of the particles on which it acts and leaves their rest mass unchanged, must be a Lorentz-type force; and as such it will be velocity-dependent in any other frame S'—unless the field in S happens to be parallel to the motion of S'. For the four-force (61.2) in S can be identified with a four-force (61.3) specialized by $\mathbf{h} = 0$; and (61.3), being a four-vector, will then give the force in all frames. As evidenced by (61.12), this force will have $\mathbf{h}$ components in S' unless $e_2 = e_3 = 0$: this is the exceptional case mentioned above. The present result has obvious implications for SR theories of gravitation.

62   *Magnetic Deflection of Charged Particles*

A free particle having rest mass m_0 and charge q enters a uniform pure magnetic field $\mathbf{h}$ at right angles to the lines of force; what happens? The exact answer to this question is important in bubble chamber magnetic analysis of elementary particles, and also in the design of accelerators. According to the Lorentz force law (61.1), the particle experiences a force

$$\mathbf{f} = \frac{q\,\mathbf{u} \times \mathbf{h}}{c} \tag{62.1}$$

at right angles to its velocity $\mathbf{u}$ and to $\mathbf{h}$. Since this implies $\mathbf{f} \cdot \mathbf{u} = 0$, (57.6) shows that m is constant and hence also u. Moreover, from (57.9), $a_{\parallel} = 0$ and $a_{\perp} = quh/cm_0\gamma$. Consequently, the angular deflection per unit time is given by

$$\omega = \frac{d\theta}{dt} = \frac{|\,d\mathbf{u}\,|}{u\,dt} = \frac{a_{\perp}}{u} = \frac{qh}{cm_0\gamma}, \tag{62.2}$$

and thus the particle traces out a circle of radius

$$r = \frac{u}{\omega} = \frac{cm_0\,u\,\gamma}{qh} \tag{62.3}$$

with angular velocity ω and therefore with period

$$T = \frac{2\pi}{\omega} = \frac{2\pi cm_0\gamma}{qh}. \tag{62.4}$$

According to classical mechanics, this formula would lack the γ factor and the period would be velocity-independent. At high speeds γ makes itself felt and this, for example, necessitated the development from the cyclotron to the synchrotron type of accelerator: the larger the orbit, the longer the period.

The Field of a Uniformly Moving Charge   *63*

As a good example of the power that special relativity brought to electromagnetic theory, we shall calculate the field of a uniformly moving charge q by that typically relativistic method of looking at the situation in a frame where everything is obvious, and then transforming to the general frame. In the present case, all is obvious in the rest frame S' of the charge, where there is a simple Coulomb field of form

$$\mathbf{e'} = (q/r'^3)(x', y', z'), \quad \mathbf{h'} = 0, \qquad (63.1)$$

if, as we shall assume, the charge is at the origin. Now we transform to the usual second frame S, in which the charge moves with velocity $\mathbf{v} = (v, 0, 0)$, at the instant $t = 0$ when the charge passes the origin. Reference to (61.12), (61.11) and (27.7) shows

$$\mathbf{h} = (v/c)(0, -e_3, e_2), \quad \mathbf{e} = (e_1', \gamma e_2', \gamma e_3') = (q\gamma/r'^3)(x, y, z)$$
$$r'^2 = \gamma^2 x^2 + y^2 + z^2 = \gamma^2 r^2 - (\gamma^2 - 1)(y^2 + z^2)$$
$$= \gamma^2 r^2 [1 - (v^2/c^2)\sin^2\theta], \qquad (63.2)$$

where θ is the angle between the vector $\mathbf{r} = (x, y, z)$ and the x axis. Thus,

$$\mathbf{h} = \frac{1}{c}\mathbf{v} \times \mathbf{e}, \quad \mathbf{e} = \frac{q\mathbf{r}}{\gamma^2 r^3 [1 - (v^2/c^2)\sin^2\theta]^{3/2}}. \qquad (63.3)$$

It is interesting to note that the electric field at $t = 0$ is directed away from the point where the charge is *at that instant*, though (because of the finite speed of propagation of all effects) it cannot be *due* to the position of the charge at that instant. Note that both the electric and magnetic field strengths in any fixed direction from the charge fall off as $1/r^2$. Also of interest is the angular dependence of the strength of the electric field: it is strongest in a plane at right angles to $\mathbf{v}$, and weakest fore and aft. We can construct a surprising model in which the density of the lines of force represents field strength as usual. Consider a block of plexiglass at rest in S', into which the isotropic lines of force of q in S' are "frozen." The solid angle of a thin pencil of lines of x-cross sectional area A at (x', y', z'), is given by $d\Omega' = A\cos\theta'/r'^2 = Ax'/r'^3$. (See Figure (12(i).) In S the block moves with velocity v and all x-coordinates are shrunk by a factor γ^{-1}; the corresponding solid angle is given by $d\Omega = Ax/r^3$, whence, by reference to (63.2),

$$\frac{d\Omega'}{d\Omega} = \frac{x'r^3}{xr'^3} = \frac{\gamma r^3}{r'^3} = \frac{1}{\gamma^2 [1 - (v^2/c^2)\sin^2\theta]^{3/2}}. \qquad (63.4)$$

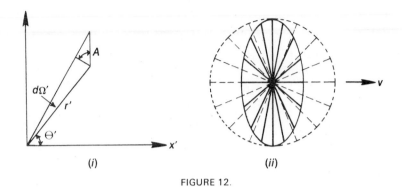

FIGURE 12.

In conjunction with (63.3), this shows that the density of the lines frozen into the block represents exactly the electric intensity in S also. Figure 12(ii) illustrates this.

Of course, this result is purely a consequence of the elementary laws of electrodynamics and can be obtained without the explicit use of SR. Lorentz so obtained it, and thereon based an "explanation" of the length contraction of material bodies: If the electromagnetic fields of the fundamental charges "contract," then so must all matter, if it is made up of such charges. (Lorentz's argument, perforce, ignored the existence of the nuclear force fields and uncharged elementary particles.)

To calculate the field of an *accelerating* charge, the above elementary method is inapplicable—unless one is willing to go to very great lengths and to make extra assumptions. The standard method involves use of the four-potential. (See, for example, RSR, page 141.) This is a four-vector of great importance in the full theory, but one which it is beyond our present scope to discuss.

The Field of an Infinite Straight Current   64

As a final example of relativistic reasoning in electromagnetic theory, we shall derive the field of an infinite straight current. We begin by calculating the field of an infinite, static, straight-line distribution of charge, of uniform line density σ, say. (See Figure 13.) Since the charge is static, there will be no magnetic field. By symmetry, the electric field at any point P will be along the perpendicular from P to the line; consequently, only field components in this direction need be considered. As reference to the figure shows, the contribution to the electric field in that direction from a line element dx is given by

$$de = [\sigma\, dx/(p \sec \theta)^2] \cos \theta, \qquad (64.1)$$

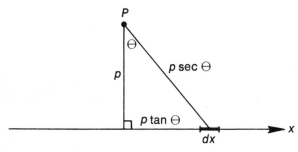

FIGURE 13.

where θ is the angle which the element subtends at P with the perpendicular p from P to the line. Since $x = p \tan \theta$, $dx = p \sec^2 \theta\, d\theta$ and thus, from (64.1),

$$e = \int_{-\pi/2}^{\pi/2} \frac{\sigma}{p} \cos \theta\, d\theta = \frac{2\sigma}{p}. \qquad (64.2)$$

Now suppose an infinite line charge with proper line density σ_0 moves with velocity v relative to a frame S. Because of length contraction, its line density in S is $\gamma \sigma_0$, and it corresponds to a current $i = \gamma \sigma_0 v$. Let us identify the line charge with the x' axis of the usual frame S'. Then, by the above calculation, the only nonvanishing component of the field at the typical point $P(0, p, 0)$ in S' is given by

$$e_2' = \frac{2\sigma_0}{p}. \qquad (64.3)$$

Transforming this field to S by use of the inverse relations of (61.11) and (61.12), obtained by interchanging primed and unprimed symbols and writing $-v$ for v, we find

$$e_1 = 0, \quad e_2 = \frac{2\gamma\sigma_0}{p} = \frac{2i}{pv}, \quad e_3 = 0,$$

$$h_1 = 0, \quad h_2 = 0, \quad h_3 = \frac{2\gamma\sigma_0 v}{pc} = \frac{2i}{pc}. \qquad (64.4)$$

Note that the strength of the magnetic field is only a fraction v/c of that of the electric field, and another factor of order u/c reduces its effect, by comparison, on a charge moving with velocity u (see (61.1)). Moreover, in a laboratory current of a few amperes, v is only about one millimeter per second. As C. W. Sherwin has said, it is hard to believe that this magnetic force, which has to suffer a denominator c^2, is the "work force" of electricity, responsible for the operations of motors and generators. And again, seeing that this force arises from transforming a purely electric field to another frame having very small velocity relative to the first, A. P. French has remarked: who says that relativity is important only for velocities comparable to that of light? The fact is that we have a very big charge: there are something like 10^{23} free electrons per cubic centimeter of wire. Their *electric* force, if it were not neutralized, would be enormous.

But that force *is* neutralized in a "real" current flowing in a wire. Such a current corresponds to *two* superimposed linear charge distributions, one at rest and one in motion: the positive metal ions are at rest while the free electrons move, say, with velocity $-v$. The respective line densities are equal and opposite, say $\pm\sigma$, and the current is given by $i = \sigma v$. The *proper* line density of the free electrons is $-\sigma/\gamma$, while that of the ions is σ. As can be seen from (64.3) and (64.4), the electric fields will exactly cancel, while the magnetic field is given as before by $2i/pc$.

A moving charge deflected by this field experiences an *electric* force in its rest frame; physically, that arises because the positive and negative line densities will no longer cancel in that frame: this is about the closest we get to a direct manifestation of length contraction.

7

Basic Ideas of General Relativity

65   Curved Surfaces

One of the most revolutionary features of general relativity is the essential use it makes of curved space (actually, of curved spacetime). Though everyone knows intuitively what a curved *surface* is, or rather, what it looks like, people are often puzzled how this idea can be generalized to three or even higher dimensions. This is mainly because they cannot visualize a *four*-space in which the three-space can *look* bent. So let us first of all try to understand what the curvature of a surface means *intrinsically*, i.e., without reference to the embedding space. Intrinsic properties of a surface are those that depend only on the measure relations *in* the surface; they are those that an intelligent race of two-dimensional beings, entirely confined to the surface (in fact, experience, and power of visualization), could determine. Intrinsically, for example, a flat sheet of paper and one bent almost into a cylinder, or almost into a cone, are equivalent (see Figure 14). (If we closed up the cylinder or the cone, these surfaces would still be "locally" equivalent but not "globally.") In the same way a helicoid (spiral staircase) is equivalent to an almost closed catenoid (a surface generated by rotating the shape of a freely hanging chain); and so on. One can visualize intrinsic properties as those that are preserved when a surface is bent without stretching or tearing.

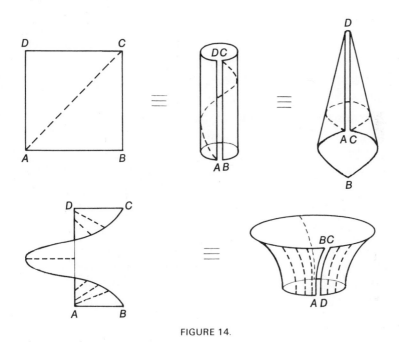

FIGURE 14.

An important intrinsic feature of a surface is the totality of its *geodesics*. These are lines of minimal length between any two of their points. Thus if, in Figure 15, A and B are two arbitrary points on a geodesic g of a surface S, then all nearby lines joining A and B on S (e.g., l and l') would have greater length than the portion of g between A and B. Since geodesics depend only on distance measurements *in* the surface, they are intrinsic, i.e., they remain geodesics when the surface is bent. (See the dotted lines in Figure 14.)

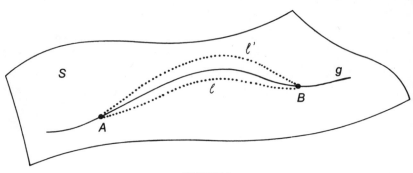

FIGURE 15.

Now let us see how the two-dimensional beings would discover the curvature of their world. As representatives of three different types of surface, consider a plane, a sphere, and a saddle. On each of these draw a small geodesic circle of radius *r*, i.e., a locus of points which can be joined by geodesics of length *r* to some center (see Figure 16). In practice this could be done by using a taut wet string like a tether —wet, so as to cling to the surface. Then we (or the flat people) can measure both the circumference *C* and the area *A* of these circles. In the plane we get the usual "Euclidean" values $C = 2\pi r$ and $A = \pi r^2$. On the sphere we get *smaller* values for *C* and *A*, and on the saddle we get *larger* values. This becomes evident when, for example, we cut out these circles and try to flatten them onto a plane: the spherical cap must tear (it has too little area), while the saddle cap will make folds (it has too much area).

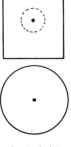
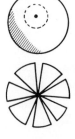
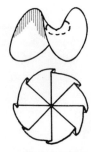

Just right.   Too little.   Too much.

FIGURE 16.

For a quantitative result, consider Figure 17, where we have drawn two geodesics subtending a small angle θ at the north pole P of a sphere of radius a. By definition, we shall assign a curvature $K = 1/a^2$ to such a sphere. At distance r along the geodesics from P, let their perpendicular separa-

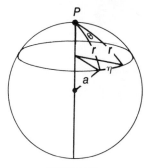

FIGURE 17.

tion be η. Then, using elementary geometry and the Taylor series for the sine, we have

$$\eta = \theta\left(a \sin \frac{r}{a}\right) = \theta\left(r - \frac{r^3}{6a^2} + \cdots\right) = \theta\left(r - \frac{1}{6} Kr^3 + \cdots\right),$$

(65.1)

and consequently,

$$C = 2\pi\left(r - \frac{1}{6} Kr^3 + \cdots\right), \quad A = \pi\left(r^2 - \frac{1}{12} Kr^4 + \cdots\right),$$

(65.2)

since $dA/dr = C$, evidently. From these expansions, we find the following two alternative formulae for K:

$$K = \frac{3}{\pi} \lim_{r \to 0} \frac{2\pi r - C}{r^3} = \frac{12}{\pi} \lim_{r \to 0} \frac{\pi r^2 - A}{r^4}. \quad (65.3)$$

We can now adopt these formulae generally as the *definition* of the curvature K at a given point of an arbitrary surface. Then, of course, the curvature of the saddle will be negative. [If the spine and the ribs of the horse, that goes with the saddle, locally approximate to circles of radii a and b, respectively, the curvature of the saddle can be shown to be $-1/ab$. In fact, for a sufficiently differentiable surface, K always equals the product of the two extremals of the curvature of the normal section, and these always occur in perpendicular directions.] It can be shown that a surface with $K = 0$ everywhere is necessarily intrinsically plane, and one with $K = 1/a^2$ everywhere is intrinsically a sphere of radius a (except for possible "topological identifications" —see Section 85).

66   *Curved Spaces of Higher Dimensions*

The ideas of the intrinsic geometry of surfaces can be extended to spaces of higher dimensions, such as, for example, the three-space of our experience. Geodesics are defined by direct generalization of the two-dimensional case. The direct generalization of curvature to three dimensions would be to draw geodesic *spheres* (instead of circles) of radius r and to compare their measured surface area or volume with the Euclidean values. It is logically quite conceivable that by very accurate measurements of this kind we might find our space to deviate slightly from flatness. The great Gauss himself made several experiments to measure space curvature, but with the available apparatus—then or now—none can be detected directly.

Actually, the direct generalization of the definitions (65.3) to areas and volumes of spheres turns out to be too unrefined. Instead, one considers *geodesic surfaces* embedded in the space of interest: at the point of interest P one draws the geodesics in two arbitrary directions $\mathbf{p}$ and $\mathbf{q}$, and then in all other directions of the "pencil" $\lambda\mathbf{p} + \mu\mathbf{q}$. The curvature K, at P, of the geodesic surface so generated is said to be the curvature $K(\mathbf{p}, \mathbf{q})$ of the space at P for the orientation $(\mathbf{p}, \mathbf{q})$. If the curvature at P is *independent* of the orientation, we say P is an *isotropic point*; then, indeed, all the information is contained in knowing the surface area S or volume V of a small geodesic sphere of radius r. These are easily seen to be given by the formulae

$$S = 4\pi(r^2 - \tfrac{1}{3}Kr^4 + \cdots), \quad V = \tfrac{4}{3}\pi(r^3 - \tfrac{1}{5}Kr^5 + \cdots).$$

$$(66.1)$$

(The first follows from (65.1), and the second from the relation $dV/dr = S$.) If *all* points of a space are isotropic, it can be shown that the curvature must be the same at all of them (*Schur's theorem*), and then the space is said to be *of constant curvature*. This theorem, as well as the above definition of curvature have direct generalizations from 3 to *n* dimensions: $K(\mathbf{p}, \mathbf{q})$ is defined alike in all dimensions ≥ 3.

Let us digress for a moment and as an example consider the three-dimensional analog of a sphere, i.e., a three-space of constant positive curvature (which is called a hypersphere). Think first what happens on an ordinary two-sphere of curvature $1/a^2$ as we draw circles about a given point: at first the circumferences get bigger with increasing geodesic radius r, but after reaching a maximum they get smaller again and finally become zero when $r = \pi a$. (Note that there is nothing illogical in the fact that the later small circles *contain* early bigger ones.) If we lived in a *hypersphere* of curvature $1/a^2$ and drew concentric geodesic *spheres* around ourselves, their surface area would at first increase with increasing geodesic radius r (but not as fast as in the Euclidean case), reaching a maximum $4\pi a^2$, with included volume $\pi^2 a^3$, at $r = \tfrac{1}{2}\pi a$. After that, successive spheres contract until finally the sphere at $r = \pi a$ has zero surface area and yet contains *all* our space: it is, in fact, a single point, our "antipode." The total volume of this space is finite, $2\pi^2 a^3$, and yet there is no boundary; again, there is no center: every point is equivalent to every other. All this is not as fantastic as it may seem. The very first cosmological model proposed by Einstein envisaged our three-space to be precisely of this kind.

Now we wish to introduce the concept of *geodesic deviation*, which is closely related to what we have already done. Differentiating the third equation in (65.1) twice with respect to r, we find, to first order,

$$\ddot{\eta} = -K\eta \quad (\cdot \equiv d/dr). \tag{66.2}$$

Thus we may use the second rate of spread (or "deviation") of two neighboring geodesics as a very direct measure of the curvature of a surface. (See Figure 18.) A question, how-

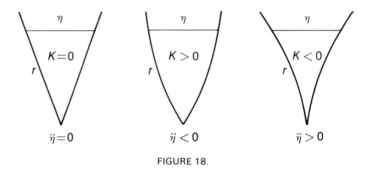

FIGURE 18.

ever, arises: we derived formula (65.1)(iii) from the sphere, a surface of maximal symmetry; is it true for a general surface that the spread of geodesics from a given point satisfies (65.1)(iii) to the order given *in all directions*? The answer turns out to be yes: all sufficiently differentiable *surfaces* possess this degree of symmetry.

In *n*-dimensional space, if two neighboring coplanar geodesics g_1, g_2 are chosen, formula (66.2) gives K for the orientation corresponding to the plane of these geodesics; for g_1 and g_2 are clearly geodesics also on the geodesic surface which determines K.

67   Riemannian Spaces

In all theorems stated in the preceding two sections, the "Riemannian" nature of the underlying spaces was implicit. This we must now discuss. On a curved surface we cannot set up Cartesian coordinates in the same way as in the plane (with "coordinate lines" forming a lattice of strict squares) —for if we could, we would *have* a plane, intrinsically. Certain surfaces by their symmetries suggest a "natural" coordinatization, like the sphere (see Figure 19) on which one

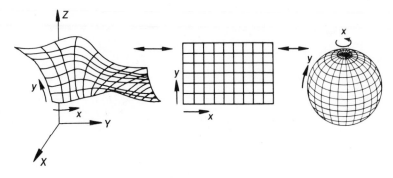

FIGURE 19.

usually chooses longitude (x) and latitude (y) to specify points. On a general surface one can "paint" two arbitrary families of coordinate lines and label them $x = \cdots -2,$ $-1, 0, 1, 2, \ldots$ and $y = \ldots -2, -1, 0, 1, 2, \ldots$, respectively, and one can further subdivide these as finely as one wishes. It can be shown that it is always possible to choose *orthogonal* coordinates on a surface, i.e., coordinates such that the lines x = constant and y = constant intersect everywhere at right angles, but this is by no means essential. In every case we can *map* the surface, or at least part of the surface, onto a Cartesian (x, y) plane simply by making points with equal (x, y) correspond (see Figure 19, where "↔" denotes a mapping). Distances in the map will generally be distorted.

If we imagine the surface embedded in a Euclidean three-space with coordinates (X, Y, Z) (see Figure 19), then it will satisfy equations of the form

$$X = X(x,y), \quad Y = Y(x,y), \quad Z = Z(x,y), \quad (67.1)$$

which we assume to be differentiable as often as required. Since the distance between neighboring points in the Euclidean space is given by

$$d\sigma^2 = dX^2 + dY^2 + dZ^2, \quad (67.2)$$

distances in the surface are given by

$$d\sigma^2 = (X_1 dx + X_2 dy)^2 + (Y_1 dx + Y_2 dy)^2$$
$$+ (Z_1 dx + Z_2 dy)^2, \quad (67.3)$$

where the subscripts 1 and 2 denote partial differentiation with respect to x and y, respectively. Evidently (67.3) is of the form

$$d\sigma^2 = E\,dx^2 + 2F\,dx\,dy + G\,dy^2, \qquad (67.4)$$

where E, F, G are certain functions of x and y. Whenever the squared differential distance $d\sigma^2$ is given by a homogeneous quadratic differential form as in (67.4), we say that $d\sigma^2$ is a *Riemannian metric*, and the corresponding space (here the surface) is called *Riemannian*. It is, of course, not a foregone conclusion that all metrics must be of this form: one could *define*, for example, a non-Riemannian metric $d\sigma^2 = (dx^4 + dy^4)^{1/2}$ for some two-dimensional space, and investigate the resulting geometry. (Such more general metrics give rise to "Finsler" geometry.) What distinguishes a Riemannian metric among all others is that it is *locally Euclidean*: At any given point P_0 the values of E, F, G in (67.4) are simply numbers, say E_0, F_0, G_0; thus, "completing the square," we have, at P_0,

$$d\sigma^2 = \left(E_0^{1/2}dx + \frac{F_0}{E_0^{1/2}}dy\right)^2 + \left(G_0 - \frac{F_0^2}{E_0}\right)dy^2 = d\tilde{x}^2 + d\tilde{y}^2,$$

where

$$\tilde{x} = E_0^{1/2}x + \frac{F_0}{E_0^{1/2}}y, \qquad \tilde{y} = \left(G_0 - \frac{F_0^2}{E_0}\right)y.$$

Hence there exists a transformation of coordinates (actually there exist infinitely many) which makes the metric Euclidean (a sum of squares) at any *one* preassigned point. Conversely, *if* there exist coordinates $\tilde{x}$, $\tilde{y}$ in terms of which the metric is Euclidean at a point P_0, then in general coordinates it must be Riemannian at P_0; for there must exist some transformation $\tilde{x} = \tilde{x}(x, y)$, $\tilde{y} = \tilde{y}(x, y)$ from the special to the general coordinates, and thus

$$d\tilde{x}^2 + d\tilde{y}^2 = (\tilde{x}_1 dx + \tilde{x}_2 dy)^2 + (\tilde{y}_1 dx + \tilde{y}_2 dy)^2,$$

which is Riemannian in x, y. Now we see that in order to predict the form of (67.4) we could have dispensed with the use of the embedding space. We could simply have postulated that the surface is locally Euclidean, i.e., that at any given point we can paint the coordinate lines so that $d\sigma^2 = dx^2 + dy^2$ *there.*

These ideas generalize directly from surfaces to spaces of higher dimensions. Such spaces, too, can (by definition) be coordinatized with arbitrary ("Gaussian") coordinates, just like surfaces. In three-space, for example, we would "paint" three families of coordinate *surfaces* and label them $x =$ constant, $y =$ constant, $z =$ constant. If there exists a metric analogous to (67.4), we say the space is Riemannian, and it *will* be so if and only if it is locally Euclidean.

A formally slight—but for our purposes vital—generalization consists in admitting metrics that are not "positive definite": on a real surface we obviously have $d\sigma^2 > 0$ for *all* $dx, dy \neq 0$, but this condition is not essential for much of the theory. A "nondefinite" Riemannian metric corresponds locally to a "pseudo-Euclidean" metric (squares only, but some with negative sign), e.g., to one with "signature" $(+ + -)$: $dx^2 + dy^2 - dz^2$.* The spacetime of special relativity (hereafter referred to as Minkowski space, M_4) with metric $ds^2 = c^2 dt^2 - dx^2 - dy^2 - dz^2$ is an example of a Riemannian space of signature $(+ - - -)$. Of course, it is rather a special example, since it is not only Riemannian, but globally pseudo-Euclidean. The fact that ds here is not just a simple ruler distance in no way affects the mathematics.

In such nondefinite spaces the idea of geodesics is a little more complicated. For example, whenever the signature has only *one* positive sign, geodesics are of three kinds: of maximal (!) *real* length between any two of their points, of minimal *imaginary* length, or of zero length and the limit of both other kinds ("null geodesics"). With the right mathematics, this is really much simpler to express formally than in words: all geodesics obey a certain differential equation that can most directly be interpreted as stating that a geo-

---

*It can be shown that the signature of a metric is invariant, i.e., no matter *how* a reduction to squares of differentials is achieved, there always emerges the same distribution of plus and minus signs (provided we adhere to *real* coordinates).

desic is "locally straight," or has "no curvature relative
to the space." In all Euclidean or pseudo-Euclidean spaces
geodesics have linear equations in the Euclidean coordinates.

In spaces of nondefinite metric, curvature is best visual-
ized via geodesic deviation. The concepts of "isotropic
point" and "constant curvature" apply to these spaces as to
others; but the isotropy of an isotropic point is here restricted purely to curvature. The points of M_4, for example,
are *not* isotropic in a general sense (because of the null
cone), but nevertheless equation (66.2) with $K = 0$ applies
in *all* directions; we shall later meet nondefinite spaces of
constant curvature in which (66.2) applies similarly in all
directions with $K \neq 0$.

Once we know the metric, we know all distance relations
in the space, and so we know all there *is* to know about the
space intrinsically. The differential equation of geodesics,
for example, involves only the coordinates and the metric
coefficients (the generalizations of the E, F, G in (67.4)); so
does the formula for the curvature K in any given orientation; etc. Two spaces which are intrinsically equivalent
clearly admit coordinates in terms of which the metrics are
identical; and conversely, if the metrics can be made
identical by a suitable choice of coordinates, the spaces are
intrinsically equivalent. Hence instead of "intrinsically
equivalent," one uses the shorter term "isometric."

This brings us to an important problem. Two spaces
may be isometric and yet their metrics may *look* quite different. For example, of the four metrics

$$dx^2 + x^2 dy^2, \quad (4x^2 + y^2)dx^2 + (2xy - 4x)dxdy$$
$$+ (1 + x^2)dy^2, \quad y^2 dx^2 + x^2 dy^2, \quad ydx^2 + xdy^2,$$

the first three *all* represent the ordinary plane; the last does
not. The first is actually the well-known polar metric $dr^2 +
r^2 d\theta^2$ in unfamiliar notation, but still "recognizable"; the
second results from the usual Cartesian (Euclidean) coordinates $\tilde{x}, \tilde{y}$ by the undistinguished transformation

$$\tilde{x} = x^2 - y, \quad \tilde{y} = xy.$$

The reader will not guess in a hurry (and should not try) how the third arises, though it too results from transforming the Cartesian $\tilde{x}$, $\tilde{y}$. For spaces of constant curvature (like the plane), we have a powerful theorem to help us: *any two spaces of the same constant curvature, dimensions, and signature, are isometric.* (As a corollary, all flat spaces ($K = 0$) must be isometric with pseudo-Euclidean space of the same signature.) But the general problem of deciding the equivalence of two arbitrary metrics (the so-called "equivalence problem" of quadratic differential forms) is very difficult, especially in practice.

A Plan for General Relativity *68*

As we have seen in Section 49, the presence of gravitating matter precludes the existence of extended inertial frames, *if* we accept the EP. General spacetime will therefore not be the familiar M_4. Yet, according to the EP, it will be *locally* M_4, i.e., locally pseudo-Euclidean, and thus Riemannian! For, according to the EP, we can find at any event E (at least, in vacuum) a local inertial frame, i.e., a local coordinate system x, y, z, t with the property, among others, that the interval between E and *neighboring* events is given by

$$ds^2 = c^2 dt^2 - dx^2 - dy^2 - dz^2. \qquad (68.1)$$

In its original form the EP does not apply inside matter, for example inside the earth, where we cannot have a material "freely falling lab"; nevertheless, by extension, we shall assume that even *inside* matter spacetime is Riemannian, with signature $(+ - - -)$. After all, matter is mostly vacuum, anyway.

The recognition of the Riemannian structure of the world led Einstein to his brilliant scheme for general relativity. Suppose spacetime in the presence of gravitating masses were curved. Perhaps it would then be true that free test particles trace out geodesics in this curved four-space—as they do, for example, in classical mechanics when confined to a smooth curved surface, and in the absence of all external forces. [Incidentally, it is impossible to suppose that our *three*-space is curved in such a way that gravitational orbits are simply geodesics in *it*. For geodesics are uniquely determined by an initial *direction*, whereas gravitational orbits depend also on initial velocity.] The geodesic law would be a beautiful law of motion, and one which incorporates Galileo's principle, according to which the path in space *and* time of a particle through a gravitational field is independent of the particle itself. It would totally eliminate from gravitational theory the concepts of inertial and passive-gravitational mass, and the question of why they are equal. It would also explain gravity without "action at a distance." By extension, light would travel along null geodesics (along which $ds^2 = 0$) in empty spacetime. In Newton's theory, absolute space provided the "rails" along which free particles moved in the absence of gravity (and of all other forces). In Einstein's theory, spacetime provides the rails in the absence of other forces; gravitational force no longer exists: it has become absorbed into the geometry.

But just *how* should spacetime be curved? Since the spacetime structure would now determine inertial *and* gravitational effects, Mach's principle suggests that it is the gravitating matter of the universe which alone must cause the structure of spacetime. The big task, and one that occupied even the genius of Einstein for many years, was to discover the *field equations*, i.e., the equations which predict quantitatively how the material contents of the world are related to its metric.

With this overall plan in mind, let us now look at some of the details. The interval *ds* between events is a more complicated concept than that of distance between points on a surface or in three-space, but it is a perfectly definite physical quantity nevertheless. Empirically the metric at any event E can be determined uniquely in a local inertial frame. And since the LIF simply provides us with one possible local coordinate system, the metric at E in any other coordinate system can then be determined by transforming away from the LIF. The determination of ds between two neighboring events can also be reduced to a *single* measurement with clock or ruler: (i) If the separation between the events in the LIF is timelike, we can send a freely falling standard clock from one to the other and its reading between the events will give the relevant ds (assuming that LIF units are chosen to make $c = 1$). [If a free standard clock follows an extended (geodesic) path through spacetime (say, an orbit round the sun), its reading therefore gives precisely the interval length s along its worldline. If the standard clock is pushed out of its free path, say by a rocket motor attached to it, or by an electric field, we adopt the "general clock hypothesis": it will still read s for the path it follows.] (ii) If the separation between two neighboring events in the LIF is spacelike, there will be one LIF in which the events are simultaneous. And ds is then i times the distance measured by a standard ruler in that frame. [As a matter of fact, it is possible to dispense with rulers altogether, and measure all intervals by use of standard clocks and light signals cleverly combined; but although this makes the logical foundations neater, it is somewhat less intuitive.] (iii) Null intervals, of course, are those corresponding to light paths.

The "grain" of special-relativistic spacetime, i.e., the existence of null cones at each event, and of three different kinds of displacement (timelike, spacelike, null), is impressed on the general-relativistic spacetime also through the LIF's. The cones will no longer be "parallel" to each other everywhere, and their generators (photon worldlines) will no longer be "straight." But still, a particle worldline will stay *within* the cone at each of its points, and a photon will travel *along* the cones.

The spacetime of special relativity, M_4, is flat, since it is pseudo-Euclidean. The worldlines of free particles in M_4 are *certainly* geodesics. For consider a free particle P

present at two events *A* and *B*. The length *s* of its worldline between *A* and *B* is simply the time measured by a
standard clock attached to *P*. The clock on any *other*
particle *P'* moving close to *P* and also present at *A* and *B*
will measure a *shorter* time, since in the rest frame of *P*, *P'*
has moved away from and back to *P*, and, like the twin in
the paradox, it gets back "younger" than *P*. Thus the path
of the free particle has *maximal* interval length between any
two of its points, and is a geodesic. This bears out Einstein's
geodesic hypothesis in a very special case.

It may be thought that the preceding argument can serve
as proof also in the general case. Suppose, for example, a
free test particle *P*, within a freely falling laboratory *L*, is in
circular orbit around a mass center. Could not a neighboring particle *P'* again be regarded as the twin in *L*? The flaw
in this argument is that it assumes a LIF to exist over an extended time, whereas, originally, LIF's are assumed to exist
only in the immediate neighborhood of any given event. As
is well known in the case of circular orbits, the larger the
radius, the smaller the angular velocity. (Recall, for example, Kepler's third law according to which the square of
the period of a planet is proportional to the cube of its mean
distance from the sun.) Hence there would be some shear-
ing of the free lattice points in *L*, and, for all we know, also
a loss of synchrony. That these effects are negligible in the
present circumstances (as indeed they are) can hardly be
assumed *a priori*.

Having embarked on a voyage inspired by two extraor-
dinarily bold though attractive hypotheses—namely the
EP and the geodesic law of motion—we shall do well to
pause for a moment and check our bearings. Our bearings,
of course, are Newton's laws of gravitation, for we must not
forget that they agree almost perfectly with the observed
phenomena throughout an enormous range of applications.
Any alternative theory must yield the same results to
the same observable accuracy. Consequently, in Sections 70
and 71 we shall make a first attempt to compare Einstein's

with Newton's theory in some simple situations. A necessary tool for this work is developed in Section 69.

The Gravitational Doppler Effect   *69*

For the argument of our next section, we shall need a quantitative formulation of the gravitational Doppler effect which was already discussed qualitatively in Section 21. Suppose an elevator cabin of height l is dropped from rest in a uniform gravitational field of strength g, and at the same time a photon of frequency ν_0 is emitted from its ceiling towards the floor. By the equivalence principle the signal takes a time $dt = l/c$ to reach the floor, at which time this floor moves at speed $du = gl/c$ relative to the elevator shaft. Also by the EP, no change in frequency is observed in the falling cabin. Hence an observer B at rest in the shaft a distance l below the emission point (we neglect the small distance moved by the floor in time dt) can be considered to move with speed du into a wave of frequency ν_0, thus observing a Doppler (blue) shift, given to sufficient accuracy by the classical formula

$$\frac{\nu}{\nu_0} = \frac{c + du}{c} = 1 + \frac{gl}{c^2}, \quad \text{or} \quad \frac{\nu_0}{\nu} = 1 - \frac{gl}{c^2}. \quad (69.1)$$

(Compare (40.4).) Of course, B is not an inertial observer. However, here (and in all similar circumstances) we can assume that B makes the same measurements as a freely falling (inertial) observer B' momentarily at rest relative to B. This is justified by the clock and length hypotheses, according to which the readings of the clocks and rulers of B, though accelerated, will momentarily coincide with those of B'.

The result (69.1) can also be obtained by appeal to Planck's relation $E = h\nu_0$ for the energy of the photon. During its "fall," it has mass $h\nu_0/c^2$ approximately (the mass does not remain constant), and thus it loses gravitational potential energy $glh\nu_0/c^2$ before reaching B. Since radiation and matter are interchangeable, radiation must obey the conservation laws of matter; consequently the photon's energy relative to B is given by

$$h\nu = h\nu_0 + \frac{glh\nu_0}{c^2}, \qquad (69.2)$$

and this is equivalent to (69.1). (The weak EP enters this argument when we equate the photon's inertial mass $h\nu_0/c^2$ with its gravitational mass.)

Of course, the Newtonian potential energy formula may be expected to be valid over small distances only; furthermore, the drop of the cabin floor was neglected in our first argument, as was the variation of the photon mass in our second argument. For these reasons, and also in order to extend the result to nonuniform static gravitational fields, let us accept (69.1) only for *small* distances l, rewriting it in the form

$$\frac{\nu}{\nu_0} = 1 + \frac{\delta\phi}{c^2} \qquad (69.3)$$

where $\delta\phi$ is the drop in potential. To find the Doppler shift over a light path along which the potential drop $\Delta\phi$ is not necessarily small, we divide the path into a sufficient number n of portions with equal potential drop $\Delta\phi/n$, at the extremities of which the frequencies are $\nu_0, \nu_1, \ldots, \nu_n = \nu$, say. By use of (69.3) we then obtain

$$\frac{\nu}{\nu_0} = \frac{\nu_1}{\nu_0}\frac{\nu_2}{\nu_1}\cdots\frac{\nu}{\nu_{n-1}} = \left(1 + \frac{\Delta\phi}{nc^2}\right)^n,$$

which, in the limit $n \longrightarrow \infty$, becomes

$$\frac{\nu}{\nu_0} = \exp\frac{\Delta\phi}{c^2} = 1 + \frac{\Delta\phi}{c^2} + \cdots. \qquad (69.4)$$

[This result can be shown to be exact for static fields, provided ϕ is so defined that the relativistic force on a particle of unit rest mass at rest in the field is $-\text{grad }\phi$ in its rest LIF.]

The theory of the gravitational Doppler effect can be applied to derive another interesting result: *gravitational time dilation.* If two standard clocks are fixed in an arbitrary static gravitational field at points whose potential differs by $\Delta\phi$, then the clock at the lower potential goes slow by the Doppler factor $D \approx 1 + \Delta\phi/c^2$ relative to the other clock. This is certainly so as judged by mutual viewing, for the clock being viewed can tick in time with the wavecrests of the light whereby it is seen; the Doppler factor then tells precisely at what frequency these ticks are observed by the viewing clock. If originally the two clocks are adjacent and synchronized, and then one is taken to a place of lower potential and left there for a time, and finally brought back, that clock will read slow by a factor D relative to the one that remained fixed—except for the error introduced by the two journeys. But whatever happens *during* the motions is independent of the total dilation at the lower potential, and can thus be dwarfed by it. Hence a "twin" at a lower potential stays younger than his twin at a higher potential. At the surface of the earth the relevant dilation factor, compared to "infinity," is 1.000 000 000 8.

Of course, like the gravitational and kinematic Doppler effects, the gravitational and kinematic time dilation effects are not different *in kind*: this is obvious from the use of the EP in the derivation. And "youth" can be bought no more cheaply by going to live on a very concentrated mass than by fast flying through space: in each case the rockets needed to make the roundtrip from one's normal abode consume comparably large amounts of energy, since in each case the energy expended is proportional to the time dilation factor attained.

The Spacetime Around a Spherical Mass   *70*

We now wish to explore, at least roughly, the metric of spacetime around a spherically symmetric mass m, far away from all other masses. We assume that before placing m the spacetime in the region of interest is approximately M_4. To set up coordinates, we shall proceed in the most physically meaningful way possible: totally arbitrary coordinates are too hard to handle at this stage. Accordingly, before placing m, imagine a series of spheres, each centered on the eventual position of m, each made of a lattice of little weightless rulers, and coordinatized by the usual spherical polar coordinates so that the spatial metric reads

$$d\sigma_0^2 = dr^2 + r^2(d\theta^2 + \sin^2\theta\,d\phi^2).$$

Now place m at $r = 0$. Possibly the space geometry will thereby be modified. For example, the spheres may expand or shrink, and thus the spheres labeled r and $r + dr$ may no longer be a ruler distance dr apart. But the sphere labeled r, being *made* of rulers, will still have ruler area $4\pi r^2$; and since there will be no tendency to twist, the loci θ, $\phi = $ constant will still correspond to radial directions, and in particular to radial light signals. In terms of the *original* coordinates on the spheres, ruler distance in the space is therefore given by

$$d\sigma^2 = f(r)dr^2 + r^2(d\theta^2 + \sin^2\theta\,d\phi^2), \qquad (70.1)$$

where $f(r)$ is unknown at this stage, but where r has the physical meaning that a sphere at coordinate r has ruler area $4\pi r^2$.

Now suppose standard clocks are attached to all the lattice points r, θ, $\phi = $ constant. To get a *static* metric, we must synchronize the *rates* of these clocks. This will be achieved when, for example, any clock looking at any other clock always sees that the other clock differs by the same amount from its own reading. Or equivalently, if it sees the other clock tick at the same rate as itself. This is where the gravitational time dilation effect comes in. From formula (69.4) we know that a standard clock at r_1 appears to a standard clock at r_2 ($< r_1$) to go fast by approximately a factor

$$D_{12} = 1 + \frac{Gm}{c^2}\left(\frac{1}{r_2} - \frac{1}{r_1}\right), \qquad (70.2)$$

where we have used the Newtonian potential $\phi = -Gm/r$. Thus if we agree to synchronize all clocks with undisturbed standard clocks "at infinity," then evidently a standard clock at r must be *speeded up* over its proper rate by a factor

$$D = 1 + Gm/rc^2. \qquad (70.3)$$

This now fixes the clock *rates* everywhere.

The clock *settings* are most conveniently standardized by requiring the *coordinate* speed of light to be the same in any two opposite directions. This will evidently ensure the absence of time-space cross terms in the metric, and conversely. (For example, if the radial part of the metric were $A dt^2 + B dt dr + C dr^2$, setting $ds^2 = 0$ and $d\theta = d\phi = 0$ for a radial light signal, and solving for dr/dt, would yield two numerically different answers *unless* $B = 0$.) Suppose a photon is bounced back and forth between two lattice clocks C and C', reading times t and t', both at equal distance from m. Suppose the photon is reflected at the following local times: $t = 0, t' = 10, t = 12, t' = 22, t = 24$, etc. Evidently in this case C' must be set back four units, so that the sequence will read, instead, 0, 6, 12, 18, 24, etc. Then the average coordinate speed of light from C to C' is the same as that from C' to C. In the same way, we can synchronize the settings of clocks on a single radius vector from m. A prerequisite, of course, is the synchronization of rates. The overall consistency of our synchronization process follows from symmetry.

Having synchronized our clocks to coordinate time t, say, whose rate differs from proper rate by a factor D as given by (70.3), we know that $dr = d\theta = d\phi = 0$ (the worldline of a clock) will imply $ds^2 = D^{-2} c^2 dt^2$, by the clock hypothesis. The desired metric will therefore be of the form

$$ds^2 = D^{-2} c^2 dt^2 - d\tilde{\sigma}^2,$$

where $d\tilde{\sigma}^2$ is independent of t and dt. For a light signal ($ds^2 = 0$) we then have $d\tilde{\sigma} = \pm D^{-1} c dt$, which shows that $d\tilde{\sigma}$ is "radar" distance (i.e., c times one-half the proper time elapsed, at one point, between the emission of a light signal and its reception after reflection at the other point). But all small rulers measure radar distance, as can be seen by per-

forming the experiment in their rest-LIF and appealing to
the clock and length hypotheses. Consequently $d\tilde{\sigma}$ is
identical with the $d\sigma$ of (70.1). Unfortunately there exists
no satisfactory thought-experiment for determining $f(r)$,
and we therefore approximate it with its flat-space value of
unity. (The GR field equations will eventually show that
there is a very slight deviation from spatial flatness—see
Section 74.) Thus we finally arrive at the metric

$$ds^2 = \left(1 - \frac{2\,Gm}{rc^2}\right)c^2 dt^2 - dr^2 - r^2(d\theta^2 + \sin^2\theta\,d\phi^2),$$

$$(70.4)$$

where the coefficient of $c^2 dt^2$ is D^{-2}, expanded to first order
in $1/r$. As can be shown by the methods of Riemannian
geometry, this represents a *curved* spacetime, which becomes more and more flat with increasing r. [Our neglecting the possible (small) deviation of $f(r)$ from unity can be
justified by the usually small contribution of dr^2 to ds^2 (for
slow motions); the main contribution comes from dt^2, since
that is multiplied by c^2.]

Let us now test Einstein's geodesic hypothesis in the
special case of circular orbits round a central mass, using
the approximate metric (70.4). It is well known that such
orbits are possible in classical mechanics, say at distance r
from m, and with constant angular velocity ω: it is merely
necessary that the centrifugal force $\omega^2 r$ should balance the
gravitational force Gm/r^2, and so

$$\omega^2 = Gm/r^3. \qquad (70.5)$$

This, of course, is a special example of Kepler's third law.

Now, starting from Einstein's point of view, let us look
for a circular orbit in the spacetime (70.4) which maximizes
s. We shall assume that the orbit lies in the equatorial plane
$\theta = \pi/2$, and that it has constant angular velocity $\omega = d\phi/dt$. Then, by (70.4),

$$s = \int ds = \int \left\{c^2\left(1 - \frac{2\,Gm}{rc^2}\right) - r^2\omega^2\right\}^{1/2} dt. \qquad (70.6)$$

This integral will be maximized by the maximum of the braced expression, and that occurs when

$$\frac{d}{dr}\{\ \} = \frac{2\,Gm}{r^2} - 2r\omega^2 = 0,$$

which is equivalent to (70.5). It therefore appears that in this particular case, at least, Einstein's geodesic hypothesis reproduces the classical orbit.

Actually, the maximizing procedure we applied to (70.6) is not quite the one relevant to geodesics. Geodesics have greater interval length than all neighboring curves between any two *fixed points*. The variation of *r* in (70.6), indeed, produces neighboring curves, but curves that have *no* points (events) in common. Nevertheless, the fact that *a* maximum can be so obtained is an indication that it is the relevant one. And, indeed, the rigorous calculation of the geodesics of the metric (70.4) yields (70.5) as a solution.

Static Fields, Geodesics, and Hamilton's Principle   71

The argument leading to the metric (70.4) can at once be generalized to yield the approximate metric of an arbitrary static gravitational field with Newtonian potential ϕ:

$$ds^2 = (1 + 2\phi/c^2)c^2dt^2 - d\sigma^2. \qquad (71.1)$$

Here we have written $d\sigma^2$ for the Euclidean three-space metric, which can be expressed in arbitrary coordinates. The coefficient of dt^2 follows, as in (70.4), from the gravitational time dilation effect and from the requirement that clock *rates* be synchronized: In an irregular field we may simply designate an arbitrary point A as the origin of potential, measure potential differences from A, and synchronize all clock rates with that of a standard clock at A. That they are then also synchronized with each other follows from the fact that the potential change round any closed path is zero, by energy conservation. The one step in the previous argument whose generalization is not obvious is the possibility of synchronizing the clock *settings* so that there are no time-space cross terms in the metric.

To this end, let us more carefully define a *static* field. By definition it shall be time-independent and also have the property that to every possible "forward" motion of a particle or photon there corresponds an identical "backward" motion; or, in other words, all motions are time-reversible. The "gravitational field" on a turntable, for example, is not static: it is merely *stationary*, which means it is the same today as tomorrow. Stationariness corresponds to the existence of *a* coordinate system in terms of which the metric coefficients are time-independent. Staticness, we assert, corresponds to the existence of a coordinate system in terms of which the metric is not only time-independent but also without time-space cross terms. To prove this, let us assume that clock *rates* have already been synchronized. Next we synchronize the settings of all clocks with *one* arbitrarily chosen master clock A among them, so that, as in Section 70, the average coordinate speed of light from A to any clock P is the same as that from P to A. Then any two clocks P and Q so synchronized with A are automatically synchronized with each other. For suppose that the elapsed coordinate times for a photon to be bounced from P to A to Q and back to P are 2, 3, 9, say (see Figure 20), and thus the total elapsed time at P is 14. By hypothesis, this motion is possible in reverse, with again a total elapsed time of 14. But since the elapsed times along

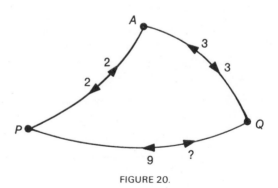

FIGURE 20.

QA and AP are 3 and 2 again, that along PQ must be 9 again, and thus the settings of P and Q are synchronized. Consequently the coordinate speed of light in *any* two directions will be equal, and the metric will have no time-space cross terms, as asserted. The converse, namely that such a metric always represents a static field according to our physical definition, is obvious.

This establishes (71.1). We have, of course, made an approximation for the time dilation factor, and an assumption for the space geometry. Consequently we shall expect (71.1) to hold, at best, for weak fields and slow motions.

Now according to Einstein's geodesic hypothesis, the free-particle worldline through two given events E_1 and E_2, if it exists, is given by the path that maximizes the integral

$$\int_{E_1}^{E_2} ds = \int_{t_1}^{t_2} \frac{ds}{dt}\, dt = \int_{t_1}^{t_2} (c^2 + 2\phi - v^2)^{1/2}\, dt, \quad (71.2)$$

where we have used (71.1) and have written v for $d\sigma/dt$, the coordinate velocity of the particle. Since $2\phi/c^2$ is small compared to unity in a weak field (see (71.1)), and v^2/c^2 is small for an "ordinary" particle,

$$(c^2 + 2\phi - v^2)^{1/2} \approx c[1 + (\phi - \tfrac{1}{2} v^2)/c^2]$$

and thus

$$\int_{E_1}^{E_2} ds = \frac{1}{c} \int_{t_1}^{t_2} (c^2 + \phi - \tfrac{1}{2} v^2)\, dt = \frac{1}{c} \int_{t_1}^{t_2} (U - T)\, dt,$$

$$(71.3)$$

where we have written U for $c^2 + \phi$ and T for $\tfrac{1}{2}v^2$. Now the definition of Newtonian potential is arbitrary up to an additive constant, and so U is as good a potential as ϕ; and in T we recognize the Newtonian kinetic energy per unit mass of the particle. Hence the requirement that the last integral of (71.3) be maximal is recognized as Hamilton's principle, which requires that $\int (T - U)\, dt$ be minimal for the path of a particle. (In our formula the terms are reversed, since U contains the large constant c^2 which makes $U - T > 0$.)

The approximate equivalence of Einstein's geodesic hypothesis with Hamilton's principle for a large class of motions, which we have just established, strongly suggests that this hypothesis has general validity.

What we have done so far is not yet GR. It merely shows the reasonableness of Einstein's plan for GR. In GR one does not have to fall back on Newtonian approximations in order to find a metric, but instead one uses the field equations. And one does not have to make do with approximate ways to work out geodesics or any other geometric features of the spacetimes under discussion: one has at one's disposal the elegant and fully developed theory of Riemannian geometry. This, incidentally, is one of the classic examples where the pure mathematicians' flights of fancy (Riemann's *n*-dimensional geometry of 1854 and Ricci's tensor calculus for it) later became the physicists' bread-and-butter. We have put off this mathematics as long as possible, but now at last we must take a quick dip into it.

8

*Formal
Development
of General
Relativity*

We shall not significantly manipulate tensors in our account of GR, but even just in order to exhibit the field equations, we need the notation of general tensors. Moreover, no idea of the flavor of actual work in GR can be conveyed without at least *some* examples of tensors in action. If he wishes, however, the reader may skim lightly over the present section and only refer back to it as need arises.

The four-tensors of SR are tied to "standard" coordinates (x, y, z, t), in the sense that it is sufficient to consider their components only relative to each such coordinate system. These systems are related to each other by general Lorentz transformations, and, as we have seen, there is a rule which tells how the components of a four-tensor transform when a LT is applied to the coordinates. In GR, as in Riemannian geometry, more general coordinate systems are forced on us, and it is therefore convenient to allow *fully* arbitrary

(Gaussian) coordinates. These need have no direct physical significance; often there is not even a preferred coordinate that can be regarded as the time. For example, even in M_4 (the flat spacetime of SR) we can go from a set of standard coordinates x, y, z, t to a set of Gaussian coordinates of no direct physical significance such as $x^1 = x + y + z + t$, $x^2 = y + z + t$, $x^3 = \exp(z + t)$, $x^4 = \exp(z - t)$.

The tensors of GR, accordingly, have components relative to *arbitrary* coordinates. These tensors are necessarily localized, i.e., associated with points in spacetime. As we transform from one general coordinate system to another, the components of any tensor undergo a typical transformation. The prototype of a "contravariant" first-rank tensor (a vector) A^μ is the coordinate differential dx^μ ($\mu = 1, 2, 3, 4$). Since contravariant tensors are traditionally written with superscripts, the coordinates themselves are also written with superscripts (x^μ) so as to make dx^μ look like what it is, a contravariant vector. The coordinate differences Δx^μ, however, behave as vector components *only* under linear transformations, and the coordinates x^μ themselves only under linear homogeneous transformations, for only then do they transform like dx^μ.

Consider now a transformation of coordinates from x^μ to $x^{\mu'}$. (It is becoming usual to denote a new coordinate system —and tensor components in the new system—by priming the indices, rather than the kernel letters, and μ, μ' are regarded as different indices, just like μ, ν.) By the chain rule, the coordinate differentials transform thus:

$$dx^{\mu'} = \sum_{\mu=1}^{4} p_\mu^{\mu'} dx^\mu, \quad p_\mu^{\mu'} = \frac{\partial x^{\mu'}}{\partial x^\mu} . \tag{72.1}$$

We can write this without the Σ sign,

$$dx^{\mu'} = p_\mu^{\mu'} dx^\mu, \tag{72.2}$$

if we adopt Einstein's *summation convention*, according to which any repeated index in one term, once up, once down, implies summation over all its values. (E.g., $A_\mu^\mu = A_1^1 + A_2^2 + A_3^3 + A_4^4$, $A_{\mu\nu\sigma} B^{\mu\nu} = A_{11\sigma} B^{11} + A_{12\sigma} B^{12} + A_{21\sigma} B^{21} +$

. . . .) If we write

$$p_{\mu'}^{\mu} = \frac{\partial x^{\mu}}{\partial x^{\mu'}},\tag{72.3}$$

the matrices $(p_{\mu'}^{\mu})$ and $(p_{\mu}^{\mu'})$ are clearly inverses of each other. These two kinds of p's are the coefficients that enter into the definition of a general tensor.

We say that the numbers $A_{\nu\cdots}^{\mu\cdots}$ are the components of a tensor, contravariant in the indices μ, . . . , and covariant in the indices ν, . . . , if under a coordinate transformation $x^{\mu} \rightarrow x^{\mu'}$ they transform according to the following (linear) scheme:

$$A_{\nu'\cdots}^{\mu'\cdots} = A_{\nu\cdots}^{\mu\cdots} \, p_{\mu}^{\mu'} \ldots p_{\nu'}^{\nu} \ldots .\tag{72.4}$$

Note that there is one p for each index on $A_{\cdots}^{\cdots}$, and all the unprimed indices on the right are summed over. (It turns out that under the "orthogonal" transformations of coordinates relevant to three-vectors, there is no distinction between covariance and contravariance, so that three-vectors can be written indifferently with superscripts or subscripts.) The most important property of general tensors, as of four-tensors, is that an identity between two sets of tensor components which is true in one coordinate system is true in all coordinate systems. The proof of this is immediate from (72.4).

The metric of a general spacetime can be written in the form

$$ds^2 = g_{\mu\nu} dx^{\mu} dx^{\nu}, \quad (g_{\mu\nu} = g_{\nu\mu}),\tag{72.5}$$

where the $g_{\mu\nu}$ are certain functions of the coordinates. Written in full, equation (72.5) reads

$$ds^2 = g_{11}(dx^1)^2 + g_{22}(dx^2)^2 + g_{33}(dx^3)^2 + g_{44}(dx^4)^2$$
$$+ 2g_{12} dx^1 dx^2 + 2g_{13} dx^1 dx^3 + \ldots .$$

Under a change of coordinates $x^{\mu} \rightarrow x^{\mu'}$ (72.5) becomes

$$ds^2 = g_{\mu\nu} dx^{\mu'} p_{\mu'}^{\mu} dx^{\nu'} p_{\nu'}^{\nu} = g_{\mu'\nu'} dx^{\mu'} dx^{\nu'},$$

where

$$g_{\mu'\nu'} = g_{\mu\nu} p_{\mu'}^{\mu} p_{\nu'}^{\nu},\tag{72.6}$$

which shows that $g_{\mu\nu}$ is a tensor.

Suppose, next, a particle has a worldline whose parametric equation is

$$x^\mu = x^\mu(s),\qquad\qquad (72.7)$$

which gives the coordinates at each moment of its proper time s. (Again we assume units chosen so that $c = 1$.) The derivative dx^μ/ds is evidently a vector since

$$\frac{dx^{\mu'}}{ds} = \frac{\partial x^{\mu'}}{\partial x^\mu}\frac{dx^\mu}{ds} = \frac{dx^\mu}{ds}\,p^{\mu'}_\mu.\qquad\qquad (72.8)$$

By choosing LIF coordinates at the particle, and interpreting dx^μ/ds in these, we see that it represents the four-velocity $\mathbf{U}$ of the particle relative to that LIF. Many general tensors can in this way be specialized to the LIF, and so be interpreted physically. The inverse process is not quite so straightforward. For example, in the LIF, d^2x^μ/ds^2 is the four-acceleration $\mathbf{A}$. But d^2x^μ/ds^2, unlike dx^μ/ds, is *not* a general vector. For, if we differentiate (72.8), we get

$$\frac{d^2x^{\mu'}}{ds^2} = \frac{d^2x^\mu}{ds^2}p^{\mu'}_\mu + \frac{dx^\mu}{ds}\frac{d}{ds}(p^{\mu'}_\mu),\qquad\qquad (72.9)$$

and the last term will not usually vanish. This argument shows quite generally that a scalar derivative of a tensor is usually not a tensor, the reason being that the p's are not constant (as they are in four-tensor theory).

There is, however, a method for defining certain "derivatives" of tensors which *are* themselves tensors, and which, moreover, conveniently reduce to the ordinary derivatives in the LIF. For this purpose one needs the so-called Christoffel symbols $\Gamma^\mu_{\nu\sigma}$, defined by the equation

$$\Gamma^\mu_{\nu\sigma} = \Gamma^\mu_{\sigma\nu} = \sum_\tau \frac{1}{2} g^{\mu\tau}\,\frac{\partial g_{\tau\nu}}{\partial x^\sigma} + \left(\frac{\partial g_{\tau\sigma}}{\partial x^\nu} - \frac{\partial g_{\nu\sigma}}{\partial x^\tau}\right),\qquad (72.10)$$

where $(g^{\mu\nu})$ is the matrix inverse of $(g_{\mu\nu})$, and $g^{\mu\nu}$ can be shown to have the tensor character indicated by its indices. The Γ's, on the other hand, are *not* tensor components. It will turn out that they vanish in each LIF.

Now, if A^μ is any contravariant vector, the object DA^μ/ds, defined by the equation

$$\frac{D}{ds} A^\mu = \frac{d}{ds} A^\mu + \Gamma^\mu_{\nu\sigma} A^\nu \frac{dx^\sigma}{ds} , \qquad (72.11)$$

can be shown to be a tensor; it is called the *absolute derivative* of A^μ in the direction of dx^μ. In each LIF it reduces to the ordinary derivative, if indeed the Γ's vanish there. Thus, for example, $\dfrac{D}{ds}\left(\dfrac{dx^\mu}{ds}\right)$ will reduce to $\dfrac{d^2 x^\mu}{ds^2}$ in the LIF, and hence it represents the acceleration vector relative to Gaussian coordinates. Its vanishing turns out to be the condition for a geodesic line (i.e., the rigorous solution of the problem of maximizing $\int ds$):

$$\frac{D}{ds}\left(\frac{dx^\mu}{ds}\right) = \frac{d^2 x^\mu}{ds^2} + \Gamma^\mu_{\nu\sigma} \frac{dx^\nu}{ds} \frac{dx^\sigma}{ds} = 0. \qquad (72.12)$$

[Let us digress to test this equation immediately for the case of the metric (71.1). There, if $x^\mu = (x, y, z, t)$, $(g_{\mu\nu}) \approx$ diag $(-1, -1, -1, c^2)$ and thus $(g^{\mu\nu}) \approx$ diag $(-1, -1, -1, c^{-2})$. All $g_{\mu\nu}$ except g_{44} are constant. Hence, by (72.10), of all $\Gamma^i_{\mu\nu} (i = 1, 2, 3)$ only

$$\Gamma^i_{44} = \frac{1}{2} \frac{\partial}{\partial x^i} g_{44} = \frac{\partial \phi}{\partial x^i} \qquad (72.13)$$

is nonzero. For a slowly moving particle, $ds \approx c \, dt$, and thus the first three of equations (72.12) reduce to

$$\frac{d^2 x^i}{dt^2} = - \frac{\partial \phi}{\partial x^i} ,$$

which coincide exactly with the Newtonian equations of motion; the last recaptures our assumption $ds \approx c \, dt$, to the same order of accuracy. So, once again, a spot-check on the geodesic law has yielded an encouraging result.]

From (72.12) we would *expect* that in every LIF the Γ's vanish locally: the equations of motion for a free particle in a LIF *should* reduce to $d^2 x^\mu/ds^2 = 0$. Now it is proved in Riemannian geometry that, given any point P, we can find an infinite set of local coordinate systems ("geodesic coordinates") in which the Γ's vanish *at P*. (And the vanishing of the Γ's can be shown to be equivalent to the vanishing of all derivatives $\partial g_{\mu\nu}/\partial x^\sigma$.) The relation between any two of these systems, x^μ and $x^{\mu'}$, is "locally linear," i.e. $\partial^2 x^{\mu'}/\partial x^\mu \partial x^\nu = 0$ at P; and any system so related to a member of the set is itself a member. In spacetime we therefore identify the locally Euclidean ones among these geodesic coordinate systems at P as the LIF's at P. This is an important finding: LIF's are not just locally Euclidean systems, but, in addition, they have a "locally constant" metric ($\partial g_{\mu\nu}/\partial x^\sigma = 0$). An example will perhaps make this clear. Suppose we are in M_4, referred to standard coordinates x,y,z,t; now introduce Gaussian coordinates by the equations

$$x = x' + y'^2, y = y', z = z', t = t'. \qquad (72.14)$$

Then the metric evidently becomes

$$ds^2 = -(dx' + 2y'dy')^2 - dy'^2 - dz'^2 + c^2 dt'^2. \qquad (72.15)$$

At the origin $x' = y' = z' = t' = 0$, this metric is Euclidean in x', y', z', t'. Yet these are not LIF coordinates at the origin, since $\partial g_{12}/\partial x^2 \neq 0$ there. If the first member of (72.14) were replaced by $x = x' + y'^3$, they would be; i.e., they would be as good a LIF coordinate system at the origin of M_4 as any we work with in GR.

This formal characterization of LIF's shows that Riemannian spacetime *fully* contains the specification of the gravitational field at each event, since it determines the LIF's uniquely, i.e. the local standards of nonacceleration. Given Galileo's principle that free paths are independent of the individual particles, it then follows that the free paths must be fully determined by the Riemannian structure. This makes the geodesic law of motion particularly plausible, since it is difficult to see what other paths could be singled out intrinsically.

It is possible to go one step further with the idea of "geodesic coordinates." One can even construct coordinates such that not only at a given point, but all along a given curve, the Γ's vanish ("Fermi coordinates"). If the given curve is a timelike geodesic, these coordinates can be interpreted as the closest possible approximation to those defined by the standard coordinates of a freely falling inertial laboratory for an extended period of time. For example, a test gyroscope (a spinning free test particle) would be expected to have its axis at rest relative to the spatial coordinate axes of such a Fermi system defined along its geodesic path. This is one theoretical basis for the recently suggested gyroscopic tests of GR, which involve sending a gyroscope into free orbit around the earth. (More satisfactory *dynamical* arguments lead to the same predictions.)

One tensor that plays a fundamental role in GR is the *Riemann curvature tensor* $R^{\mu}_{\nu\rho\sigma}$ defined as follows:

$$R^{\mu}_{\nu\rho\sigma} = \frac{\partial}{\partial x^{\rho}} \Gamma^{\mu}_{\nu\sigma} - \frac{\partial}{\partial x^{\sigma}} \Gamma^{\mu}_{\nu\rho} + \Gamma^{\mu}_{\tau\rho} \Gamma^{\tau}_{\nu\sigma} - \Gamma^{\mu}_{\tau\sigma} \Gamma^{\tau}_{\nu\rho}. \quad (72.16)$$

That this *is* a tensor of the type indicated by its four indices is not obvious, but it can be verified from the definition. It has $4^4 = 256$ components in four-dimensional spacetime; but in fact only 20 of these are independent, because $R^{\mu}_{\nu\rho\sigma}$ can be shown to possess certain symmetries, such as

$$R^{\mu}_{\nu\rho\sigma} = -R^{\mu}_{\nu\sigma\rho}, \quad R^{\mu}_{\nu\rho\sigma} + R^{\mu}_{\rho\sigma\nu} + R^{\mu}_{\sigma\nu\rho} = 0, \quad R^{\mu}_{\mu\rho\sigma} = 0. \quad (72.17)$$

Note that, because of the structure of the Γ's (cf. (72.10)), $R^{\mu}_{\nu\rho\sigma}$ is entirely built up of the $g_{\mu\nu}$ and their first and second derivatives. Being a tensor, it cannot be made to vanish by a special choice of coordinates—for it would then vanish in all coordinates, by (72.4). Thus even in a LIF it will in general be nonzero. Of course, in *flat* space (e.g., M_4) there exist coordinates which make the g's constant and thus the Γ's zero everywhere; consequently, in flat space $R^{\mu}_{\nu\rho\sigma} = 0$. The converse is also true: $R^{\mu}_{\nu\rho\sigma} = 0$ is necessary *and* sufficient for a space to be flat (i.e., Euclidean or pseudo-Euclidean).

One way of seeing how $R^{\mu}_{\nu\rho\sigma}$ is connected with the geometric concept of curvature is to study "geodesic deviation." Consider two nearby and almost parallel geodesics, and let η^{μ} be a vector joining them and orthogonal to both. Then it can be shown from the geodesic equation (72.12) that

$$\frac{D^2\eta^\mu}{ds^2} = (R^\mu_{\nu\rho\sigma}\, U^\nu\, U^\rho)\,\eta^\sigma, \quad \left[\frac{D^2\eta^\mu}{ds^2} = \frac{D}{ds}\left(\frac{D\eta^\mu}{ds}\right)\right], \quad (72.18)$$

where $U^\nu = dx^\nu/ds$ for one of the geodesics. Compare this with (66.2). [It is not difficult to deduce from (72.18) a formula for $K(U^\mu, \eta^\mu)$, the space curvature for the orientation (U^μ, η^μ); but we shall not need it.] Here, incidentally, we have a practical way of discovering the components of $R^\mu_{\nu\rho\sigma}$ in spacetime: Take a set of neighboring free test particles (four will generally be enough), adopt quasi-LIF coordinates and measure their four-velocities U^μ and 20 of their mutual acceleration components $D^2\eta^\mu/ds^2$; substitute in (72.18) and solve for the 20 independent components of the curvature tensor.

73   The Vacuum Field Equations of GR

In the neighborhood of any given event E_0, the Newtonian gravitational field **f** can be split as follows:

$$\mathbf{f} = \mathbf{f}_0 + \Delta_0\mathbf{f}, \qquad (73.1)$$

where $\mathbf{f}_0$ is the field *at* E_0 and $\Delta_0\mathbf{f}$ is defined by this equation. Since $\mathbf{f}_0$ can be "transformed away" by going to any (freely falling) local inertial frame S_0 at E_0, all that is felt of **f** in S_0 is the so-called *tidal* field $\Delta_0\mathbf{f}$. For example, as the name implies, this is the kind of field that produces the tides on earth, since the earth (except for its rotation and its *own* gravitational field) is a kind of local inertial frame in the combined sun-moon gravitational field. Again, it is the tidal field in a freely falling elevator on earth that causes two free particles on a common horizontal to accelerate towards each other, and two free particles on a common vertical to accelerate away from each other. Tidal forces always indicate the presence of an *intrinsic* gravitational field, i.e., one that cannot be ascribed to a "wrong" choice of reference frame. The way to detect these forces is to observe a set of neighboring free test particles. If there are relative accelerations between them, then there are tidal forces. In the contrary case the particles are in an extended inertial frame.

Now, every Newtonian gravitational field **f** is derivable from a potential ϕ in the usual way,

$$f_i = -\partial\phi/\partial x^i = -\phi_i, \quad (i = 1, 2, 3), \qquad (73.2)$$

where ϕ_i is defined by the last equation. (Similarly, ϕ_{ij} will denote $\partial^2\phi/\partial x^i \partial x^j$.) The relative acceleration of two test particles separated by a small connecting three-vector η^i is therefore given by

$$d^2\eta^i/dt^2 = df_i = -\phi_{ij}\,\eta^j, \qquad (73.3)$$

again using the summation convention. Thus it is the *second* derivatives of the potential that indicate an intrinsic field. We next recall that these second derivatives satisfy the so-called Poisson equation

$$\sum_{i=1}^{3} \phi_{ii} = 4\pi G\rho, \qquad (73.4)$$

which is the "field of equation" of Newtonian gravitational theory, relating the sources of the field with the field itself. It is essentially the local version of the inverse square law. At first, however, we shall be interested in *vacuum* fields—such as the field around the sun—and then $\rho = 0$, and Poisson's equation reduces to Laplace's equation

$$\sum_{i=1}^{3} \phi_{ii} = 0. \qquad (73.5)$$

If we compare (73.3) with (72.18), we see that $R^\mu_{\nu\rho\sigma} U^\nu U^\rho$ corresponds to ϕ_{ij} and that the following is therefore an analog of Laplace's equation (73.5) in spacetime:

$$R^\mu_{\nu\rho\mu} U^\nu U^\rho = 0, \qquad (73.6)$$

summation being implied again over the repeated index μ, as well as over the indices ν and ρ. If this is to hold for *all* U^μ, we need

$$R^\mu_{\nu\rho\mu} = R_{\nu\rho} = 0. \qquad (73.7)$$

The tensor $R_{\nu\rho}$, defined by this equation, is called the *Ricci* tensor. (It is easy to show that it *is* a tensor, since it arises from the "contraction" of another tensor, $R^{\mu}_{\nu\rho\sigma}$.) Because of (72.17) (ii) and (iii) it possesses the symmetry

$$R_{\mu\nu} = R_{\nu\mu}, \tag{73.8}$$

and so the number of its independent components is not 4^2 but only 10. The vanishing of the ten components of the Ricci tensor, then, is what the Newtonian analogy suggests as the vacuum field equations of GR. And this, indeed, was Einstein's proposal (1915). It has been strikingly vindicated: not only does GR, completed by these field equations (and their generalization to the inside of matter—see Section 79) reproduce to within experimental error all those Newtonian results that agree with observation, but where GR differs observably from Newton's theory, such as in the last two of the original "three crucial effects" (the gravitational Doppler effect, the bending of light, and the advance of the perihelia of the planets), it is GR that is found to be correct.

But how is it that instead of the *one* field equation (73.5) of Newtonian theory, there should be *ten* in GR? The reason is that the field equations are required to determine the whole metric, i.e., the $g_{\mu\nu}$. And there are just ten of these, since $g_{\mu\nu} = g_{\nu\mu}$. In fact, these ten $g_{\mu\nu}$ are the analogs of the *one* potential ϕ of Newton's theory. This analogy can be illustrated in many ways. The metric (71.1) already showed the (approximate) essential identity of g_{44} with the Newtonian ϕ in that particular coordinate system. An arbitrary change of coordinates would, of course, relate *all* the g's with ϕ. Again, let us recall the basic role of *any* potential: its first derivatives are directly related to the force (i.e., the acceleration), as in (73.2). In Maxwell's theory there is, instead of the Newtonian *scalar* potential ϕ, a *four-vector* potential Φ_{μ}, such that the four-acceleration is given by

$$\frac{d^2 x^{\mu}}{ds^2} = \frac{1}{c} \sum_{\tau, \nu} g^{\mu\tau} \left(\frac{\partial \Phi_{\nu}}{\partial x^{\tau}} - \frac{\partial \Phi_{\tau}}{\partial x^{\nu}} \right) \frac{dx^{\nu}}{ds} . \tag{73.9}$$

(See RSR, Chapter VI.) The corresponding equation in GR is (72.12), which can be written in the form

$$\frac{d^2 x^\mu}{ds^2} = -\frac{1}{2} \sum_{\tau,\nu,\sigma} g^{\mu\tau} \left(\frac{\partial g_{\tau\nu}}{\partial x^\sigma} + \frac{\partial g_{\tau\sigma}}{\partial x^\nu} - \frac{\partial g_{\nu\sigma}}{\partial x^\tau} \right) \frac{dx^\nu}{ds} \frac{dx^\sigma}{ds}. \quad (73.10)$$

This shows the g's in their role as potentials. GR, then, can be formally regarded as a gravitational field theory with a tensor potential.

The field equations (73.7), accordingly, are *second* order differential equations in the potential (i.e., they involve second but no higher derivatives of the $g_{\mu\nu}$), as is clear from the definition of $R^\mu_{\nu\rho\sigma}$. And this, too, is analogous to the Newtonian (vacuum) case (73.5), and the Maxwellian (vacuum) case

$$\sum_{\mu,\nu} g^{\mu\nu} \frac{\partial^2 \Phi_\sigma}{\partial x^\mu \partial x^\nu} = 0. \quad (73.11)$$

(See RSR, Chapter VI, Exercise (5).) Unlike the Newtonian or Maxwellian field equations, however, Einstein's field equations are *nonlinear*: they contain products of the g's and their derivatives. Linearity always implies that the sum of any two solutions of the field equations is itself a solution of the field equations; thus linearity permits the "superposition" of solutions. For example, in Newtonian theory if we know the field of a mass m_1 placed at a point P, and that of a mass m_2 placed at a point Q, we merely have to *add* these solutions to get the field of a mass m_1 at P and a mass m_2 at Q. The analog is true in Maxwell's theory, too, but it is *not* true in GR, and it is easy to see why. The mechanism is similar to that causing the "mass defect" of atoms (see Section 53), except that now it is the gravitational "binding energy" which itself has (negative) gravitational mass. The moon, for example, exerts a gravitational force equal to that of two half moons *minus* the mass equivalent of the energy it takes to separate these halves. Nonlinearity is therefore *necessary* if the field equations are to take into account a dependence of mass on energy. On the other hand, whether Einstein's equations always give results exactly consistent with $E = mc^2$ is not clear: the solutions are too complicated to handle and the energy concept in the large is too ill defined.

And now a final point: do we not have too many field equations in (73.7)? Do not ten differential equations determine the ten unknowns $g_{\mu\nu}$ uniquely, given suitable boundary conditions? Yet surely we do not *want* to find the $g_{\mu\nu}$ uniquely since we ought to be at liberty to change coordinates in spacetime and so transform the metric into any equivalent metric. In fact, we would like to have four degrees of freedom in the determination of the $g_{\mu\nu}$, corresponding to the four arbitrary functions $x^{\mu'} = x^{\mu'}(x^\mu)$ which specify a change of coordinates. As it happens, however, the field equations satisfy four differential identities (see Section 79), and thus they effectively impose only six differential restrictions on the g's, which is precisely what is needed.

From every theoretical point of view, therefore, the field equations $R_{\mu\nu} = 0$ seem just right. Certainly there exist none that are simpler and still consistent with the fundamental ideas of GR. And it should be remembered that field equations are a matter of choice and not of proof. (Newton, too, *chose* the inverse square law!) The next logical step is to see whether they correctly predict verifiable results.

74   *The Schwarzschild Solution*

The first and most important exact solution of Einstein's field equations was found in 1916 by Schwarzschild. It is the metric for the spacetime around a spherically symmetric mass. To obtain it, we set up coordinates exactly as we did in Section 70, defining r by the area of a two-sphere $r = constant$, and synchronizing clock rates and clock settings. The metric at this stage, then, must be of the form

$$ds^2 = e^A dt^2 - e^B dr^2 - r^2(d\theta^2 + \sin^2\theta d\phi^2), \quad (74.1)$$

where e^A and e^B are unknown functions of r, written like this for computational convenience. This time, however, we shall use no hybrid arguments to find A and B, but rather let the field equations speak for themselves. For this purpose we must calculate the Γ's of the metric (74.1) (which involve A and B and their derivatives), and then the Ricci tensor components $R_{\mu\nu}$. The algebra is tedious, and we shall merely state the results (indices 1, 2, 3, 4, refer to r, θ, ϕ, t, respectively, and primes denote differentiation with respect to r)*:

$$R_{11} = \tfrac{1}{2} A'' - \tfrac{1}{4} A'B' + \tfrac{1}{4} A'^2 - B'/r \qquad (74.2)$$
$$R_{22} = e^{-B} [1 + \tfrac{1}{2} r(A' - B')] - 1 \qquad (74.3)$$
$$R_{33} = R_{22} \sin^2 \theta \qquad (74.4)$$
$$R_{44} = -e^{A-B} (\tfrac{1}{2} A'' - \tfrac{1}{4} A'B' + \tfrac{1}{4} A'^2 + A'/r) \qquad (74.5)$$
$$R_{\mu\nu} = 0 \quad \text{when } \mu \neq \nu. \qquad (74.6)$$

The field equations require $R_{\mu\nu} = 0$ for all indices. Thus, (74.2) and (74.5) yield

$$A' = -B', \qquad (74.7)$$

whence $A = -B + k$, where k is a constant. Reference to (74.1) shows that a simple change in the time scale $t \rightarrow e^{-k/2} t$ will absorb the k; let us suppose this done, and then

$$A = -B.$$

With that, (74.3) yields

$$e^A (1 + rA') = 1,$$

or, setting $e^A = \alpha$,

$$\alpha + r\alpha' = (r\alpha)' = 1.$$

This equation can at once be integrated, giving

$$\alpha = 1 - 2m/r,$$

where $-2m$ is simply a constant of integration. It can be verified that all $R_{\mu\nu}$ indeed vanish for this solution. Ac-

---

*See, for example, A. S. Eddington, "The Mathematical Theory of Relativity," p. 85, Cambridge University Press, 1924. For a more modern computational technique see Appendix A of C. W. Misner, *J. Math. Phys.* **4**, 924 (1963).

cordingly, we have found the following metric:

$$ds^2 = \left(1 - \frac{2m}{r}\right)dt^2 - \left(1 - \frac{2m}{r}\right)^{-1} dr^2 - r^2(d\theta^2 + \sin^2\theta d\phi^2).$$

$$(74.8)$$

Now compare this with (70.4) whose geodesics, as we already know, approximate to the Newtonian orbits round a mass m. Consequently the m in (74.8) is identified with the mass of the central body, in units in which $G = c = 1$. (To restore conventional units we must write Gm/c^2 for m and ct for t.) In the present units the mass of the earth is 0.44 cm, and that of the sun 1.47 km.

Note that nowhere in our derivation did we have to *assume* flatness at infinity, yet the metric (74.8) possesses this property; it must therefore be a consequence purely of spherical symmetry, staticness, and the vacuum field equations. The argument for (74.8) would go through even if m were surrounded by a spherically symmetric mass distribution beyond a sphere Σ of coordinate radius r: *between* m and Σ the metric (74.8) would apply. This, in turn, leads to the relativistic analog of the Newtonian theorem according to which there is *no* gravitational field inside such a sphere Σ if it is empty. For then we must put $m = 0$ in (74.8) in order to avoid a singularity, and the result is Minkowski space inside Σ, which indeed corresponds to the absence of gravity.

Birkhoff has shown (1923) that even the assumption of staticness is unnecessary in order to obtain the metric (74.8): spherical symmetry is all that is needed.* Thus even a pulsating mass, surrounded by spherically symmetric pulsating matter beyond Σ, would give rise to the same metric between it and Σ.

Inspection of this metric now shows that, contrary to our assumption of Section 70, a mass *does* curve the three-space around it. Of course, the curvature is generally very small.

---

*For a rigorous proof, see W. B. Bonnor's article in "Recent Developments in General Relativity," p. 167, New York, Pergamon Press, Inc., 1962.

For a "plane" through the origin (e.g. the locus $\theta = \pi/2$) it turns out to be $-m/r^3$ at coordinate r. At the surface of the earth this is $-2 \times 10^{-27}\,\mathrm{cm}^{-2}$, and at the surface of the sun it is $-4 \times 10^{-28}\,\mathrm{cm}^{-2}$. It can be verified that the intrinsic spatial geometry of a "plane" such as $\theta = \pi/2$ with its metric $d\sigma^2 = dr^2/(1 - 2m/r) + r^2 d\phi^2$ is identical to that of the upper half of *Flamm's paraboloid*, generated by rotating the parabola

$$z^2 = 8m(y - 2m), \quad x = 0, \tag{74.9}$$

about the z axis in Euclidean three-space; r corresponds to $(x^2 + y^2)^{1/2}$ and ϕ to the angle about the z axis. (See Figure 21.)

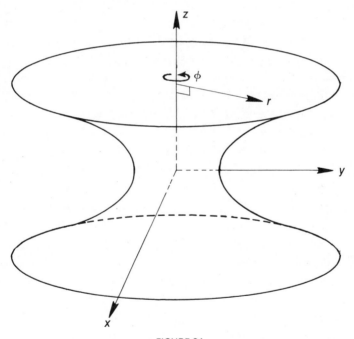

FIGURE 21.

Minute though it is, the spatial curvature contributes significantly to two well-known "post-Newtonian" effects of GR, namely the bending of light and the advance of the perihelia of planets. If one calculates the geodesics of (74.8) with simply $-dr^2$ as the second term on the right, one gets only two-thirds of the advance of the perihelia, and one-half of the bending of light.

Still, for gravitational effects on slowly moving particles it is the coefficient of dt^2 in the metric that vastly predominates. And this is not surprising, since in ordinary units it is multiplied by c^2. For the same reason it also predominates in Minkowski space, to the extent that we can often approximate ds^2 by $c^2 dt^2$. Consider *any* static metric of the form $ds^2 = \alpha dt^2 - d\sigma^2$, where $\alpha \approx 1$. Then for a particle moving with coordinate speed $v = d\sigma/dt$, we have $ds^2 = dt^2 (\alpha - v^2)$, and thus the relative contributions to ds^2 of its spatial and temporal parts are in the ratio $v^2 : \alpha$. For all the sun's planets, for example, $v < 50$ km/sec; in present units this implies $v^2 < 3 \times 10^{-8}$, which illustrates the magnitude of the spatial contribution. The small "corrections" to their Minkowskian values suffered by the spatial and temporal coefficients in (74.8) are about equal; hence *their* effects, too, are in the ratio $v^2 : \alpha$. Since gravitational orbits depend on ds^2 only, it should now be clear how little the spatial geometry affects the paths of slow particles. For high-speed particles, on the other hand, it can become significant.

It is perhaps of some interest to understand directly how the space geometry contributes to the advance of the perihelion and other phenomena. Suppose that on the assumption of flat-space geometry an orbit is nearly circular, with mean radius a, and possibly with some perihelion advance, like the curve C in Figure 22 (i). To first approximation, the "plane" of the orbit is really the tangent cone to Flamm's paraboloid at radius $r = a \cos \psi$ (see Figure 22 (ii)), where the small angle ψ is given by

$$\psi \approx \frac{dz}{dy} = \frac{4m}{z}, \tag{74.11}$$

as we calculate easily from (74.9). To make the plane of the flat-space calculation into this cone, we must cut out of it a wedge of angle δ such that

$$a(2\pi - \delta) = 2\pi r = 2\pi a \cos\psi$$
$$\approx 2\pi a(1 - \tfrac{1}{2}\psi^2). \qquad (74.12)$$

Clearly, δ will be the contribution of the spatial geometry to the perihelion advance. Solving (74.12) and substituting

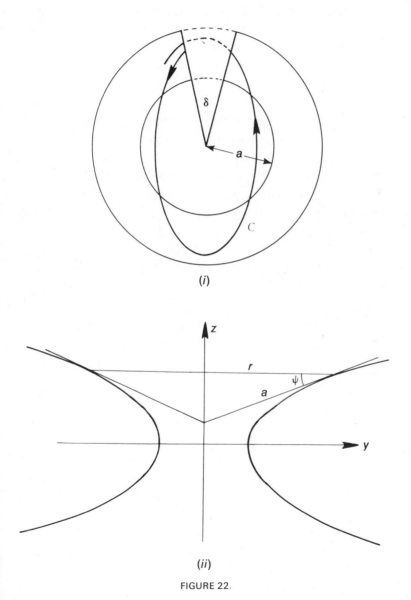

(i)

(ii)

FIGURE 22.

from (74.11) and (74.9) (with $y = r$), we get

$$\delta = \frac{2\pi m}{r}, \qquad (74.13)$$

which is one-third of the full perihelion advance, as we shall see in Section 75.

The contribution of the space geometry to the bending of light can be understood in the same kind of way. If a long, thin, rectangular strip of paper, with a straight line drawn down its middle (corresponding to a straight light path in flat space), is glued without wrinkles to the upper half of Flamm's paraboloid, and then viewed from the z axis at large z, the center line will appear bent: this is precisely the contribution of the space geometry to the bending of light. If the center line is already bent slightly relative to the strip, as implied by the EP for a light ray, then it will appear even more bent when applied to the paraboloid. (A crude application of the EP, as in Section 21, predicts curved light paths relative to the LIF's, which correspond to little tangent planes on Flamm's paraboloid.)

The angle δ, evaluated in (74.13) and illustrated in Figure 22, is also fairly obviously the contribution of the space geometry to the advance of the axis of a test gyroscope in circular orbit around a mass m at radius r, if the axis lies in the plane of the orbit (or of the projection of the axis onto this plane, otherwise). There is a second contribution to this advance, namely the so-called *Thomas precession*, which is a flat-space phenomenon: imagine a set of inertial frames moving so that the spatial track of each origin is tangent to a circle of radius r, and in such a way that we meet these origins at zero relative velocity as we go round the circle at constant angular speed ω; if any two successive such frames consider their axes to be oriented without relative rotation, then, as we complete the circle, the axes of the last frame are nevertheless rotated relative to those of the first by an angle $\pi r^2 \omega^2$. (See RSR, page 44.) In the present case, by (70.5), this amounts to $\pi m/r$. The total effect, geometric and Thomas, gives the well-known *Fokker-de Sitter precession* of $3\pi m/r$.

The reader may have noticed that something strange happens in (74.8) at the so-called *Schwarzschild radius r* = 2*m*. Remembering the significance of ds^2, one sees that standard clocks stand still and radial rulers shrink to zero length there. We shall discuss this phenomenon later. At the moment we merely note that for all "ordinary" bodies the Schwarzschild radius lies well inside them, where the *vacuum* solution (74.8) is in any case not applicable; for example, for the sun it is 2.9 km, for the earth, 0.88 cm, and for a proton, 2.4×10^{-52} cm. (But see Sections 76, 77.)

When applying the Schwarzschild metric (74.8), especially in astronomy, one must, of course, understand the physical significance of the coordinates. That of the coordinate time *t* was already discussed in Section 70. And the meanings of θ and ϕ are clear enough: for example, an event *seen* at the origin at angular coordinates θ, ϕ *has* these coordinates, since, by symmetry, radial light rays must follow paths θ = constant, ϕ = constant. It remains to relate *r* to various physical distances. By definition, *r* is "distance from apparent size," i.e., the known diameter of an object divided by the angle it is seen to subtend at the origin. (This is equivalent to the definition involving the area of spheres.) However, this is only one possible method of measuring distance in large-scale physics. Another, for example, is by radar. Suppose we send a radial signal from the surface of the earth ($r = r_E$, say) to be reflected at an event as far away as the sun ($r = r_S$, say) and clock the total time elapsed, $2T$, before the return of the signal. Then we ascribe a radar distance $R = T/c$ to the event. (In present units $c = 1$.) How does this compare with the coordinate distance $r_S - r_E$? To gain an insight into the earth's field, we shall ignore all other fields. For a radial light (or radio) signal, we have $ds = 0$ and $d\theta = d\phi = 0$, and thus, from (74.8),

$$dt = \pm \frac{dr}{1 - 2m/r} = \pm \left(1 + \frac{2m}{r - 2m}\right) dr. \quad (74.14)$$

Because of the static nature of the metric, the coordinate times for the outward and return trips are equal (cf. Section 71), and thus

$$R = \int_{r_E}^{r_S} \left(1 + \frac{2m}{r - 2m}\right) dr = r_S - r_E + 2m \log\left(\frac{r_S - 2m}{r_E - 2m}\right).$$
$$(74.15)$$

The last term on the right gives the excess of radar distance over coordinate distance; in the present case ($m = .44$ cm, $r_S = 1.5 \times 10^{13}$ cm, $r_E = 6.4 \times 10^8$ cm), this amounts to only 10 cm! To see how the same distance would come out as measured with standard rulers laid end to end, we again refer to (74.8) and find that ruler distance σ is related to co-ordinate distance r by the equation

$$d\sigma = \frac{dr}{(1 - 2m/r)^{1/2}} \approx \left(1 + \frac{m}{r}\right) dr,$$

whence, as in (74.15),

$$\sigma \approx r_S - r_E + m \log \frac{r_S}{r_E}. \qquad (74.16)$$

The excess of ruler distance is seen to be essentially one-half of the excess of radar distance, and thus about 5 cm. Both, of course, are quite negligible in practice. (Incidentally, σ represents radial distance along Flamm's paraboloid.) Other physical (i.e., operational) methods of defining distance, e.g., by parallax, by apparent brightness, etc., can all be similarly related to coordinate distance. They are in general inequivalent, and this points to the need for caution when talking about "distance" in GR.

75   Rays and Orbits in Schwarzschild Space

The easiest result to read off from the Schwarzschild metric (74.8) is the exact gravitational Doppler shift in the light from a point at radial coordinate r_1 to a point at radial co-ordinate r_2 (and correspondingly labeled other coordinates). We need not assume that these points lie on the same radius vector. Along the light path $ds^2 = 0$ and thus

$$dt = \pm(1 - 2m/r)^{-1/2} d\sigma,$$

where $d\sigma$ is the square root of the spatial part of the metric. Because the metric is static, the light path between two given points has the same space track at all times, and therefore

$$\int_{t_1}^{t_2} dt = \int_{(r_1,\theta_1,\phi_1)}^{(r_2,\theta_2,\phi_2)} \frac{\pm d\sigma}{(1 - 2m/r)^{1/2}} = \int_{t_1+\Delta t_1}^{t_2+\Delta t_2} dt. \quad (75.1)$$

This gives $\Delta t_1 = \Delta t_2$, i.e., for a later signal the coordinate time increments at emission and reception are equal. (Of course, this merely recovers one of our assumptions, namely that the coordinate clock rates are synchronized.) If Δt_1 is thought of as the time between two successive wavecrests, it is seen that the corresponding *proper time* increments are in the ratio of the locally observed wavelengths; and thus

$$D = \frac{\lambda_2}{\lambda_1} = \frac{\Delta s_2}{\Delta s_1} = \frac{(1 - 2m/r_2)^{1/2} \Delta t_2}{(1 - 2m/r_1)^{1/2} \Delta t_1} = \left(\frac{1 - 2m/r_2}{1 - 2m/r_1}\right)^{1/2}.$$

$$(75.2)$$

To first order, this is the same formula as that obtained by elementary arguments from the EP and Newton's potential without the GR field equations. Its first order verification consequently provides support for the EP but not specifically for the field equations. (Second order verification cannot presently be contemplated.) The possibility of verification exists in observing the light from the surface of very massive and dense stars. The m then refers to the mass of the star, r_1 to its radius, and r_2 to its distance from earth (essentially infinite); the earth's own field can be neglected by comparison. Unfortunately the existing astronomical results are still rather inconclusive because of the many observational difficulties. The most accurate verification to date of the gravitational Doppler shift formula (to about 1%) has been provided by the recent terrestrial experiments mentioned in Section 21.

In order to obtain the exact light and particle paths in the Schwarzschild metric, we must solve the geodesic equations (72.12). Again we shall omit some of the details.* It turns

*They may be found, for example, in A. S. Eddington, *loc. cit.*

out that the equation with $\mu = 2$ implies that if a particle (or ray) initially moves in the plane $\theta = \frac{1}{2}\pi$, then it continues to do so; consequently we assume, without loss of generality, that the motion takes place in that plane. The remaining equations can then be reduced to the following most convenient pair:

$$r^2 \frac{d\phi}{ds} = h, \qquad (h = \text{constant}), \qquad (75.3)$$

$$\frac{d^2u}{d\phi^2} + u = \frac{m}{h^2} + 3mu^2, \qquad \left(u = \frac{1}{r}\right). \qquad (75.4)$$

[It may be of interest to note that for the flat-space metric (70.4) (with $G = c = 1$) the only difference would be in the last term of (75.4); that equation would read, instead,

$$\frac{d^2u}{d\phi^2} + u = \frac{m}{h^2} + \frac{4m^2u}{h^2}. \qquad (75.5)]$$

Now *in Newton's theory*, angular momentum is conserved, i.e.,

$$r^2 \frac{d\phi}{dt} = h, \qquad (75.6)$$

and the inverse square law then implies

$$\frac{d^2u}{d\phi^2} + u = \frac{m}{h^2}. \qquad (75.7)$$

(This last equation follows quite easily from $d^2r/dt^2 = -m/r^2$, by use of (75.6) and repeated application of the chain rule.) It therefore appears that GR has added a small "correction" term to the Newtonian orbital equation, and has given a slightly different meaning to the conserved quantity h. The smallness of these corrections can be judged, respectively, from the ratio $3mu^2$: m/h^2 which for the earth's orbit, for example, is .000 000 03, and from the ratio ds/dt which for the earth is .999 999 995. (Of course, it is not clear that the Newtonian t is to be identified with GR coordinate time t rather than with proper time s, since Newtonian theory does not distinguish between these.)

Now a suitable solution of the Newtonian equation (75.7), if we are interested in planetary orbits, is given by the usual polar equation of an ellipse,

$$u = \frac{m}{h^2}(1 + e\cos\phi),\tag{75.8}$$

where e is the eccentricity. Substituting this into the right side of (75.4) as a first approximation, we get

$$\frac{d^2u}{d\phi^2} + u = \frac{m}{h^2} + \frac{3m^3}{h^4}(1 + 2e\cos\phi + e^2\cos^2\phi).\tag{75.9}$$

For the further solution of this equation, we need particular integrals of the following three types of equations,

$$\frac{d^2u}{d\phi^2} + u = A, \quad = A\cos\phi, \quad = A\cos^2\phi,$$

where each A is, in fact, a constant of order m^3/h^4. These must then be added to (75.8). As can be verified easily, such particular integrals are, respectively,

$$u_1 = A, \quad = \tfrac{1}{2}A\,\phi\sin\phi, \quad = \tfrac{1}{2}A - \tfrac{1}{6}A\cos2\phi.\tag{75.10}$$

Of these, the first simply adds a minute constant to u, while the third adds a minute constant and "wiggle," all quite unobservable. But the second cannot be neglected, since it has a "resonance" factor ϕ and thus produces a continually increasing and ultimately noticeable effect. Thus our second approximation is

$$u = \frac{m}{h^2}\left(1 + e\cos\phi + \frac{3m^2}{h^2}e\phi\sin\phi\right)$$

$$\approx \frac{m}{h^2}\left[1 + e\cos\left(1 - \frac{3m^2}{h^2}\right)\phi\right],\tag{75.11}$$

where we have used the formula $\cos(\alpha - \beta) = \cos\alpha\cos\beta - \sin\alpha\sin\beta$, and the approximations $\cos\beta \approx 1$, $\sin\beta \approx \beta$ for a small angle β. This equation shows u (and therefore r) to be a periodic function of ϕ with period

$$\frac{2\pi}{1 - 3m^2/h^2} > 2\pi.$$

Thus the values of r, which of course trace out an approximate ellipse, do not begin to repeat until somewhat *after* the radius vector has made a complete revolution. Hence the orbit can be regarded as an ellipse that rotates ("pre-

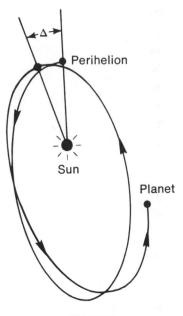

Perihelion

Sun

Planet

FIGURE 23.

cesses") about one of its foci (see Figure 23) by an amount

$$\Delta = \frac{2\pi}{1 - 3m^2/h^2} - 2\pi \approx \frac{6\pi m^2}{h^2} = \frac{6\pi m}{a(1 - e^2)} \qquad (75.12)$$

per revolution. Here we have used the Newtonian equation

$$\frac{2m}{h^2} = \frac{1}{r_1} + \frac{1}{r_2} = \frac{2}{a(1 - e^2)}, \qquad (75.13)$$

which follows from (75.8) on setting $\phi = 0, \pi$; a is the semi-major-axis, and r_1, r_2 are the maximum and minimum values $a(1 \pm e)$ of r. This Δ is the famous Einsteinian advance of the perihelion. For the flat-space metric (70.4) we have, from (75.5),

$$\frac{d^2u}{d\phi^2} + \left(1 - \frac{4m^2}{h^2}\right)u = \frac{m}{h^2},$$

whose solution is *immediately* recognized as having period $2\pi/(1 - 4m^2/h^2)^{1/2}$, which leads to exactly two-thirds of the perihelion advance (75.12). The remaining third comes from the spatial geometry (as we saw in (74.13), at least for nearly circular orbits).

The relative difficulty of observing the advance of planetary perihelia depends not only on the size of Δ, but also on the eccentricity of the orbit. The case of Mercury* is by far the most favorable. Its actually observed perihelion advance, in *one hundred terrestrial years*, is 5599".74 ± 0".41 (seconds of arc). All but 43" of this total was explained by Newtonian perturbation theory as due to the remaining planets and other causes. The 43" discrepancy, however, had long been a notorious puzzle. It is precisely these missing 43" that were explained by GR in what must surely have been one of the most striking denouements ever of a natural mystery. (Consider such pedestrian alternatives as changing Newton's $1/r^2$ law to $1/r^{2.000\ 000\ 16}$—as had been seriously proposed!) The secular advances of the perihelia of the earth and of Venus have also been observed lately, and they agree to within the rather large observational uncertainties with the GR predictions of 3".8 and 8".6, respectively.

Next we investigate the deflection of light. We can again start with equations (75.3) and (75.4). But since now $ds = 0$, $h = \infty$ and (75.4) reduces to

$$\frac{d^2u}{d\phi^2} + u = 3mu^2. \tag{75.14}$$

A suitable solution of this equation *without* the small right-hand term is given by the straight line

$$u = \frac{\sin \phi}{R}, \tag{75.15}$$

in which R can be regarded as the radius of the sun, if we are primarily interested in rays grazing the sun's edge (see Figure 24). Substituting (75.15) into the right side of (75.14) gives

---

*$a = 4.8 \times 10^{12}$ cm, $e = 0.2$, period = 88 days, m(sun) = 1.5 × 10^5 cm in present units.

$$\frac{d^2\mu}{d\phi^2} + u = \frac{3m}{R^2}(1 - \cos^2\phi),$$

of which a particular integral is (cf. (75.10))

$$u_1 = \frac{3m}{2R^2}(1 + \tfrac{1}{3}\cos 2\phi).$$

Adding this to (75.15) yields the second approximation

$$u = \frac{\sin\phi}{R} + \frac{3m}{2R^2}(1 + \tfrac{1}{3}\cos 2\phi). \qquad (75.16)$$

For large r, ϕ is evidently very small, and so $\sin\phi \approx \phi$, $\cos 2\phi \approx 1$. Going to the limit $u \to 0$ in (75.16), we thus find $\phi \to \phi_\infty$ (see Figure 24), where

$$\phi_\infty = -\frac{2m}{R}.$$

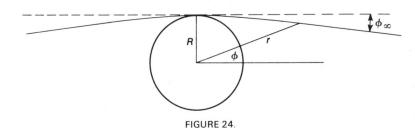

FIGURE 24.

Consequently the magnitude of the total deflection of the ray, by symmetry, is

$$\frac{4m}{R}$$

in circular measure.

For a ray grazing the sun, for example, this comes to $1''.75$. It can be tested by comparing the observed with the known positions of stars seen near the sun's limb during a total eclipse. The agreement is quite satisfactory, though some observations seem to give values slightly in excess of the GR prediction. They certainly do *not* support the prediction

$$\frac{2m}{R},$$

which can be made on the basis of Newtonian theory. [Consider the orbit (75.8) with $\sin\phi$ in place of $\cos\phi$ (to conform with Figure 24). For a photon grazing the sun, $h = Rc$, and thus, setting $\phi = \frac{1}{2}\pi$ in (75.8) (and $c = 1$), we have

$$\frac{1}{R} = \frac{m}{R^2}(1 + e), \quad \text{or} \quad e = \frac{R}{m} - 1 \approx \frac{R}{m},$$

since $R/m \gg 1$. Then going to the limit $u \to 0$ in (75.8), just as we did in (75.16), we get $\phi_\infty = -1/e = -m/R$.] Also the flat-space metric (70.4) yields, via equation (75.5) and the above procedure, only one-half of the full GR deflection.

A somewhat different point in connection with the "photon equation" (75.14) is the existence of circular light paths: evidently that equation possesses the particular solution $u = 1/3m$, or $r = 3m$. These orbits are three times larger than the corresponding "Newtonian" circular light orbits obtainable from (70.5) by setting $\omega = c/r = 1/r$ and $G = 1$; *that* yields $r = m$.

A General-Relativistic "Proof" of E = mc²   76

In this section we give two possibly amusing applications of the gravitational Doppler shift formula in the Schwarzschild field. First we use it to calculate the exact proper acceleration felt by a particle fixed at coordinate r: it differs slightly from the Newtonian m/r^2. Then we use that result and the Doppler formula again to show how the full energy equivalent mc^2 can be extracted from a mass m:* As we saw in Section 53, it is easy enough to establish by the methods of SR that all energy *contributes* to mass according to the relation $E = mc^2$ (—since kinetic energy does, and all energy is convertible to kinetic energy). But the converse, that all mass is energy, i.e., convertible energy, was originally a pure hypothesis whose experimental justification had to wait for

---

*I owe to Professor Roger Penrose the suggestion that "one must be able to get mc^2 by slowly lowering m down to a Schwarzschild radius."

decades. In GR one can actually give a prescription for extracting up to mc^2 units of energy from a mass m.

We recall equation (69.1) for the Doppler effect in an acceleration field g over a small *proper* length l. Now, the proper length $d\sigma$ corresponding to a small radial coordinate increment dr in the Schwarzschild field is, by (74.8),

$$d\sigma = (1 - 2m/r)^{-1/2} dr, \tag{76.1}$$

and the corresponding Doppler ratio (75.2) is

$$D = \left[\frac{1 - 2m/(r - dr)}{1 - 2m/r}\right]^{1/2} \approx \left[\frac{1 - (2m/r)(1 + dr/r)}{1 - 2m/r}\right]^{1/2}$$

$$= \left[1 - \frac{2m\,dr}{r^2(1 - 2m/r)}\right]^{1/2} \approx 1 - \frac{m\,d\sigma}{r^2(1 - 2m/r)^{1/2}}. \tag{76.2}$$

Here we have treated dr but *not* m/r as small. Comparison of (76.2) with (69.1) yields the proper acceleration of a particle at rest in the Schwarzschild field:

$$g = \frac{m}{r^2(1 - 2m/r)^{1/2}}. \tag{76.3}$$

We observe that this becomes infinite at $r = 2m$, and thus a "particle" at rest at $r = 2m$ must be a photon. (See the remark after (37.3).)

For our next argument, we shall need an object with Schwarzschild radius outside itself. Theoretically this is certainly possible: Consider, for example, a spherical object of uniform density ρ and radius R. Its mass, naively (i.e., not allowing for the mass equivalent of gravitational binding energy, etc.) is $4\pi R^3 \rho/3$ and so its Schwarzschild radius is $8\pi R^3 \rho/3$. For this to exceed R we simply need

$$\frac{8}{3}\pi R^2 \rho > 1 \quad \text{or} \quad R > \left(\frac{3}{8\pi\rho}\right)^{1/2} \tag{76.4}$$

Thus, spheres of any density can have their Schwarzschild radius showing, provided only R is big enough. For a sphere of the density of iron the critical R is 1.4×10^8 km, or about the distance from the sun to the earth. In Section 77 we shall see some more realistic examples.

Suppose, then, we have a spherical object of mass M with accessible Schwarzschild radius. Let us stand at coordinate distance r_1 from the center of M and hold a particle of mass m whose energy we wish to extract. We place assistants at rest all along the radius vector joining us to the center of M. They will hand the particle on from one to the next, each receiving it with zero velocity, and each collecting the potential energy lost by the particle in transit. Then each will faithfully send all collected energy back to us in the form of a photon.* At the Schwarzschild radius of M, this process comes to a natural end. Now, according to (76.3), the force per unit mass at r is

$$\frac{M}{\alpha^{1/2}r^2}, \qquad \left(\alpha = 1 - \frac{2M}{r}\right).$$

Ruler distance corresponding to dr is $\alpha^{-1/2}\,dr$, and thus the potential energy gathered from m locally is

$$\frac{mM\,dr}{\alpha r^2}.$$

When converted into a photon and dispatched, this reaches us with diminished energy

$$\frac{mM\,dr}{\alpha_1^{1/2}\alpha^{1/2}r^2}, \qquad \left(\alpha_1 = 1 - \frac{2M}{r_1}\right),$$

because of Planck's relation $E = h\nu$ and the Doppler shift (75.2). Consequently, the total energy received by us will be

$$\int_{2M}^{r_1} \frac{mM\,dr}{\alpha_1^{1/2}\alpha^{1/2}r^2} = \left[\frac{m\alpha^{1/2}}{\alpha_1^{1/2}}\right]_{2M}^{r_1} = m,$$

which is precisely mc^2 when ordinary units are restored. And so our assertion that mc^2 units of energy can be extracted from a mass m is proved.

This "proof," however, is not fully satisfactory unless m at the Schwarzschild radius of M just dissolves into nothing.

---

*For more realistic physics (momentum conservation!) the energy could be converted into *two* oppositely moving photons, which are then suitably diverted by mirrors.

But it does not: as we shall see in the next section, it goes through and adds mass to M. The question then arises: do we not violate global energy conservation by our process, since we end up (at least, in the infinite future) with the *same* mass at r_1 and *more* mass at the origin? Of course, there is now more (negative) binding energy between these masses, but that does not balance the books unless $m \approx r_1$. However, no global energy conservation theorem has yet been proved in GR and thus, legalistically, none can be violated. In Newtonian gravitational theory the situation is even worse: there is *no* limit to the energy that can be extracted from two point-masses by allowing them to approach under their mutual attraction. Thus all mass would have an *infinite* energy equivalent unless non-Newtonian forces exist which prevent unlimited approach.

77   The Schwarzschild Radius

We shall now discuss a feature of the Schwarzschild field that was long misunderstood, namely the "singularity" $r = 2m$ of the metric

$$ds^2 = \alpha dt^2 - \alpha^{-1} dr^2 - r^2(d\theta^2 + \sin^2 \theta d\phi^2),$$
$$(\alpha = 1 - 2m/r), \qquad (77.1)$$

when it occurs outside the mass m. For years it was believed that spacetime itself has a singularity there, in the sense that at $r = 2m$ its local properties would be distinguishable from those of "regular" regions. (Indeed, as Bondi points out, if active gravitational mass were negative instead of positive, the Schwarzschild singularity would undoubtedly have been used as an argument to show that it *must* be negative, since a positive mass leads to a singularity ...). However, in 1933 Lemaître found that the Schwarzschild singularity is not a *physical* singularity at all, but merely a *coordinate* singularity, i.e., one entirely due to the choice of the coordinate system: an observer in a small, freely falling cabin would pass through the sphere $r = 2m$ without noticing anything special at all.

It is very easy to *produce* coordinate singularities. Consider, for example, the Euclidean plane referred to the standard metric $d\sigma^2 = dx^2 + dy^2$; then simply introduce a new x coordinate ξ by the equations

$$\xi = \tfrac{1}{4}x^2 (x \geq 0), \quad \xi = -\tfrac{1}{4}x^2 (x < 0), \qquad (77.2)$$

which gives a one-to-one relation between x and ξ. Thereupon the metric evidently becomes

$$d\sigma^2 = \frac{1}{|\xi|} d\xi^2 + dy^2,$$

and this now has a singularity at $\xi = 0$: a *coordinate* singularity! For it is fully removable by introducing a "new" variable x by the equations (77.2). Of course, in general it will not be so obvious how to remove a coordinate singularity, or even whether a given singularity is due to the coordinates or not. One way of deciding this last question is to calculate the invariants of the curvature tensor (14 coordinate-independent combinations of its components, which are constructed by standard tensor methods) and testing whether these remain finite as the singularity is approached: if they do, the singularity is probably not a physical one. (But it *could* be: for example, near the vertex of a cone all curvature components are zero!)

After Lemaître, a number of others rediscovered the coordinate nature of Schwarzschild's singularity, but the general appreciation of this fact came inexplicably slowly. It was finally helped by a widely read paper by M. D. Kruskal.* Many of the proposed coordinate transformations

---

*Phys. Rev. **119**, 1743 (1960). Kruskal mistakenly seems to credit E. Kasner with the original discovery in 1921; Kasner's work is discussed and modified by C. Fronsdal in *Phys. Rev.* **116**, 778 (1959). Actually, it was A. S. Eddington (*Nature* **113**, 192 (1924)) who first transformed Schwarzschild's metric into a form not singular at $r = 2m$, but he seems not to have noticed this. (His paper, incidentally, contains a misleading misprint: eq. (2) should have $r - 2m$ instead of $r - m$.) Eddington's transformation was rediscovered by D. Finkelstein (*Phys. Rev.* **110**, 965 (1958)). G. Lemaître's paper is in *Ann. Soc. Sci. Bruxelles* **A53**, 51 (1933).

are purely formal, but Lemaître's is based on a very simple physical idea: At infinity, there is a collection of synchronized standard clocks, and these are dropped from rest at regular time intervals, along each radius vector. Let the clocks for one radius vector be labeled $R = R_1, R_2, \ldots$, as they are dropped, and let T be the time as read by these freely falling clocks. Moreover, let R_n be just the value of T when the clock R_n strikes the origin. The coordinates assigned to any event E are the usual θ and ϕ, plus the R of the clock at which E occurs, and the T indicated by that clock at E. (Of course, we must make R into a continuous variable—either by having a continuous stream of clocks, or by interpolating.) Lemaître found that the metric will then be

$$ds^2 = dT^2 - \frac{2m}{r} dR^2 - r^2(d\theta^2 + \sin^2\theta d\phi^2), \qquad (77.3)$$

where

$$r = \left[\frac{3\sqrt{(2m)}}{2} (T - R)\right]^{2/3}. \qquad (77.4)$$

This becomes singular only at $T = R$, and that, of course, is the equation of the origin. The actual transformation between Schwarzschild's r, t and Lemaître's R, T is given partly by (77.4) and partly by the further relation

$$T = t - 2\sqrt{(2mr)} - 2m \log\left|\frac{\sqrt{r} - \sqrt{(2m)}}{\sqrt{r} + \sqrt{(2m)}}\right|. \qquad (77.5)$$

It is interesting that the *proper* time for a particle to fall into the origin from a finite height (right through the Schwarzschild sphere $r = 2m$) is finite. Of course, Lemaître's method of assigning coordinates is based on just this fact. To see how this comes about, we shall briefly study the equations for a radial geodesic in Schwarzschild's coordinates:

$$\theta, \phi = \text{constant}, \quad dr/ds = \pm(k^2 - \alpha)^{1/2}, \quad dt/ds = k/\alpha, \qquad (77.6)$$

where k is a constant. Of these, only the last need really be calculated from the geodesic differential equations: the

θ, ϕ equations follow from symmetry, and the r equation then results on substituting into the metric (77.1) (divided by ds^2).

[Even the last equation can be obtained indirectly, at least for $r > 2m$. Suppose a particle P of unit rest mass is dropped radially from coordinate r_1 with total energy k_1 relative to the LIF momentarily at rest at r_1, and is then absorbed in a LIF S_0 momentarily at rest at coordinate $r < r_1$. Standard time t_0 in S_0 is related to coordinate time t by $dt_0 = \alpha^{1/2} dt$. Let ds refer to events at P; then, by (44.3), $dt_0/ds \; (= \alpha^{1/2} dt/ds)$ represents P's energy relative to S_0. Let this be converted into a photon (or photon pair) and returned to r_1. By the Doppler formula (75.2) and Planck's relation $E \propto \nu$, it arrives at r_1 with energy

$$\alpha^{1/2} \frac{dt}{ds} \frac{\alpha^{1/2}}{\alpha_1^{1/2}} = \frac{\alpha dt}{\alpha_1^{1/2} ds}, \quad \left(\alpha_1 = 1 - \frac{2m}{r_1} \right),$$

which must equal k_1 if we assume energy conservation. Hence

$$\frac{dt}{ds} = \frac{k_1 \alpha_1^{1/2}}{\alpha}, \tag{77.7}$$

which is equivalent to the last of the equations (77.6), and also gives an interpretation of k: it is the energy at infinity.]

From the last two equations of (77.6), we find for a particle dropped from rest at infinity,

$$\frac{dt}{dr} = \frac{-r^{3/2}}{(r - 2m)\sqrt{(2m)}}, \quad \frac{ds}{dr} = -\frac{r^{1/2}}{\sqrt{(2m)}}.$$

Integration between two levels r_1 and $r_2 (< r_1)$ then gives

$$\int dt = \frac{1}{\sqrt{(2m)}} \int_{r_2}^{r_1} \frac{r^{3/2} dr}{(r - 2m)},$$

$$\int ds = \frac{1}{\sqrt{(2m)}} \int_{r_2}^{r_1} r^{1/2} dr. \tag{77.8}$$

The first of these integrals diverges as $r_2 \to 2m$, and thus the particle reaches the Schwarzschild sphere at coordinate time $t = \infty$. The second integral, on the other hand, remains proper at $r_2 = 2m$ and finite right up to $r_2 = 0$. Lemaître's relation (77.4) is simply an integrated form of this integral. The state of affairs here illustrated holds more generally: *all* freely falling particles meet the Schwarzschild sphere at $t = \infty$ but reach the origin in finite proper time. The time-reflected situation also holds: if the motion of any *outgoing* free particle is produced backwards, it is found that it left the origin a finite proper time earlier, but passed the Schwarzschild sphere at $t = -\infty$.

[The remainder of this section gets a little complicated, and may well be omitted at a first reading.]

In calculating a particle's proper time during its fall through the Schwarzschild sphere, we have blithely used the Schwarzschild coordinates both outside *and* inside that sphere.   This is justifiable for the following reasons: (i) r, θ, ϕ, t form a perfectly acceptable Gaussian coordinate system inside as well as outside, (ii) the metric satisfies Einstein's vacuum field equations inside as well as outside, and (iii) the geodesic equations (77.6) hold inside as well as outside.   Yet r and t clearly do *not* have the same physical interpretation inside and outside.   For one thing, we cannot *fix* clocks at constant r inside, since $r, \theta, \phi = $ constant inside implies $ds^2 < 0$, and this cannot be the case along the worldline of a particle. In fact, one sees from (77.1) that whereas, outside, $ds^2 > 0$ implies

$$dr^2 < dt^2 \left(1 - \frac{2m}{r}\right)^2, \qquad (77.9)$$

it implies the opposite inequality inside:

$$dr^2 > dt^2 \left(\frac{2m}{r} - 1\right)^2. \qquad (77.10)$$

This is illustrated in Figure 25, which represents a radius vector ($\theta, \phi = $ constant) in the Schwarzschild metric. Various light cones are drawn, the shaded portions being in timelike relation to the vertex.   Note that inside the Schwarzschild radius r is a *timelike* coordinate, i.e., the displacement vector $(0, 0, dr, 0)$, corresponding to an increment

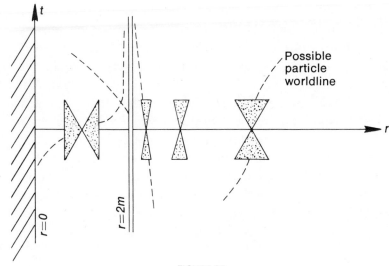

FIGURE 25.

of *r* only, is timelike. Moreover, *r* is the *only* timelike coordinate inside and must therefore change along the worldlines of *all* particles and photons. (This can be seen either
from Figure 25, or directly from the metric (77.1) in which
$ds^2 \geq 0$ is impossible with $dr = 0$.) For causality uniqueness
inside, either all particles must move in the direction of
increasing *r*, or all in the direction of decreasing *r*. It turns
out that there must be a strange "flip-over" in the metric:
for the first half of eternity all particles stream *out* of the
Schwarzschild sphere, and for the second half they stream
in. We have already seen that a particle *on* the Schwarzschild sphere is, in fact, a photon. Hence this sphere can be
thought of as a stationary light front: for half of eternity it
"points in" (when particles and photons stream out across
it), and for half of eternity it "points out" (when particles
and photons stream in). Relative to any LIF *at* the
Schwarzschild sphere, of course, that sphere has the velocity
of light.

The worldline of the origin *r* = 0 is a genuine physical
singularity. Though ds^2 is undefined on it, that line is the
limit of a spacelike line, as suggested by Figure 25. For the

understanding of the locus $r = 2m$, however, Figure 25 is totally misleading. This locus can be crossed by particle and photon worldlines, but in Figure 25 such lines "cross" at $t = \pm\infty$. On the other hand, worldlines which in this diagram approach $r = 2m$ from the left at *finite* t continue *not* into the region $r > 2m$ but "into another universe." For these reasons, Figure 25 should be considered as *two separate* diagrams with a definite break at $r = 2m$.

Many of the strange properties of the Schwarzschild metric can be nicely illustrated, and thus better understood, by analogy with the relatively simple case of the uniformly accelerated rod of Section 37. Consider the following transformation from the special relativistic coordinates x, y, z, t to new coordinates X, Y, Z, T:

$$t = X \sinh T, \quad x = X \cosh T, \quad y = Y, \quad z = Z. \quad (77.11)$$

This implies the relations

$$x^2 - t^2 = X^2, \quad t/x = \tanh T \quad (77.12)$$

and

$$ds^2 = dt^2 - dx^2 - dy^2 - dz^2$$
$$= X^2 dT^2 - dX^2 - dY^2 - dZ^2. \quad (77.13)$$

Comparing the first of (77.12) with (37.4), one sees that any point moving with constant X performs hyperbolic motion parallel to the x axis with proper acceleration $1/X$ ($c = 1$). Equation (77.13) shows that for observers at rest relative to the coordinates X, Y, Z, T, the first three of these represent true ruler distances, while T is an acceptable time coordinate for a static field (no cross terms in the metric, no time dependence.) These coordinates, in fact, refer to the hyperbolically moving skyscraper discussed at the end of Section 37. The hyperbolas in region I of Figure 26 represent fixed points in that skyscraper. Actually, each point in Figure 26 represents a whole (y, z) plane at right angles to the x axis; the only motions, however, that can be well illustrated in the figure are those parallel to the x axis. The straight lines diverging from the origin represent lines of equal T, i.e., "moments" in skyscraper time.

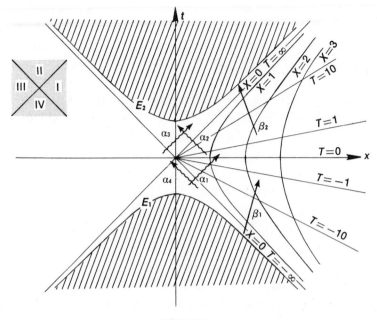

FIGURE 26.

This skyscraper is analogous to the Schwarzschild field
outside $r = 2m$; and X, Y, Z, T are analogous to Schwarzschild's r, θ, ϕ, t. Each "vertical" (Y, Z = constant) in the
skyscraper corresponds to a radius vector in the Schwarzschild field. Of course, in the skyscraper the force is $1/X$,
i.e., it falls off inversely as the first rather than the second
power of the distance. But it becomes infinite at $X = 0$
(just as the Schwarzschild force does at $r = 2m$) and $X \equiv 0$
corresponds to photons which "sit" at the bottom of the
skyscraper, apparently at rest (just like the photons at
$r \equiv 2m$). For these photons there is a "change of the guard"
halfway through eternity: at $t = 0$ the photons at the bottom
of the skyscraper fly off and are replaced by others, moving
in the opposite direction. The former are "guards" that
allow traffic to flow only *into* the skyscraper (see the photon
and particle paths α_1 and β_1 in Figure 26), while the latter
allow traffic to flow only out (see the paths α_2 and β_2). A
particle such as β_2 that has dropped through the bottom of

the skyscraper can never get back. The analog is true also in Schwarzschild space. (Light fronts such as $X = 0$, $T = \infty$, which causally shuts the skyscraper off from all events beyond, play a role in cosmology too: they are called "event horizons.")

In Figure 26 we have cut out of the special-relativistic spacetime M_4 the region $t^2 - x^2 > 1$, so that the locus $t^2 - x^2 = 1$ (E_1 and E_2) becomes a singular "edge of the world." This is the analog of the Schwarzschild origin $r = 0$. All free particles and photons that are *rising* in the skyscraper can be traced back to a beginning on E_1; all that are *falling* can be traced forward to an end on E_2. The regions II and IV in Figure 26 correspond to the *inside* of the Schwarzschild sphere: for half of eternity traffic flows out, and for the other half traffic flows in.

All this makes good sense in M_4—but the analogous happenings in Schwarzschild space, which we have stated rather than proved, are a little puzzling. How can the *disconnected* edges E_1 and E_2 *both* correspond to $r = 0$? And what of the Schwarzschild analog of the region III in the figure? This region is causally quite disconnected from the skyscraper: no signals can pass from one to the other. There is one single moment of contact, at $t = 0$, when "bottom photons" are exchanged. Yet an observer in region II, in the short time left to him before disaster at E_2, can receive signals from *both* regions I and III. Hence logically one cannot forget about III—it is needed to complete the picture. We can put a second skyscraper into III, moving in the opposite direction. There also exists an analogous second "outside" Schwarzschild field, totally disconnected from the first, except for a momentary interchange of "bottom photons." The imagination boggles about where to put this second field, since the first already seems to fill all space: one simply must imagine it "in another universe."

But even for the people in the skyscraper, the visualization of region III is not totally trivial. Let us see how *they* would regard their world (see Figure 27). First, it is easy to

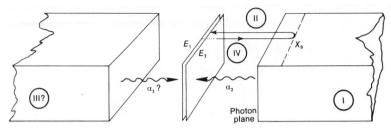

FIGURE 27.

show that all particles dropped from a given height X_0 reach the singularity E_2 in always the same finite proper time $(1 + X_0^2)^{1/2}$. Consequently these people will picture E_2 as a plane parallel to, and at constant distance from, their bottom photon plane. Moreover, since all particles rising and coming to rest at height X_0 have also taken a proper time $(1 + X_0^2)^{1/2}$ since leaving E_1, the people may be tempted to identify E_1 with E_2. Now, can they imagine region III as a mirror image of themselves on the opposite side of E_1, E_2, as indicated in Figure 27? Remember that there is one moment of contact. Can they imagine E_1 to be in place for half of eternity, then momentarily disappearing to allow the contact of I with III, and then E_2 taking its place? No: for every photon (e.g., α_2 in Figure 26) getting to E_2 from I meets photons (e.g., α_3) from III *before* hitting E_2. So after all, the people have no choice but to imagine region III on the *same* side of the singularity as themselves, but somehow in another universe. It is only when they finally realize that they are living in x, y, z, t space that the visualization of all their experiences unravels into the simple picture of Figure 26.

It was Kruskal's achievement (and, independently, C. Fronsdal's) to have found a similar unraveling of the Schwarzschild field. It would take us a little too far to discuss it here, but the unraveled picture of Schwarzschild space looks exactly like Figure 26. Only the basic space is not flat M_4: it cannot be, since, unlike the hyperbolic field,

the Schwarzschild field is an intrinsic gravitational field.*
[The reader may find it instructive to make and consider an
(X, T) diagram analogous to Figure 25 for the skyscraper.
X can take negative values up to $X = -1$ on E_1 and E_2. The
transformation corresponding to (77.11) for regions II and
IV of Figure 26 must then be taken, respectively, as $t =
\pm \mid X \mid \cosh T, x = \pm \mid X \mid \sinh T$.]

Why have we given so much space to a subtle concept
like the Schwarzschild radius which, it is often said, is
purely theoretical (since it occurs deep inside all "ordinary"
masses where the Schwarzschild vacuum metric ceases to
hold anyway)? Well, first, it is an instructive exercise, involving ideas of much wider applicability in GR. But there
is a second reason: the Schwarzschild radius has recently
gained much prominence in connection with the question of
gravitational collapse. This arose as a possible explanation
of the energy of the *quasars*, those very puzzling objects,
apparently far out in the universe, which were discovered in
the early nineteen-sixties.

The Schwarzschild radius of a typical galaxy of mass
$\sim 10^{45}$ gm is $\sim 10^{17}$ cm. Since a typical galaxy has radius
$\sim 10^{23}$ cm, a contraction by a linear factor of 10^6 would
bring it within its Schwarzschild sphere. In a typical galaxy
the stars are spaced like pinheads 50 km apart; the shrinkage would bring the pinhead-stars to within 5 cm of each
other—still far from touching. Thus, unless a galaxy has
some mechanical prevention device (like rotation), it *will* be
sucked into its Schwarzschild sphere by its own gravity.†
Such catastrophes are not discounted by astronomers. Once
a galaxy is inside the Schwarzschild sphere, its total collapse
can no longer be halted by any means, and will proceed
very rapidly. The galaxy can then no longer be seen from

*For further details of the analogy between Kruskal space and the hyperbolic
field, see W. Rindler, *Am. J. Phys.* **34,** 1174 (1966).

†Theoretically, intelligent beings could stop each star in a galaxy in its motion
by ejecting a (small) part of its substance. (See exercise 5-16.) The residual stars
would then fall towards the galactic mass center under their mutual gravitation,
and eventually disappear through the galactic Schwarzschild radius.

the outside, except by photons which it emitted still outside the Schwarzschild sphere; the last of these, of course, will take an infinite time to reach us, and will arrive infinitely red-shifted. Theoretically visible forever, such a galaxy would nevertheless soon vanish from our photographic plates. On the other hand, the external gravitational field of the galaxy will persist unchanged, and could lead to its detection. Some astronomers believe that collapsed galaxies may substantially increase the average density of the universe over the density of *visible* matter in it. Some also believe that quasars may be collapsing galaxies, though the process whereby gravitational energy could be converted into radiative energy is still a matter of debate.

Stars, too, can collapse—though the mechanism is more complicated and always involves thermonuclear reactions. A stable, burnt-out state can only be reached by objects of mass less than 1.2 solar masses. Heavier stars must either explode eventually or collapse. Indications are, however, that only the most massive stars can follow the latter course.

At the other end of the spectrum we have the whole universe, and here the numbers are strangely disturbing: A universe of radius 10^{10} light years and density 10^{-29} gm/cm^3 would just about be at its Schwarzschild radius. And these numbers are not too far from the ones sometimes believed to apply to the actual universe we live in. Of course, the Schwarzschild theory cannot be applied on this scale unless the universe were an insular blob in otherwise empty and ultimately flat spacetime—which is an unconventional view. But still, the numbers are suggestive. And even the rigorous calculations of conventional cosmology indicate the possibility of collapsing universes, as we shall see in the final chapter.

The Laws of Physics in Curved Spacetime   78

Our investigations so far have led to the recognition that the real spacetime we live in is curved, and that SR, which presupposes flat spacetime, is therefore only an approximate and local theory—just as Euclidean geometry would be only an approximate and local geometry in a curved three-space. What, then, are the *real* laws of physics whose approximate form we discover in SR? Lest the reader despair at the prospect of yet another major revision, let us quickly assure him that for most laws the transition from flat to curved spacetime is essentially trivial. However, it needs the full machinery of the tensor calculus, and we shall therefore have to be content with a rather vague description here.

The need for tensors, of course, is not surprising since they constitute the natural mathematical language of GR. All Gaussian coordinates are admissible in GR, and thus all laws must be written in a form equally valid in all coordinate systems ("principle of covariance"). The obvious way to do this is to write them as tensor equations. Indeed, it was Einstein's primary aim in constructing GR to produce a theory in which especially the laws of mechanics are equally valid in all coordinate systems; he thought thereby to satisfy Mach's demand for the exclusion of absolute space, i.e., of preferred coordinates. There, however, he was mistaken, as was soon pointed out by Kretschmann, and acknowledged by Einstein (1918). For even if all spacetime were Minkowskian (in violation of the EP) and there existed a satisfactory theory of gravitation within SR, all the laws of SR could be written in a form equally valid in all coordinate systems, as we shall see. Yet this would in no way diminish the pre-eminence of Minkowski space, and thus of an absolute standard of nonacceleration. One suspects that additional conditions may give physical content to the principle of covariance. A recent attempt to clarify these ideas has been made by Anderson.* But nowadays these dark origins of GR are mainly of historical interest.

---

*J. L. Anderson, "Principles of Relativity Physics," New York, Academic Press, 1967; see also his Chapter 9 in "Gravitation and Relativity," Chiu and Hoffmann, editors, New York, W. A. Benjamin, 1964.

Einstein's discovery of the fact that our world is a Riemannian spacetime, and of the field equations, is regarded as
primary; the need for tensor laws of physics is then an obvious corollary.

The first step in finding a GR law that corresponds to a
known SR law is always to write the SR law in four-tensor
form. Here the indicial notation of Section 45 is more useful, because it is more general, than the bold-face notation
of Section 44. Take a simple law like that of momentum
conservation, (51.4). We can write it in the form

$$P_1^\mu + P_2^\mu = P_3^\mu + P_4^\mu, \tag{78.1}$$

where each four-momentum P^μ is defined by an equation
like

$$P_1^\mu = m_1 U^\mu = m_1 \frac{dx^\mu}{ds}. \tag{78.2}$$

(Again we use units in which $c = 1$ and thus $ds = d\tau$.) Now,
any four-vector has a well-defined meaning in any LIF. We
can make a *general* vector out of it by *defining* its components relative to an arbitrary coordinate system in spacetime by an equation like (72.4), in which we regard the unprimed symbols as relating to the LIF. The next step is
simply to adopt the SR equations, for example, (78.1) and
(78.2), as the GR law, with this changed interpretation of
all vectors (and tensors) that occur in them. Of course, this
is not the only possible way to make the transition. Logically, all we can require of the GR law is that it should reduce to the SR law in flat spacetime. But that would be the
case also if the GR law contained additional terms involving
the curvature tensor. For example, the GR definition corresponding to (78.2) *could* be

$$P_1^\mu = m_1 \frac{dx^\mu}{ds} + R^\mu_{\nu\rho\sigma} g^{\nu\rho} \frac{dx^\sigma}{ds}. \tag{78.3}$$

However, it is a basic principle of science that one never
chooses a law more complicated than need be. And consequently we adopt the *simplicity postulate* never to add
curvature terms unnecessarily. Note also that, although

(78.3) would reduce to (78.2) in flat spacetime, it would not in general reduce to (78.2) in a LIF, since a LIF is only a particular coordinate system in actual spacetime and curvature can never be "transformed away." Our simplicity postulate therefore amounts to the attempt to have the laws in the LIF as nearly as possible the same as in flat spacetime. This is evidently closely related to the equivalence principle. It may even be considered to *be* the equivalence principle.

A slight difficulty occurs when the SR law contains derivatives, either ordinary or partial, of tensors. Take a law (or definition) like (57.4). In four-tensor (indicial) notation, it reads

$$F^\mu = m_0 \frac{d}{ds} U^\mu = m_0 \frac{d}{ds} \left(\frac{dx^\mu}{ds} \right). \tag{78.4}$$

This cannot be simply reinterpreted in Gaussian coordinates, since the last member is not a general tensor. As we have seen in Section 72, the unique general tensor which reduces to this in the LIF, apart from the scalar m_0, is

$$\frac{D}{ds} \left(\frac{dx^\mu}{ds} \right) = \frac{d^2 x^\mu}{ds^2} + \Gamma^\mu_{\nu\sigma} \frac{dx^\nu}{ds} \frac{dx^\sigma}{ds}.$$

The rule, accordingly, is to replace all *ordinary* derivatives by *absolute* derivatives before adopting an SR law in GR. Thus the GR definition of force is

$$F^\mu = m_0 \frac{D}{ds} \left(\frac{dx^\mu}{ds} \right). \tag{78.5}$$

Note, incidentally, how this rule leads from the SR law of free motion $\frac{d}{ds} \left(\frac{dx^\mu}{ds} \right) = 0$ to the GR law of geodesics $\frac{D}{ds} \left(\frac{dx^\mu}{ds} \right) = 0$; of course, it constitutes no proof.

There is a similar procedure for dealing with *partial* derivatives. Given a second-rank general tensor $A^{\mu\nu}$, for example, its partial derivative $\frac{\partial}{\partial x^\sigma} A^{\mu\nu}$, often written $\partial_\sigma A^{\mu\nu}$ or $A^{\mu\nu}{}_{|\sigma}$, is *not* a general tensor. But the *covariant derivative* defined by

$$A^{\mu\nu}{}_{,\sigma} = A^{\mu\nu}{}_{|\sigma} + A^{\tau\nu} \Gamma^\mu_{\tau\sigma} + A^{\mu\tau} \Gamma^\nu_{\tau\sigma} \tag{78.6}$$

is a third-rank general tensor. Similarly one can define covariant derivatives of tensors of all ranks. The rule, then, is to replace all partial derivatives by covariant derivatives before adopting a law in GR. And now we have said practically all there is to say on this subject! (Unfortunately there are still certain cases in which the above rules are ambiguous; e.g., two forms of a law which are equivalent in SR may lead to inequivalent generalizations. Other criteria must then decide.)

One law we shall be particularly interested in is that which governs the behavior of continuously distributed matter. We saw in Section 60 that this law is expressible in the form (60.4), which we may now write as

$$M^{\mu\nu}{}_{|\nu} = 0.$$

Its GR form will therefore be

$$M^{\mu\nu}{}_{,\nu} = M^{\mu\nu}{}_{|\nu} + M^{\tau\nu}\Gamma^{\mu}_{\tau\sigma} + M^{\mu\tau}\Gamma^{\nu}_{\tau\nu} = 0. \qquad (78.7)$$

By the methods of this section one can rewrite Maxwell's equations, the SR equations of collision mechanics, of optics, etc., against the new background of curved space-time. In particular, all the *forces* of SR (electromagnetic, elastic, impact, etc.) have their counterparts in GR, i.e., they are now players on a new stage. Of all the classical forces, only gravity has no counterpart in GR: instead of being one of the players, it has become "part of the stage" (in E. T. Whittaker's phrase). Gravity has become "geometrized." For many years it was hoped that it might be possible also to absorb electromagnetism into the geometry ("unified field theories") by somehow enlarging the geometry. But with the discovery of yet other basic forces (the nuclear forces), these attempts have lost much of their attraction.

The Field Equations in the Presence of Matter 79

The Einstein vacuum field equations $R_{\mu\nu} = 0$ are, as we have seen in Section 73, the GR analog of the Laplace equation

$\Sigma \phi_{ii} = 0$, which governs Newton's potential in empty space. If we wish to discuss the gravitational field in the presence of matter—for example, in a dust cloud, or inside the earth, or, indeed, in the universe (where for a first crude oversimplification the actual contents are replaced by continuous dust)—in all such cases we need a GR equivalent not of Laplace's equation but of Poisson's equation

$$\Sigma \phi_{ii} = 4\pi G\rho. \qquad (79.1)$$

The GR field equations will have to relate the matter with the *geometry* (the analog of ϕ). Since in the vacuum case the equations should reduce to $R_{\mu\nu} = 0$ (this we have already accepted), an obvious candidate for the left-hand side of the GR field equations is $R_{\mu\nu}$. And an equally obvious candidate for the right-hand side is the matter tensor $M^{\mu\nu}$, of which, as we have seen, the density ρ is one component (in LIF coordinates). However, we cannot equate covariant with contravariant tensors, and so we first define the *contravariant* Ricci tensor $R^{\mu\nu}$ by the equations

$$R^{\mu\nu} = g^{\mu\rho} g^{\nu\sigma} R_{\rho\sigma}. \qquad (79.2)$$

(This is the standard method of converting from covariance to contravariance, and vice versa.) The most obvious field equations, then, would be

$$R^{\mu\nu} = -\kappa M^{\mu\nu}, \qquad (79.3)$$

where κ is some suitable "coupling" constant, and the minus sign is inserted for later convenience.

An immediate implication of these equations would be $M^{\mu\nu} = 0$ in flat spacetime, which would seem to vitiate our work with continuous media in SR: there could be no continuous media in SR. But this was to be expected: the presence of matter curves the spacetime. On the other hand, we have seen in Section 74 how very small a curvature results locally from even an enormous mass like the earth, or the sun. Hence the κ in equations (79.3) would be exceedingly small, and the presence of "ordinary" matter distributions in a flat-spacetime laboratory would not produce appreciable curvature.

Even so, how seriously can we then take, for example, an equation like (78.7), obtained by generalizing a result from SR, which in SR already was only approximate? Very seriously: for the arguments advanced in Section 60 for the flat-spacetime version of this equation would go through also in a LIF, even if the curvature due to external causes was not negligible.

If we accept (78.7), however, (79.3) implies

$$R^{\mu\nu}_{\ ,\nu} = 0. \tag{79.4}$$

On the other hand, it is known in Riemannian geometry (from *Bianchi's* identity) that

$$(R^{\mu\nu} - \tfrac{1}{2}g^{\mu\nu}R)_{,\nu} = 0, \quad (R = g^{\mu\nu}R_{\mu\nu}), \tag{79.5}$$

and thus (79.4) implies

$$R_{,\nu} = 0, \tag{79.6}$$

(since the covariant derivative is linear and satisfies Leibniz's rule, and since the covariant derivative of all g's is zero; these facts are clear when it is recalled that the covariant derivative reduces to the partial derivative in a LIF.) But (79.3) also implies $R = -\kappa M (M = g_{\mu\nu}M^{\mu\nu})$, and so (79.6) would imply $M_{,\nu} = 0$, which is clearly false. (For example, in the dust case, $M = c^2\rho_0$, and this need not be constant.) Hence equations (79.3) are not acceptable.

On the other hand, as reference to (79.5) shows, the equations

$$R^{\mu\nu} - \tfrac{1}{2}g^{\mu\nu}R = -\kappa M^{\mu\nu} \tag{79.7}$$

would meet our present objection: they satisfy $M^{\mu\nu}_{\ ,\nu} = 0$ *automatically*. They are, in fact, the equations that Einstein proposed as his general field equations. Multiplying them by $g_{\mu\nu}$ we find

$$R - 2R = -\kappa M, \quad \text{i.e.,} \quad R = \kappa M, \tag{79.8}$$

and so (79.7) can also be written in the alternative form

$$R^{\mu\nu} = -\kappa(M^{\mu\nu} - \tfrac{1}{2}g^{\mu\nu}M). \tag{79.9}$$

Note: (i) In vacuum $M^{\mu\nu} = 0$, and then these field equations reduce to $R^{\mu\nu} = 0$, which is equivalent to $R_{\mu\nu} = 0$. (ii) The four differential identities (79.5), satisfied by both sides of the field equations, are the ones that ensure that we do not get the g's uniquely but have four degrees of freedom left to apply arbitrary transformations of the coordinates (cf. end of Section 73). (iii) As Ehlers has pointed out, the "correction" (79.3) $\rightarrow$ (79.7) is quite analogous to the usual introduction of the displacement current into Maxwell's equations: there it is required by charge conservation, here by energy and momentum conservation (i.e., by $M^{\mu\nu}{}_{|\nu} = 0$).

It can be shown that the field equations (79.7) are the most general that satisfy the following desiderata: they should (i) have tensorial character; (ii) involve no higher derivatives of the g's than the second, and these and $M^{\mu\nu}$ only linearly (in analogy with Poisson's equation); (iii) satisfy $M^{\mu\nu}{}_{,\nu} = 0$ identically; and (iv) permit flat space-time as a particular solution in the absence of matter. Eventually Einstein dropped the last requirement, and then a slightly more general set of equations becomes possible, namely

$$R^{\mu\nu} - \tfrac{1}{2}Rg^{\mu\nu} + \Lambda g^{\mu\nu} = -\kappa M^{\mu\nu}, \qquad (79.10)$$

where Λ is a universal constant which, like R, has the dimensions of a space curvature, namely (length)$^{-2}$. It has come to be called the "cosmological" constant, because only in cosmology does it play a significant role; there, however, it seems to be forced on us by the observations.* Current estimates suggest $0 < \Lambda < 10^{-54}$ cm^{-2} (see Section 91), and we shall show below that this makes Λ quite negligible in all noncosmological situations. *A priori*, of course, Λ could be negative as well as positive.

Analogously to (79.8) we find from (79.10) that

$$R = \kappa M + 4\Lambda, \qquad (79.11)$$

which allows us to rewrite (79.10) in the alternative form

$$R^{\mu\nu} = \Lambda g^{\mu\nu} - \kappa(M^{\mu\nu} - \tfrac{1}{2}g^{\mu\nu}M). \qquad (79.12)$$

---

*The effect of a positive Λ, as will be seen, is to counteract gravity. Einstein needed this because he wanted to construct a *static* universe. Today we need it even more, because we want to construct an acceleratingly expanding one.

Clearly these equations are *not* satisfied by *flat* spacetime in the absence of matter, for then they reduce to

$$R^{\mu\nu} = \Lambda g^{\mu\nu}, \tag{79.13}$$

which implies curvature. [*Any* space satisfying (79.13) is called an *Einstein space*; it turns out that every space of constant curvature is an Einstein space, but not vice versa, unless its dimension is two or three.]

The numerical value of κ in Einstein's field equations must be obtained experimentally, just like that of Newton's gravitational constant. In practice, one compares Einstein's field equations in first approximation with Poisson's equation, which can be regarded as experimentally confirmed. (However, if we try to get Λ in this "local" way, we find $\Lambda = 0$.) We have already seen that the metric (71.1) approximately represents the spacetime corresponding to a weak static Newtonian potential field ϕ. The argument given in Section 71 presupposes a vacuum field, but it can be pushed through even in the nonvacuum case, in spite of the complication that light will then not move along null geodesics. That metric, with $d\sigma^2 = dx^2 + dy^2 + dz^2$, is further discussed in the paragraph containing (72.13). It can be shown to have the property that all $R_{\mu\nu}$ except R_{44} vanish approximately (technically: to first order in ϕ/c^2), and

$$R_{44} \approx -\sum_{i=1}^{3} \frac{\partial}{\partial x^i} \Gamma^i_{44} = -\sum_{i=1}^{3} \phi_{ii},$$

where the second step follows from (72.13). Consequently all $R^{\mu\nu}$ vanish too except R^{44}, and

$$R^{44} = g^{44} g^{44} R_{44} \approx -c^{-4} \sum \phi_{ii}. \tag{79.14}$$

If the matter is approximately static dust, with $M^{\mu\nu}$ given by (60.2), all $M^{\mu\nu}$ vanish except M^{44}, and

$$M^{44} = \rho_0, \quad M = \rho_0 c^2, \quad M^{44} - \tfrac{1}{2} g^{44} M = \tfrac{1}{2} \rho_0. \tag{79.15}$$

Moreover, $\rho_0 = \rho$. Substituting these values into (79.9) and comparing it with (79.1), we obtain

$$\kappa = \frac{8\pi G}{c^4} \approx 2.1 \times 10^{-48} \ \text{sec}^2/\text{cm gm}. \tag{79.16}$$

We are now in a position to justify the omission of the Λ term in all but cosmological applications. (See also the remark after (80.6) below.) The "curvature invariant" R is a certain mean of the various curvatures at a given point; for example, in a space with *constant* curvature K it can be shown that $R = -12K$. Now it is seen from (79.11) and the cosmological value of Λ that the contribution of Λ to the curvature invariant is at most of the order $4\Lambda \approx 4 \times 10^{-54}$ cm^{-2}; as a curvature this is *locally* quite indistinguishable from zero. The contribution of M due to "ordinary" matter is much larger by comparison. In the case of air, for example ($\rho = .0013$ gm/cm^3, $M \approx c^2\rho$), the ratio $\kappa M/\Lambda$ turns out to be $> 10^{24}$! In cosmology, on the other hand, where we deal with a "cosmic density" of about 10^{-30} gm/cm^3, the contributions of M and Λ can become comparable.

In obtaining κ above, we regarded the metric (71.1) as "established" and showed that the field equations, when applied to it, approximate to Poisson's equation. One can do better, and *use* the field equations to establish the metric in the first place, and under more general conditions. Suppose we begin with an arbitrary "weak-field" and "quasi static" metric (i.e., with g's that differ only slightly from their Minkowskian values, and vary only slowly in time), and permit matter to be "ordinary" rather than "dust." Applying the field equations by an approximation as we did before, we now *find* that $g_{44} = 1 + 2\phi/c^2$ with $\Sigma\phi_{ii} = 4\pi G\rho$ (and also $g_{11} = g_{22} = g_{33} = c^2/g_{44}$.) Newton's law of motion can be shown (as in the paragraph containing (72.13)) to approximate to Einstein's law of geodesics also for this more general metric. In other words, Newton's theory can be regarded as a first approximation to Einstein's theory, and on close examination it is even seen to be a very *good* theoretical approximation. Consequently all the classical observations of celestial mechanics, which are in such excellent agreement with Newtonian gravitational theory, can now be adduced as support for Einstein's theory too. One must marvel that, beginning with such utterly novel assumptions, GR can nevertheless contain so much that is familiar.

If we go one step further, to a "post-Newtonian" approximation (in which $R^\mu_{\nu\sigma\tau}$ is small but the sources need not move slowly) we find that GR reduces to a linear theory that has pronounced Maxwellian features, such as induction. Since interesting *exact* solutions of the GR field equations are difficult to get except in situations of high symmetry, much work has been done instead with this "linearized theory" (although it is not always clear how good an approximation to the full theory one gets in this way). For example, it was used to obtain verifications of the various "induction" effects predicted on the basis of Mach's principle (cf. Section 16). And it was also with this theory that gravitational waves were first investigated. But much progress has recently been made in dealing with this subject in the full theory. In spite of the theoretically expected weakness of gravitational waves, experiments trying to detect them have been in progress for some years.* However, these matters are all somewhat beyond our present scope, and we shall not pursue them further.

A most interesting property of the Einstein field equations is that they, by themselves, imply the geodesic law of motion, which had originally been introduced as a separate hypothesis. The proof in the general case is long and difficult; suffice it to say that it has been given (in a series of papers by Einstein and collaborators beginning in 1927), though perhaps still not with sufficient rigor to satisfy the mathematicians. In the special case of *dust* particles, however, the proof is quite easy: Because of the differential identities (79.5), the field equations (79.7) imply

$$M^{\mu\nu}_{,\nu} = 0.$$

(Of course, they were constructed with this in view.) In dust, that implies

*See, for example, J. Weber, "Gravitational Waves," *Phys. Today* **21**, 34 (April 1968).

$$(\rho_0 U^\mu U^\nu)_{,\nu} = 0,$$

or, in expanded form,

$$U^\mu(\rho_0 U^\nu)_{,\nu} + \rho_0 U^\mu_{,\nu} U^\nu = 0. \tag{79.17}$$

Multiplying this by $g_{\mu\tau} U^\tau$, we have

$$c^2(\rho_0 U^\nu)_{,\nu} + \rho_0 g_{\mu\tau} U^\tau U^\mu_{,\nu} U^\nu = 0. \tag{79.18}$$

But $U^\mu_{,\nu} U^\nu = A^\mu$, the four-acceleration (as can be seen in LIF coordinates), and hence the second term in (79.18) vanishes, being $\rho_0 \mathbf{U} \cdot \mathbf{A}$. Hence the first term vanishes also. When that is substituted into (79.17), we get

$$U^\mu_{,\nu} U^\nu = 0, \quad \text{i.e.,} \quad \mathbf{A} = 0, \quad \text{i.e.,} \quad \frac{D}{ds}\left(\frac{dx^\mu}{ds}\right) = 0,$$

and this is precisely the equation of a geodesic. If a dust particle in a dust cloud (which may be a very *small* dust cloud) follows a geodesic, it seems very likely, of course, that *any* free test particle follows a geodesic.

Finally a word about "solving" the field equations. In GR the situation is very different from that in any other field theory. For example, in Newtonian theory we start with a well-defined coordinate system, relative to which we can specify the density distribution ρ, and then we simply *solve* the relevant Poisson equation for the potential ϕ. It is much the same in Maxwell's theory. But in GR we do *not* start with a well-defined coordinate system: on the contrary, that is what we are trying to find. Hence we cannot simply "plug in" the given $M^{\mu\nu}$ on the right-hand side of the field equations, since there is no way of knowing the components of $M^{\mu\nu}$ except with reference to a coordinate system. Ideally, one could make a catalog by inventing arbitrary $g_{\mu\nu}$ and listing the corresponding $M^{\mu\nu}$ from (79.7); in any given situation one would then try to find the relevant pair $(g_{\mu\nu}, M^{\mu\nu})$. In practice, one often works from both ends: for example, the symmetry of the physical situation may suggest a certain pattern of g's involving unknown functions; the M's can then be expressed also in terms of these functions, which are finally determined by the field equations when the M's and g's are substituted into them.

Modified Schwarzschild Space   *80*

In Section 74 we found the most general spherically symmetric static metric subject to Einstein's original vacuum field equations. (It will be recalled that according to Birkhoff's theorem the assumption of staticness can be omitted: it is a *consequence* of spherical symmetry.) We can now easily adapt that argument to the case of Einstein's "modified" vacuum field equations (79.13). Again we shall assume staticness, although again there exists a Birkhoff theorem which says that the result is independent of this assumption. Thus we begin with a metric of form (74.1) and the relevant $R_{\mu\nu}$ as given by (74.2)–(74.6). Now, however, we require $R_{\mu\nu} = \Lambda g_{\mu\nu}$ instead of $R_{\mu\nu} = 0$. Still, as before, we find $A' = -B'$ and $A = -B$. The equation $R_{22} = \Lambda g_{22}$ then yields

$$e^A(1 + rA') = 1 - \Lambda r^2, \qquad (80.1)$$

or, setting $e^A = \alpha$,

$$\alpha + r\alpha' = (r\alpha)' = 1 - \Lambda r^2.$$

Hence

$$\alpha = 1 - \frac{2m}{r} - \tfrac{1}{3}\Lambda r^2, \qquad (80.2)$$

where $-2m$ is again a constant of integration. It is now easily verified that this solution indeed satisfies *all* the equations $R_{\mu\nu} = \Lambda g_{\mu\nu}$. Thus we have found the following essentially unique metric satisfying our conditions:

$$ds^2 = \left(1 - \frac{2m}{r} - \tfrac{1}{3}\Lambda r^2\right)dt^2 - \left(1 - \frac{2m}{r} - \tfrac{1}{3}\Lambda r^2\right)^{-1}dr^2$$
$$- r^2(d\theta^2 + \sin^2\theta d\phi^2). \qquad (80.3)$$

Comparison with the metric (71.1) shows that the orbits in the space (80.3) approximately correspond to Newtonian orbits under a central potential

$$\phi = -\frac{m}{r} - \tfrac{1}{6}\Lambda r^2, \qquad (80.4)$$

in units in which $c = G = 1$. The first term is recognized as the Newtonian effect of a mass m, and thus again we must identify the constant m with a spherically symmetric mass centered at the origin. The effect of the Λ term can be found by retracing the calculations that led to the previous orbit equations (75.3) and (75.4). The former reappears unchanged, but instead of the latter we now get*

$$\frac{d^2u}{d\phi^2} + u = \frac{m}{h^2} + 3mu^2 - \frac{\Lambda}{3h^2u^3}. \qquad (80.5)$$

The main effect of the extra Λ term in this equation can be shown to be an *additional* motion of the perihelion by an amount

$$\Delta = \frac{\pi\Delta h^6}{m^4} = \frac{\pi\Lambda a^3(1 - e^2)^3}{m}. \qquad (80.6)$$

In the case of Mercury, for example, this would amount to one second of arc per century if Λ were $\sim 5 \times 10^{-42}$ cm^{-2}. Since this would be detectable, Λ *cannot* be that big.

This conclusion is one useful by-product of obtaining the metric (80.3). Another is the space we get on letting $m \rightarrow 0$:

$$ds^2 = (1 - \tfrac{1}{3}\Lambda r^2)dt^2 - (1 - \tfrac{1}{3}\Lambda r^2)^{-1}dr^2$$
$$- r^2(d\theta^2 + \sin^2\theta d\phi^2). \qquad (80.7)$$

Apart from the usual possibility of transforming coordinates, this is the *unique* static solution of Einstein's modified vacuum field equations that is spherically symmetric about a given point and regular at that point: any nonzero m in (80.3) makes the origin an intrinsic singularity. (According to Birkhoff's theorem quoted earlier, there is no other solution even if we relinquish staticness.) The spacetime (80.7) is therefore the successor of Minkowski space *if* the equations $R_{\mu\nu} = \Lambda g_{\mu\nu}$ govern an empty world. Of course, it would be a serious flaw of these equations if the resulting spacetime could be spherically symmetric about one point only, for we would expect the successor of Minkowski space at least to possess the symmetries of Minkowski space. In

*Cf. Eddington, *loc. cit.*, Section 45.

fact, it does: (80.7) is a four-dimensional spacetime of constant curvature $-\frac{1}{3}\Lambda$, with every point (event) equivalent to
every other. [This is *a priori* likely because of the theorem
quoted in Section 79 to the effect that every space of constant curvature is an Einstein space (and the results $R =
-12K, R = 4\Lambda$). We would surely expect the existence of *a*
four-space of constant curvature $-\frac{1}{3}\Lambda$ with Minkowskian
signature (proved below), which must therefore be a Λ-Ein-
stein space, and which must also be spatially isotropic about
every point. But the unique Λ-Einstein space spatially isotropic about *one* point is (80.7). Hence it is spatially isotropic about every point.]

To see this in detail, suppose first that $\Lambda > 0$. Now consider *five*-dimensional Minkowski space M_5, with
coordinates X, Y, Z, W, T and metric

$$ds^2 = dT^2 - (dX^2 + dY^2 + dZ^2 + dW^2), \qquad (80.8)$$

i.e., having one timelike and four spacelike dimensions. In
M_5 construct a pseudosphere of radius a,

$$X^2 + Y^2 + Z^2 + W^2 - T^2 = a^2. \qquad (80.9)$$

For displacements *on* this sphere we have

$$XdX + YdY + ZdZ + WdW - TdT = 0, \qquad (80.10)$$

which shows that any such displacement is perpendicular to
the vector (X, Y, Z, W, T) which, by (80.9), is always spacelike. Thus the normal to the pseudosphere is spacelike, and
the sphere itself must contain the remaining one timelike
and three spacelike dimensions. It has, therefore, the right
signature for a spacetime.

To show that *any* point $P_0(X_0, Y_0, Z_0, W_0, T_0)$ on the
pseudosphere can be transformed into the origin $r = t = 0$
of (80.7) (and thus, incidentally, to demonstrate the homogeneity of the pseudosphere) we can first make an ordinary
three-rotation in X, Y, Z to ensure $Y_0 = Z_0 = 0$, then a two-
rotation in X and W to ensure $X_0 = 0$, and finally a Lorentz
transformation in W and T to ensure $T_0 = 0$ (each of these
preserves (80.8) and (80.9)). Having done this, we apply the
following coordinate transformation to (80.7):

$$X = r \sin \theta \cos \phi$$
$$Y = r \sin \theta \sin \phi$$
$$Z = r \cos \theta, \tag{80.11}$$

and, according as $r \lessgtr (3/\Lambda)^{1/2} \equiv a$, respectively,

$$W = a\left(1 - \frac{r^2}{a^2}\right)^{1/2} \cosh \frac{t}{a}$$

$$T = a\left(1 - \frac{r^2}{a^2}\right)^{1/2} \sinh \frac{t}{a} \tag{80.12}$$

or

$$W = a\left(\frac{r^2}{a^2} - 1\right)^{1/2} \sinh \frac{t}{a}$$

$$T = a\left(\frac{r^2}{a^2} - 1\right)^{1/2} \cosh \frac{t}{a}. \tag{80.13}$$

Any point (r, θ, ϕ, t) thereby transforms into a point which satisfies $X^2 + Y^2 + Z^2 + W^2 - T^2 = a^2$, and thus lies on the pseudosphere; and clearly $r = t = 0$ maps into P_0, as desired. Furthermore it is easily verified that the metric (80.7) is the transform of (80.8), which, restricted by (80.9), is the metric of the pseudosphere. We have therefore mapped the entire space (80.7) (except for the locus $r = a$) into that sphere; but actually into only one *half* of it: for the mapping always satisfies $W + T \geq 0$. We note incidentally, from the relations $K = -\tfrac{1}{3}\Lambda = -1/a^2$, that the pseudosphere (80.9) has constant *negative* curvature $-1/a^2$.

It was de Sitter who in 1917 discovered the space (80.7) with $\Lambda > 0$ in connection with cosmology, and we shall refer to it, and more generally to its "extension" (80.9), as *de Sitter space S_4^-*.

Going back to the metric (80.7), we see that it has a coordinate singularity at the locus

$$r = (3/\Lambda)^{1/2} = a.$$

This is *only* a coordinate singularity, since the equivalent space (80.9) remains perfectly regular there. Still, that locus is not without peculiarity. It is, in fact, quite analogous to the Schwarzschild singularity, and, *like* the

Schwarzschild singularity, it was at first thoroughly misunderstood. Even Einstein and Weyl, though fully aware of the distinction between real and coordinate singularities, regarded this one as real and indicative of the presence of mass—hence its early name "mass horizon." However, clarification came much sooner than in the case of the Schwarzschild sphere. Certainly by 1920 Eddington understood it perfectly.* It is easy to see, by tracing the paths of radially moving free particles or photons forward or backward, that every event *on* the mass horizon has $t = \infty$ or $t = -\infty$. Consequently that locus corresponds to $X^2 + Y^2 + Z^2 = a^2$ and $W^2 - T^2 = 0$ on the pseudosphere. Like the Schwarzschild singularity, the de Sitter singularity can thus be seen to be a light front. Like that one, too, it changes its direction of "motion" relative to the origin "half way through eternity" (at $T = 0$). We shall not pursue these matters here, but some further discussion of de Sitter space will be found in Section 90.

The case of (80.7) with $\Lambda < 0$ is of less practical appeal, mainly because we do not now believe that Λ is negative. Nevertheless, it is not without theoretical interest, and we can treat it quite analogously to the case $\Lambda > 0$. We must here consider a five-dimensional *pseudo*-Minkowski space $\tilde{M}_5$ with metric

$$ds^2 = dT^2 + dW^2 - (dX^2 + dY^2 + dZ^2), \quad (80.14)$$

and in it pseudosphere

$$X^2 + Y^2 + Z^2 - W^2 - T^2 = -a^2 \quad (80.15)$$

with $a^2 = -3/\Lambda$. The necessary transformations from (80.7) into the *whole* of this sphere are given by (80.11) together with

$$W = a \left(1 + \frac{r^2}{a^2}\right)^{1/2} \cos \frac{t}{a}$$

$$T = a \left(1 + \frac{r^2}{a^2}\right)^{1/2} \sin \frac{t}{a}. \quad (80.16)$$

---

*See A. S. Eddington, "Space, Time, and Gravitation," Chapter X, Cambridge University Press, 1920 (and New York, Harper Torchbooks, 1959). Also Eddington, *loc. cit.* (Mathematical Theory) p. 166.

We shall call *this* space S_4^+. It has constant *positive* curvature $1/a^2$.

The above mapping has the strange property that the world lines of fixed spatial points in (80.7), (r, θ, ϕ = constant) are *closed* in the pseudosphere (80.15): by sitting still at such a point and letting time go by we would *retrace* our existence-events after a time $t = 2\pi a$ has elapsed! This possibility is perhaps interesting, but to avoid its embarrassment we can modify the mapping topologically: Under suppression of two dimensions (but with no loss of generality), (80.15) corresponds to a hyperboloid of revolution $W^2 + T^2 - Z^2 = a^2$; now instead of regarding this as an ordinary hyperboloid we can regard it as a "hyperboloidal scroll" wrapped round itself; when we have gone round any circle Z = constant ($t: t_0 \rightarrow t_0 + 2\pi a$) we simply are on the next layer of the scroll rather than back where we started; and thus we run into no difficulties of causality.

9

Cosmology

The Basic Facts 81

Modern scientific man has largely lost his sense of awe of the universe. He is confident that, given sufficient intelligence, perseverance, time and money, he can understand all there is beyond the stars. He believes that he sees here on earth and in its vicinity a fair exhibition of nature's laws and objects, and that nothing new looms "up there" that cannot be explained, predicted, or extrapolated from knowledge gained "down here." He believes he is now surveying a fair sample of the universe, if not in proportion to its size—which may be infinite—yet in proportion to its large-scale features. Little progress could be made in cosmology *without* this presumptuous attitude. And nature herself seems to encourage it, as we shall see, with certain numerical coincidences that could hardly be accidental.

Accordingly, cosmologists construct theoretical "models" which they believe represent the universe as a whole,

213

concentrating on its largest-scale features, and they compare these models with the universe as observed by astronomers. Modern theoretical cosmology found its greatest inspiration in Einstein's general relativity, which provided it with such exciting possibilities as closed and yet unbounded universes; even more significantly, GR had already yielded expanding models (de Sitter, Friedmann) by the time astronomers found that these were needed. Yet, it happened in cosmology as it so often happens in mathematics: when old and difficult problems are solved at long last by intricate methods, much simpler solutions become suddenly apparent. In pre-relativistic days it was thought that Newtonian theory was inadequate for dealing with the dynamics of the universe as a whole, mainly because of apparently unavoidable infinities in the potential. But twelve years after relativistic cosmology had been developed, it was suddenly realized that Newtonian theory (with a few now almost "obvious" modifications) could, after all, be used to obtain many model universes essentially similar to those of GR, and in any case a sufficient variety to survive comparison with the actual universe for a long time to come.

However, before we discuss cosmological theories, we must look at some of the facts. Evidently the first concern of cosmologists must be with the spatial distribution of stars and galaxies. Newton already realized that the stars are immensely far apart. Assuming that stars are essentially like the sun, and knowing that the light from luminous objects falls off inversely as the square of their distance, he compared the apparent luminosity of the stars with portions of the sun, and so estimated that the stars must be at least 100,000 times farther away from us than the sun. In fact, the correct figure for the nearest star is about 270,000.

For Copernicus, as for Ptolemy, all the stars had still been fixed to a "crystalline" sphere, though now centered on the sun rather than on the earth. But as early as 1576, Thomas Digges boldly replaced that sphere by an infinity of stars extending uniformly through all space. The same extension was also made by Giordano Bruno, and mystically foreshadowed a century earlier by Nicholas of Cusa. But, whereas to Digges the sun was still king of the heavens, one who "raigneth and geeveth lawes of motion to ye rest," Bruno recognized it for what it was: just a star among many. The infinite view was later supported by Newton, who believed that a finite universe would "fall down into the middle of the whole space, and there compose one great spherical mass. But if the matter was evenly disposed throughout an infinite space... some of it would convene into one mass and some into another.... And thus might the sun and the fixed stars be formed." (1692)

The next revolutionary idea was born sometime around 1750 and has been variously ascribed to Swedenborg, Lambert, Wright and Kant. They all wrote on the subject of "island universes," recognizing the finiteness of our galaxy and conjecturing the existence of similar stellar systems far out in space. Various "nebulae" seen by the astronomers were candidates for this new role. Kant well understood the shape of our own galaxy ("stars gathered together in a common plane"—as indicated by the Milky Way) and so explained the observed elliptical appearance of some of the nebulae as discs seen obliquely. In 1783 Messier catalogued 103 such nebulae, and William Herschel with his extraordinary 48-inch reflector telescope located no fewer than 2500 before his death in 1822. He became the great observational supporter of the multi-island universe theory, though, ironically, many of his arguments turned out to be quite false. Still, he came to foresee the important division of nebulae into two main classes—galactic and extragalactic. Herschel's theory had its ups and downs in favor, but essentially it had to wait for the slow development of observational capacity to its huge demands. The waiting period culminated in a historic wrangle, continued at one astromers' conference after another from 1917 to 1924—until it suddenly ended on January 1, 1925: Hubble, with the help of the brand-new 100-inch telescope at Mount Wilson, had resolved star images in three of the nebulae, and, as some of these were Cepheids, he was able to establish beyond all doubt their extragalactic distances. Only one main feature of the universe as we know it today was still missing: its expansion. From 1912 onwards, Slipher had observed the spectra of some of the brighter spiral nebulae, and found many of them redshifted, which presumably meant that these nebulae were receding. But distance criteria were still lacking. Hubble now applied his "brightest star" measure of distance, and, together with Humason, extended the red shift studies to ever fainter nebulae. Finally, in 1929, he was able to announce the famous law: all galaxies recede from us (apart from small random motions) at velocities proportional to their distance from us. The modern era of cosmology had begun.

We must draw a curtain over the further detailed development of observation and content ourselves with simply listing the main astronomical findings relevant to our purpose. Stars, to begin with, are now known to be tremendous thermonuclear reactors, going through reasonably well understood life cycles—whose exact course depends mainly on their mass. Their size can be appreciated by considering that the earth *with* the moon's orbit would comfortably fit into most stars, including the sun. About 7000 of them are visible to the naked eye; about 10^{11} are contained in a typical galaxy, in exceedingly sparse distribution, being separated by distances of the order of ten light years. In a scale model in which stars are represented by pinheads, these would be 50 km apart, and the solar system (out to the orbit of Pluto) would be a 20-meter circle centered on a pinhead sun. A galaxy *on this scale* is 300,000 km in diameter, or three-quarters of the distance from the earth to the moon. A typical galaxy, in fact, has a radius of 3×10^4 light years, is 3×10^6 light years from its nearest neighbor, and rotates differentially with a typical period of 100 million years. Like a dime, it has a width only about a tenth of its radius, and dimes spaced about a meter apart make a good model of the galactic distribution. About 10^{11} galaxies are visible with the 200-inch telescope. *On the dime scale*, the farthest of these are 1.5 km away from us, but objects 6 km away would represent the farthest known quasars, which apparently have a velocity of recession equal to about four-fifths of the speed of light. Consequently *nothing* could be seen beyond 7.5 km, no matter how powerful our telescope.*

There is one more complication: galaxies, too, are not distributed uniformly throughout space but instead tend to cluster. Single galaxies are exceptional; most belong to clusters of from 2 to 1000 to even 10,000, apparently bound by gravity. There are some indications that the clusters themselves may cluster and so form "superclusters." This is perhaps a convenient point to mention the so-called "hierarchical" model universe of Charlier, which, though it has found little favor, is based on an interesting idea. Already in 1761 Lambert had loosely speculated that various solar systems might revolve about a common center, that such supersystems in turn might combine and revolve about another center, "and where shall we stop?" Analogously to this scheme, Charlier between 1908 and 1922 developed a cosmological theory in which galaxies form clusters, clusters form superclusters, and so on *ad infinitum*. By arranging the dimensions suitably it is evidently possible in this way to create a model with zero average density, and thus to avoid the infinities inherent in the Newtonian treatment of *homogeneous* universes (which, of course, have a *finite* density). Charlier's model is not homogeneous. It can be constructed in stages from a primordial homogeneous gas: (i) form stars, and expand by a given factor; (ii) form galaxies, and expand again; (iii) form galaxy clusters, and expand again; etc. At each completed stage there is homogeneity for volumes large enough to contain several of

---

*We shall refine this statement when we talk about *horizons* in Section 86 and about distance in Section 87.

the highest-order clusters; but when the process is driven to the limit, *no* volume is large enough to be "typical."

Other basic facts concern the distribution of galaxies over the sky (isotropy) and in depth (homogeneity); the rate of expansion of the universe; its average density; and its age. Isotropy, in principle at least, is easy to check: do the galaxies appear to be uniformly distributed in all directions (allowing for obscuring matter within our Milky Way)? The answer has long been: very roughly, yes. Recently our faith in the isotropy of the universe, from our vantage point, has been reinforced by observation of the so-called "background" microwave radiation of temperature $\sim 3°K$—an apparent left-over from a primordial "big-bang" origin of the universe. This happens to be incident with a very high degree of isotropy.

Checking for homogeneity in depth is much harder, since it is complicated by many factors, such as the finite speed of light, the relativistic definition of time, the possible evolution of galaxies (which affects distance-from-brightness estimates), the expansion of the universe, and the unknown space geometry. The first two factors are easily allowed for, but the others are so flexible that practically all observations of the really distant galaxies could be compatible with homogeneity. Among the nearer ones, however, approximate homogeneity seems well established.

For the rate of expansion of the universe, Hubble in 1929 gave the figure of 540 km/sec/megaparsec. [The parsec (pc) is an astronomical unit equal to 3.087×10^{18} cm, or 3.26 light years, and one megaparsec (Mpc) equals 10^6 parsec.] This figure, *Hubble's constant*, has undergone several drastic revisions, all caused by revisions of the cosmic distance scale. Values as low as 60 km/sec/Mpc have been proposed recently, but a conservative present estimate would be in the region of 100. It must be stressed that Hubble's "constant" may well vary in time—though not, of course, as quickly as the above estimates! An analogy with a rubber sheet that is isotropically expanded should make this clear: If at any instant two points on the sheet one inch apart have relative velocity H, then points x inches apart will have relative velocity xH, and H is Hubble's constant. But there is no reason why point-pairs one inch apart should always have the same relative velocity; the expansion rate may well vary, and H could even change from positive values to negative values (contraction). Constant H would imply exponential expansion: $x = x_0 \exp(Ht)$.

The average density of the *visible* contents of the universe (luminous galaxies) is judged to be at least 10^{-30} gm/cm^3. But this, of course, is only an approximate lower bound for the present average density of *all* matter; *that* may well be higher, owing to the presence of undetected intergalactic matter, collapsed (and therefore invisible) galaxies, etc. Very recent X-ray observations made from rockets high above the earth's atmosphere (Henry, 1968) have suggested the presence of extremely hot (and therefore radiating) intergalactic hydrogen in sufficient concentration to increase the density over that of visible matter a hundredfold. An upper limit to the cosmic density is probably that of rich clusters of galaxies obtained *dynamically* (which therefore includes intergalactic matter), the very existence of clusters being taken as evidence that their density exceeds that of intercluster space; this upper limit has been set at 6×10^{-28} gm/cm^3.* As we shall see later, the cosmic density is a very critical datum, which may determine whether the universe is positively or negatively curved, and also whether it is infinitely expanding or "oscillating."

An equally critical datum is the age of the universe—that is, if it *has* an age: it could, of course, be infinitely old. The age of the earth since the formation of its crust can be quite accurately determined from considerations of radioactive decay. It turns out to be $(4.5 \pm 0.3) \times 10^9$ years. Evidently the universe cannot be younger than this. The best estimate for the present age of our galaxy is $\sim 2 \times 10^{10}$

*G. O. Abell, *Annual Review of Astronomy and Astrophysics* **3**, 1 (1965).

years. This comes partly from dynamical considerations, but mainly from a study of the so-called Hertzsprung-Russell diagram, which charts the life and death of stars in terms of their color, brightness, and age. Some of the same considerations have been applied to other galaxies, whose ages also appear to be at least 2×10^{10} years, though higher estimates have at times been given.

Two extremely useful pieces of information to have would be the exact spectrum of an average galaxy, and the variation of its intrinsic brightness with age: evidently a galaxy cannot burn evenly forever. The spectrum is partially hidden from us by the earth's atmosphere, which absorbs much of the ultraviolet radiation. And since galactic distances are judged by photographic brightness, and since the Doppler shift displaces the spectrum across the photographic range of color-sensitivity, our uncertainty about the full spectrum results in uncertainties of distance. There is, however, hope that extraterrestrial spectroscopy (from rockets and satellites) will soon solve this problem. Unfortunately, our distance estimates are also affected by our ignorance of galactic evolution. It must be remembered that as we see farther out into space we also see farther back into time. (In fact, we see precisely the events on our past light cone, and from this essentially instantaneous "snapshot," or world-picture, we must try to construct a suitable world-map.) Thus when we see one galaxy fainter than another, we presumably see it not only at a greater distance, but also at an earlier age; and we cannot be totally sure how to apportion the dimming effect between these two causes. The usual procedure is simply to *ignore* galactic evolution, but this clearly has its pitfalls.

In the remainder of this book we must content ourselves with a study of what may be called post-galactic cosmology —the kinematics and dynamics of the universe of galaxies. Pre-galactic cosmology, or "cosmogony"—the study of the formation of matter, of the stars, and of galaxies, out of some primordial gas—depends on nuclear physics and chemistry and is well beyond our present scope. It has, of course, great philosophical interest, since, in a sense, it takes over where Darwin left off. If Darwin and modern biology can explain the rise of man from a lifeless earth, cosmogony can explain the rise of earths, suns, and galaxies from an amorphous gas, given only the immutable laws of nature.

Apparent Difficulties of Pre-Relativistic Cosmology   *82*

In retrospect, it may seem hard to understand why nineteenth-century astronomers were so bent on the idea that the universe must be infinite and static. A finite shower of stars (or galaxies) shot out in all directions from some primordial "big bang," its expansion finally halted and reversed by gravity, and ending in another holocaust, is certainly well within Newtonian possibilities. And so is a finite universe that rotates forever and thereby avoids gravitational collapse. Was the *appearance* of an infinite static universe so compelling that it must not be questioned? Again, how could generations brought up on the idea of energy conservation expect the stars to burn forever, without, evidently, receiving comparable energies from their surroundings? But here we must remember that the source of stellar energy was still totally unknown, $E = mc^2$ was undreamed of, and thus it was still legitimate to imagine an infinite reservoir of energy hidden in a finite mass (like that which results from the indefinitely close approach of two point-particles under Newtonian gravitation).

Whatever the reason, an infinite static universe it had to be. And this led to difficulties. The first was with Newton's theory. Consider an infinite, homogeneous and initially static distribution of mass (e.g., stars) throughout all space; what happens? To judge from the quotation given in Section 81, Newton apparently thought that this was an equilibrium configuration. For, believing in absolute space, he might well appeal to symmetry and argue that the resultant force on each star must vanish, whence no motions could occur.   However, if we abandon the idea of absolute space, a general homogeneous contraction under gravity of the infinite distribution becomes possible. No star would move in a preferred manner *relative to the rest.* The *local* application of Newton's theory actually *demands* such a contraction.   But we anticipate.   Before Einstein, absolute space was still an article of faith with most astronomers.   And Newton's theory as such was confounded by the above problem, since the potential due to all the masses is infinite at each point.   Although the large-scale dynamics (equilibrium) could be settled by symmetry, small-scale problems like planetary motions could only be handled by subtracting out infinities, or, in other words, by *ignoring* the universe.

This led Neumann and Seeliger in 1896 to suggest that the Newtonian potential of a point mass be replaced by

$$\phi = -\frac{mG}{r} e^{-r\sqrt{\lambda}}, \quad (\lambda = \text{constant} \approx 0), \qquad (82.1)$$

whose integral would remain finite.   (Note that this is identical in form with Yukawa's mesonic potential put forward in 1935.)   Poisson's equation* $\nabla^2\phi = 4\pi G\rho$ then becomes

$$\nabla^2\phi - \lambda\phi = 4\pi G\rho, \qquad (82.2)$$

which possesses the obvious solution

$$\phi = -\frac{4\pi G\rho}{\lambda} \qquad (82.3)$$

in a homogeneous universe.   (This results also on integrating (82.1) throughout space for a continuous distribution of matter.)

It is interesting to observe the striking *formal* analogy between Einstein's modification (79.10) of his original field

---

*From now on we write $\nabla^2\phi$ for our previous $\Sigma\phi_{ii}$ to stress the coordinate-independent meaning of the operation.   We recall that in the case of spherical symmetry $(\phi = \phi(r)) \ \nabla^2\phi = \phi'' + (2/r)\phi'$.

equations (79.7) and Neumann and Seeliger's modification (82.2) of Poisson's equation. However, in first approximation (79.10) does *not* reduce to (82.2) but rather to another modification of Poisson's equation, namely

$$\nabla^2 \phi + c^2 \Lambda = 4\pi G\rho, \qquad (82.4)$$

as can be shown by methods similar to those of Section 79. This *also* admits a constant solution in the presence of homogeneous matter, namely $\phi = 0$, *provided* $c^2\Lambda = 4\pi G\rho$ —a situation which obtains in Einstein's static universe, for which, indeed, Einstein originally introduced his Λ term.

The most general modification of Poisson's equation, *in the spirit* of Einstein's modification of *his* field equations, would be subject only to three conditions: (i) preservation of the scalar character, (ii) preservation of linearity, (iii) occurrence of no derivatives of the potential higher than the second. And this leads uniquely to the form

$$\nabla^2 \phi + A\phi + B = 4\pi G\rho, \qquad (A, B \text{ universal constants}),$$
$$(82.5)$$

of which *both* (82.2) and (82.4) are special cases. If A or B or both are nonzero, this equation has the somewhat disturbing property of admitting *nonconstant* solutions for *empty* space ($\rho = 0$): assuming local isotropy and regularity, let us substitute a Taylor series in r into (82.5) (with $\rho = 0$) and solve; the result is

$$\phi = a - \tfrac{1}{6}Br^2 - \tfrac{1}{6}aA\{r^2 + 0(r^4)\},$$
$$(a = \text{arbitrary constant}). \qquad (82.6)$$

To simplify matters, assume $A = 0$, $B = c^2\Lambda$—i.e., equation (82.4). Then (82.6) can be superimposed on any solution of Poisson's equation to yield a solution of (82.4). But (82.6) represents a distance-proportional acceleration $\tfrac{1}{3}c^2\Lambda r$ away from *every* point. Such an extra acceleration, being totally independent of whether matter is present or not, is perhaps best regarded as a homogeneous expansion or contraction *of space itself* (or of the inertial field) with Hubble constant $\pm(\tfrac{1}{3}c^2 \Lambda)^{1/2}$ if $\Lambda > 0$, and $n\cot nt(n^2 =$

$-\frac{1}{3}c^2\Lambda$) if $\Lambda < 0$. The static solution $\phi = 0$, for example, can be regarded as a combination of the naturally collapsing Newtonian solution $\phi = \frac{2}{3}\pi G\rho r^2$ and the neutralizing effect of space expansion. Alternatively, the Λ term in (82.4) may be regarded as equivalent to a permanent density $-c^2\Lambda/4\pi G$ superimposed on ρ, but, unlike ρ, not subject to change with expansion.

Another famous objection to the pre-relativistic static infinite homogeneous universe, quite independent of gravitational theory, is what has come to be known as *Olbers' Paradox*.* This simply states that *if* the stars shine with unvarying and equal light, and space is Euclidean, the whole sky in such a universe must appear uniformly as bright as the sun. For consider any narrow cone of rays entering the eye. That cone must come from the surface of *some* star. But since its cross-sectional area varies as r^2, whereas the apparent luminosity of a unit area of star surface decreases as $1/r^2$, the light gathered into this cone is independent of where it originates; hence it is the same as if it originated on the sun, and the paradox is established. Today the most immediately questionable assumption is the eternal burning of the stars. A more popular explanation (Chéseaux, 1744) was absorption by some interstellar medium, but, as Bondi has pointed out, this would soon radiate as much as it absorbs. Nor can a finite and closed geometry help: our cone of rays may have to be traced back several times "round the universe" before it strikes a star, and it will not spread as r^2; but its spread and the stellar luminosity still vary inversely, and the argument is unimpaired. Best relief is provided by a sufficient expansion of the universe, for this ensures that light from the distant sources is so Doppler-shifted (and thus, by Planck's relation $E = h\nu$, so de-energized) that the paradox is easily avoided—even in the case of "steady

---

*For its interesting historical antecedents, see S. L. Jaki, "Olbers', Halley's, or Whose Paradox?" *Am. J. Phys.* **35**, 200 (1967), which should also stand as a warning to all armchair historians.

state" theories, in which the mean light emission per unit volume remains constant.

Cosmological Relativity: The Cosmological Principle *83*

Though little value is placed these days on the Euclidicity of the universe, and none on its staticness, practically all modern cosmologies make the assumption that the universe is homogeneous, and usually also that it is isotropic. In other words, no galaxy, and no direction at any galaxy, is thought to be in any way preferred. [In our theoretical discussion we shall use the term "galaxy" in the conventional sense of a basic unit, or building brick, of the universe. It may well be that these units, whose homogeneous distribution is assumed, correspond to clusters of galaxies rather than just galaxies. To avoid inaccuracies, some authors prefer to speak of the "fundamental particles" of model universes, and refer to observers fixed to these as "fundamental observers," a usage which we shall occasionally adopt.] This assumed absence of preference is not merely an expression of Copernican humility, whereby one capriciously eliminates such "sensible" alternatives as single-island universes, Charlier universes, etc.: it is cold common sense. For, as long as it is not contradicted by the observations, it is a simplifying hypothesis of great power. Whereas nonhomogeneous model universes involve us in *global* questions, the beauty of homogeneous models is that they can be studied mainly locally: any part is representative of the whole. The demand for isotropy can more easily be relaxed than that for homogeneity, though such relaxation, too, leads quickly to complications.

The assumption of large-scale homogeneity, usually together with—but sometimes explicitly without—the assumption of large-scale isotropy, has come to be known as the *Cosmological Principle* (CP). As far as present-day observations go, there are certainly no compelling indications to abandon this principle. On the contrary, the fairly good isotropy observed from our position in the universe provides us with an argument *for* the CP: By mere considerations of probability, *we* are hardly likely to be in a special position in the universe; hence we suspect isotropy everywhere. But this implies homogeneity, since a non-homogeneous universe can appear isotropic only from very special vantage points—e.g., from its center, if it were spherically symmetric.

There exists also a *Perfect Cosmological Principle* (PCP), on which, in fact, the *steady state* cosmology is built. This asserts that, in addition to being spatially homogeneous and isotropic, the universe is also temporally homogeneous, i.e., it presents the same average aspect at all times. As Bondi (who with Gold in 1948 originated the PCP) once put it, "geography doesn't matter, and history doesn't matter either." The PCP implies that as the universe expands, sufficient new matter is created to fill the gaps.* (Deliberate violation of local energy conservation!) Also there is no beginning or end in time—a very attractive feature philosophically. The PCP has the further advantage of leading to a unique model which, as such, is highly vulnerable to empirical disproof (see Section 85). It is probably fair to say that no such disproof has yet occurred, though at times it seemed close.

The CP and the PCP (and all similar symmetry assumptions) may be thought of as defining a "relativity of the universe," i.e., a group of coordinate transformations under which the large-scale universe transforms into itself. For this reason alone we may consider *any* cosmology based on such principles as a relativity theory, and it is in this sense that the term "cosmological relativity" appears in the title of this book and of this section. (Cf. Section 1.)

So far we have used the notion of homogeneity purely intuitively. In an expanding universe, however, spatial homogeneity is not quite as simple a concept as it is in static

---

*About one hydrogen atom per 6 km^3 of space per year is all that is needed.

situations. Intuitively we think of it as meaning that all sufficiently large spatial "samples" of the universe are equivalent. But when? Our neighborhood *now* probably differs even from *itself*, let alone from other regions, one hundred million years ago. Thus the comparison involves time, and relativity has taught us to be wary of time. The following definition, due to A. G. Walker, avoids this difficulty: Homogeneity means that the totality of observations that any fundamental observer can make on the universe is identical with the totality of observations that any other fundamental observer can make on the universe. In other words, if throughout all time we here, as well as observers on all other galaxies, could log all observations— e.g., the density and directional distribution of galaxies, their rate of expansion, etc., together with the times at which the observations are made (as measured, say, by standard cesium clocks) then homogeneity would be equivalent to the coincidence of all these logs (up to a possible translation in time, of course).

A most important corollary of such homogeneity is the existence of *cosmic time*, i.e., of an absolute universe-wide sequence of moments. In fact, the universe itself, *if it is evolving*, acts as the relevant synchronization agent at each point. For we need merely reset the time origins of the various cesium clocks in the preceding paragraph to make the logs *identical*. Then their readings define τ, the cosmic time; clearly τ is the *proper* time at each galaxy. If the universe is static, or in steady state, the clock setting to cosmic time can be achieved by two-way signaling experiments similar to those of Section 71. We shall in all cases assume this has been done.

Milne's Model **84**

Breaking the historical sequence, we shall now describe a most ingenious and simple model universe, invented by

E. A. Milne* in 1932, which nicely illustrates many of the features shared by the more complicated models. And, though it will not be immediately apparent, Milne's model in fact satisfies the CP.

Against a background of empty Minkowski space M_4, and totally neglecting gravity, Milne considered an infinite number of test particles (no mass, no volume), all shot out (for reasons unknown) in all directions, and with all possible speeds, at a unique creation event E. Let us look at this situation in some particular inertial frame $S(x, y, z, t)$, and suppose E occurred at its origin O at $t = 0$. All the particles, being free, will move uniformly and radially away from O, with all possible speeds short of c. Hence the picture in S will be that of a ball of dust whose unattained boundary expands at the speed of light. At each instant, Hubble's velocity-distance proportionality is accurately satisfied in S. Still; at first sight, this seems an unlikely candidate for a modern model universe, since (i) it appears to have a unique center, and (ii) it clearly is a "single island" universe. Leaving aside the second objection for the moment, let us dispose of the first: The boundary of the cloud behaves kinematically like a spherical light front emitted at E, and thus each particle, having been present at E, will consider *himself* to be at the center of this front! Moreover, since all particles coincided at E, *each* particle will consider the whole motion pattern to be radially away from himself, and of course uniform. There remains the question whether we can have an isotropic density distribution around each particle.

To study this, let τ denote the proper time elapsed at each particle since creation. Then n_0, the proper particle density at any given particle P, is of the form

$$n_0 = N/\tau^3, \quad (N = \text{constant}), \qquad (84.1)$$

because a small sphere around P, containing a fixed number of particles, expands with the constant velocity du of the

*Nature **130**, 9 (1932).

farthest particles, and thus has radius $du\tau$ and volume $(4\pi/3)\,du^3\tau^3$. Evidently, for maximum symmetry, we must choose N the same at all particles. If particle P is at distance r from the origin in S, then for events *at P* we have

$$\tau = \frac{t}{\gamma(u)}, \quad u = \frac{r}{t}; \qquad (84.2)$$

therefore, since a unit proper volume at P is decreased to $\gamma(u)$ in S, the particle density at P *relative to S* is given by

$$n = \frac{\gamma(u)\,N}{\tau^3} = \frac{\gamma^4(u)\,N}{t^3} = \frac{Nt}{(t^2 - r^2/c^2)^2}. \qquad (84.3)$$

It is clear that, conversely, a density *defined* by (84.3) reduces to N/τ^3 at each particle, and this is therefore the density distribution we must require to hold around *any* particle in SR coordinates. Observe how this density approaches infinity at the "edge" $r = ct$.

Milne's model is now seen to satisfy the CP—i.e., homogeneity and isotropy. In pre-relativistic kinematics the conflict of "single-island" universes with the CP arises because galaxies at (or even near) the edge are evidently not typical. Milne's model demonstrates how in relativistic kinematics this conflict can be avoided: there are no galaxies *at* the edge, and there are no galaxies *near* the edge by their own reckoning.

Note that the restriction to *point* particles is necessary. It may be thought that because of the length contraction of the galaxies near the edge it is possible to fill Milne's sphere with particles of finite proper volume. But first, there must be infinitely many particles (otherwise some would be *at* the edge), and second, there would be a definite proper time τ_0 at which particles touch locally. Therefore, since τ gets arbitrarily small as we approach the edge at any fixed t, particles at a certain r would touch and beyond that they would have to overlap, which is absurd.

We now give an alternative description of Milne's model which is not only instructive in itself, but which is in fact standard for *all* models satisfying the CP, and thus prepares the way for later comparisons. When the CP is satisfied, and a cosmic time consequently exists, models are conveniently described in terms of what we may call *cosmic maps.* Each such map is a composite or patchwork of *local* space maps, all made at the same cosmic instant τ. Moreover, the spatial coordinates are usually chosen to be *comoving,* which means that the fundamental particles, though mutually moving, have fixed space coordinates—like the lattice points in a permanently labeled expanding Cartesian lattice. For example, in Milne's model, the set (u, θ, ϕ) relative to the origin of the inertial frame S could serve as comoving coordinates, but u could also be replaced by any function of u.

Consider, then, the usual metric of M_4 relative to a given frame S in spherical polar coordinates,

$$ds^2 = c^2dt^2 - dr^2 - r^2(d\theta^2 + \sin^2\theta\, d\phi^2), \qquad (84.4)$$

and suppose the origin $r = t = 0$ coincides with Milne's creation-event E. Now make the following coordinate transformation to cosmic time τ (see (84.2)) and to a new comoving coordinate $\rho*$:

$$\tau = t(1 - u^2/c^2)^{1/2}, \quad c\rho = u(1 - u^2/c^2)^{-1/2}, \quad (u = r/t).$$
$$(84.5)$$

A simple computation, aided by the realization that

$$r = c\tau \sinh\psi, \quad t = \tau \cosh\psi, \quad (\sinh\psi = \rho), \quad (84.6)$$

then yields the new form of the metric,

$$ds^2 = c^2d\tau^2 - c^2\tau^2\left\{\frac{d\rho^2}{1 + \rho^2} + \rho^2(d\theta^2 + \sin^2\theta\, d\phi^2)\right\}. \quad (84.7)$$

It is well known in Riemannian geometry that the expression in braces in (84.7) represents the metric of a three-space of constant negative curvature $K = -1$. (Its symmetry is such that if the origin of ρ is moved to any other of its points, and angles are then measured from there, the metric transforms into itself. This is clear also from our present

---

*Not to be confused with density. The use of ρ in this context is unfortunate but traditional.

derivation, since *any* galaxy could be identified with $r = \rho = 0$.)   Multiplied by $c^2\tau^2$, as in (84.7), the brace represents a space of constant curvature $K = -1/c^2\tau^2$.*
Milne called this the *public* three-space of his model (our "cosmic map"), because it is shared by all galaxies, as compared with the *private* Euclidean three-space which constitutes the inertial frame attached to a given galaxy. The metric of public space, as can be seen from (84.7), represents ruler distance measured locally by the fundamental observers. Milne's public space expands uniformly "at the speed of light" (it is the negative-curvature analog of a hypersphere of radius $c\tau$), but it is always of infinite extent, except at $\tau = 0$, when it becomes singular. Figure 28 illustrates the model in terms of the x and t

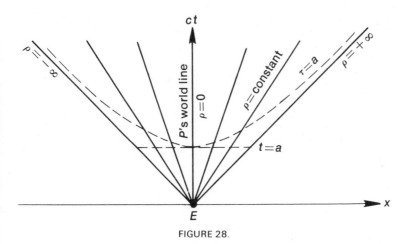

FIGURE 28.

coordinates of a particular fundamental particle P. The lines ρ = constant *between* $\rho = \pm\infty$ (i.e., u = constant between $\pm c$) represent the worldlines of the fundamental particles, while the lines $\rho = \pm\infty$ represent the boundary. Any horizontal line $t = a$ = constant represents one of P's private three-space sections of the model, while any hyperbola $\tau = a$ = constant (i.e., $c^2t^2 - r^2 = c^2a^2$) represents a public space section.

*Assuming a present age of the universe $\tau \approx 10^{10}$ years, $K \approx -10^{-56}$ cm^{-2}.

Note that (84.4) merely gives the metric of the spacetime *background* of Milne's model, without further characterizing the model itself; the metric (84.7), on the other hand, together with the information that ρ, θ, ϕ are comoving coordinates, *fully describes the motion pattern of the model*, as well as the background. And therein lies much of its utility. (Cf. (85.5) and (85.6) below.)

Finally let us state a blemish of sorts, inherent in all "island universes": there can be events in the world at which no galaxy is present, but which can nevertheless interact with the galaxies. The public coordinates used in (84.7) obscure this fact, but it is very clear in the original description of the model. There are no galaxies outside the sphere $r = ct$, yet events beyond that sphere could, for example, be seen at the galaxies. World models possessing this property are called "incomplete."

85   *The Robertson-Walker Metric*

To discuss the kinematics of general model universes, we idealize the material part of the universe by a smooth distribution of virtual particles whose motion pattern (or velocity field) constitutes the "substratum" of the model. Actual galaxies will coincide with only a subset of these particles. We assume that the galactic distribution is sufficiently sparse not to interfere appreciably with the null-geodetic propagation of light. For we now accept also the validity of GR. In this section we derive a standard form of the metric, in terms of cosmic time and comoving coordinates, which will characterize the most general model satisfying the CP (homogeneity *and* isotropy).

As we have seen in Section 83, there will exist a cosmic time (*which we now denote by* t), which reduces to proper time at each galaxy, and which correlates identical observations at different galaxies. If for the moment we denote arbitrary comoving coordinates by x^i ($i = 1, 2, 3$), there can be no cross terms $dt\,dx^i$ in the metric. For consider a pair of fundamental particles separated, say, by dx^1, with $dx^2 = dx^3 = 0$. Then, as in Section 70 (except that now the metric coefficients may depend on t), the presence of a $dt dx^1$ term would imply that signals *emitted* at equal t at the two particles, towards each other, *arrive* at unequal t, which contradicts the CP. Since, furthermore, $dx^i = 0$ (all i) must imply $ds = c dt$ (since t is proper time on each galaxy), the metric must be of the form

$$ds^2 = c^2 dt^2 - d\sigma^2, \qquad (85.1)$$

where $d\sigma^2$, the metric of public space, contains the dx^i but not dt, with coefficients possibly dependent on t. Consider next the development in time of a small triangle formed by three neighboring fundamental particles. By isotropy, the motion relative to each must be radial, and thus the angles must remain constant; hence the ratios of the sides must remain constant (since locally we have Euclidean geometry), and this means that time can enter $d\sigma^2$ only through a common factor, say $R^2(t)$. Thus

$$ds^2 = c^2 dt^2 - R^2(t) dl^2, \qquad (85.2)$$

where dl^2 is time-independent and comoving. We have derived this form of the metric by symmetry arguments only: for consistency with GR we can now verify that the comoving point x^1, x^2, x^3 = constant traces out a timelike geodesic in any metric (85.2), or, indeed, (85.1). (We need only check that $\Gamma^\mu_{44} = 0$, for all μ.)

Evidently $R(t)$ represents the expansion of the universe, or, more accurately, the expansion of public space. If a dot denotes differentiation with respect to t, we find that the separation between neighboring galaxies, $d\sigma = R dl$, satisfies

$$(d\sigma)^{\cdot}/d\sigma = \dot{R}/R, = H(t) \quad \text{say}, \qquad (85.3)$$

and this is just Hubble's law, instantaneously. Consequently we recognize $H(t)$ as Hubble's constant.

Now, because of the assumed isotropy of the model, *all* points of the public space must be "isotropic points" (see Section 66) and thus, by Schur's theorem, dl^2 must represent a Riemannian three-space of constant curvature. It can be shown that the metric of such a space can always be brought to the form

$$dl^2 = A^2 \left\{ \frac{dr^2 + r^2(d\theta^2 + \sin^2 \theta \, d\phi^2)}{(1 + \frac{1}{4}kr^2)^2} \right\}. \qquad (85.4)$$

The curvature of this space is k/A^2; we shall agree that k (the "curvature index") takes only the values ± 1 and 0, and that the factor A^2 is absorbed into $R^2(t)$ in (85.2). Then (85.2) finally assumes the form

$$ds^2 = c^2 dt^2 - R^2(t) \left\{ \frac{dr^2 + r^2(d\theta^2 + \sin^2 \theta \, d\phi^2)}{(1 + \frac{1}{4}kr^2)^2} \right\}. \qquad (85.5)$$

The curvature of public space is now k/R^2, and r, θ, ϕ, of course, are comoving. We recognize the numerator inside the brace as the metric of Euclidean three-space in spherical polars. The effect of an r-dependent denominator is like stretching all rulers equally at a given distance r; it does not affect the meaning of θ, ϕ as the usual angular coordinates. By isotropy, therefore, θ and ϕ must be constant along light rays (null geodesics) through the origin, which can of course be placed on any fundamental particle P. Thus θ and ϕ are the familiar visual angular coordinates relative to P; and r is a radial coordinate.

An alternative form of (85.5) is occasionally useful:

$$ds^2 = c^2 dt^2 - R^2(t) \left\{ \frac{d\rho^2}{1 - k\rho^2} + \rho^2(d\theta^2 + \sin^2 \theta \, d\phi^2) \right\}. \qquad (85.6)$$

It is readily obtained from (85.5) by introducing a new radial comoving coordinate ρ defined by

$$\rho = r/(1 + \tfrac{1}{4}kr^2). \qquad (85.7)$$

Note that Milne's model (84.7) corresponds to (85.6) with $k = -1$, $R(t) = ct$. It is of course not surprising to find Milne's model again in this context, since it satisfies all present hypotheses. Like (84.7), (85.5) and (85.6) specify not merely the spacetime, but also the substratum.

Though we have presupposed GR in this section, we have used of that theory so far only (i) the Riemannian nature of spacetime, and (ii) the fact that light travels along null tracks. In two independent and most significant papers, H. P. Robertson and A. G. Walker almost simultaneously discovered by group-theoretic methods around 1935 that both (i) and (ii) are actually implicit in the CP, i.e., they follow purely from the (rather strong) assumptions of the perfect homogeneity and isotropy of the substratum. Consequently the metric (85.5), which is now justly called the Robertson-Walker (RW) metric (though in GR it was known earlier) *applies to all models satisfying the* CP, even to those outside of GR. Without GR, however, its properties are fewer: Its coefficients are unrestricted by the GR field equations, its timelike geodesics do not necessarily represent the paths of free particles, and $c^{-1}\int ds$ does not necessarily measure proper time along arbitrary paths. But *t does* represent cosmic time, light *does* travel along null geodesics, and the spatial part *does* represent a distance element ("radar distance") of public space in comoving coordinates.

This, then, is as far as we can go with the CP alone. The two *free* elements of the RW metric, k and $R(t)$, can only be determined by additional *assumptions*—if we approach the task theoretically—or possibly by *observation* of the actual universe. Observation without further theory, however, is of very limited scope. The curvature k/R^2 of public space, for example, is somewhat conventional and cannot be measured locally as space curvature (recall Milne's model where local curvature is strictly zero); in any case, it is extremely small (recall its present value -10^{-56} cm^{-2} in Milne's model). Nevertheless, as we shall see in Section 87, in principle it is obtainable from astronomical observations if these can be pushed "to third order." Such observations also yield the present value of Hubble's constant $\dot{R}/R$, and potentially that of the first few of the ratios $\ddot{R}/R$, $\dddot{R}/R$, ... But that is all. Thus, inevitably, we must bring in more theory to make further progress.

One theoretical approach is to appeal to general principles, e.g., to the desirability of having a closed and finite universe. This has sometimes been thought to necessitate the choice $k = +1$ (e.g., by Einstein), but in fact it does not. Closed and finite if somewhat artificial universes can be constructed also with $k \leq 0$ (see exercise 7-5) by making "topological identifications" which spoil the global isotropy of the model but retain its homogeneity and *local* isotropy.* One must bear in mind that a *metric* determines a space only locally. For example, if we are given the metric $dx^2 + dy^2$, it would be very naive to assume that we are necessarily dealing with an infinite plane: we may be dealing with a cylinder, or even with a closed and finite surface, topologically equivalent to a torus, which results on cutting a square from the plane and identifying any two directly opposite points on the edges. Again, the metric of a unit sphere does not necessarily imply that we are dealing with a closed surface of area 4π. We may be dealing with one of area 2π: such a surface results on identifying diametrically opposite points of the sphere; by the time we go half-way round, we are already back where we started. (And, apart from our biased experience, such a surface is, *per se*, no more "unlikely" than a sphere.) These examples illustrate the kind of technique involved in closing the public space of an RW model with $k = -1$ or 0, though in the case $k = -1$ it is not so trivial. In the case $k = 0$, on the other hand, it is quite analogous to the closing of the plane. The opposite process, incidentally, that of "opening up" a space of constant *positive* curvature and making it complete and infinite, is impossible.

Another essentially *a priori* assumption, but a very fruitful one, is Bondi and Gold's perfect cosmological principle: by imposing a further symmetry on the model they made it unique. As we mentioned in Section 83, the

---

*It is sometimes asserted in the literature that the RW metric can be derived (without presupposing Riemannian geometry) from the weaker assumption of *local* isotropy alone, rather than global isotropy and homogeneity. The proof is seen in certain results that Walker has derived in another context; but, in fact, neither proof nor disproof exists to date. On the other hand, if we assume Riemannian geometry (as in GR) then the RW metric is indeed derived from local isotropy alone.

steady state model not only satisfies the CP but also presents the same aspect at all times. It *must* violate local energy conservation, and thus it *cannot* satisfy GR, which has energy conservation built into it. (But see Section 89.) Nevertheless, the RW metric (85.5) is applicable. Since $H(t)$ must be constant in this model, (85.3) implies $R = a \exp(Ht)$ for some constant a, which we can absorb into the exponential by a translation of t. And since the curvature $k/R^2(t)$ must also be constant, k must necessarily vanish. Hence the relevant metric is

$$ds^2 = c^2 dt^2 - e^{2Ht} \{dr^2 + r^2(d\theta^2 + \sin^2\theta \, d\phi^2)\}, \quad (85.8)$$

and now the model is fully specified, *kinematically*.

A very different theoretical approach to the narrowing of the RW model is *dynamical*, namely the application of gravitational theory. In GR this amounts to subjecting the metric to the field equations. In a pseudo-Newtonian theory it amounts to applying a Poisson or a pseudo-Poisson equation. We shall discuss these methods in Sections 88 and 89. But first we wish to describe a useful "model of the model," which helps us visualize the formalism.

Rubber Models, Red Shifts, and Horizons *86*

Suppressing one spatial dimension, and choosing the simplest topological spaceforms, we can illustrate the public spaces of the three types of RW metric (corresponding to $k = 1, 0, -1$) by a sphere, an infinite plane, and an infinite surface which is everywhere locally similar to a saddle (see Figure 29*). Since the public space generally expands or contracts, we shall think of the sphere as a rubber balloon which can be inflated or deflated at will, and of the other two surfaces as also made of rubber membrane and similarly subject to uniform expansion or contraction. The

*This figure, as well as Figures 31, 33, and 34, is reproduced, by permission of the publishers, from the author's article "Relativistic Cosmology" in *Phys. Today* **20**, 23 (November 1967).

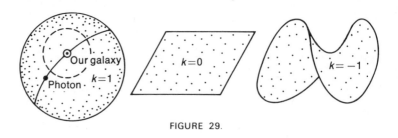

FIGURE 29.

motion of the balloon is perhaps the easiest to visualize, and we shall mainly talk about *it* as representative of all three cases. Actual distance on the membrane corresponds to $d\sigma$ in (85.1). The material points of the membrane represent the substratum, and a selected subset of them corresponds to galaxies. These are marked by dots on the membrane, in roughly uniform distribution. Since $\pm 1/R^2(t)$ is the curvature of public space in the cases $k = \pm 1$, $R(t)$ corresponds to the radius of our balloon, or to the radius of either of the two spheres fitting into the saddle (one above, one below). In all cases the distance between galaxies as a function of time is proportional to $R(t)$, and in the plane case this is the *only* interpretation of $R(t)$, since there is then no intrinsic normalization for it.

The assumption of absolute time throughout the Euclidean three-space in which the rubber models are embedded, and of no time dilation on the fundamental particles, is consistent with the definition of cosmic time: each fundamental clock indicates it, and equal readings of t correspond to equal local measurements, e.g., of curvature.

Now it can easily be shown formally that null geodesics in the RW metric correspond to ordinary geodesics in the public space; in any case, this is obvious from symmetry. Hence in the rubber model light propagates along geodesics, e.g., along great circles on the sphere and straight lines in the plane. For a light signal we have $ds^2 = 0$ whence $d\sigma/dt = c$ (see (85.1)). This means that in the rubber model photons crawl, like ideal bugs, at constant speed c over the membrane, and along geodesics.

All features of the RW metric are now accurately represented by the rubber model. As a first simple application let us establish the cosmological red shift formula

$$1 + z = R(t_0)/R(t_1), \qquad (86.1)$$

where $z = \Delta\lambda/\lambda$, λ being the wavelength of light emitted by a distant galaxy at cosmic time t_1 and received by us at t_0 with wavelength $\lambda + \Delta\lambda$. If two closely successive "bugs" crawl over a nonexpanding track, they arrive as far apart as when they left. But if the track expands—or contracts—proportionally to $R(t)$, then their distances apart at reception and emission will be in the ratio $R(t_0)/R(t_1)$. Replacing the bugs by two successive wavecrests, we get equation (86.1). Note that the cosmological red shift is really an *expansion* effect rather than a *velocity* effect.

The fact that the red shift in the light of all presently observed cosmic objects depends only on the "radius of the universe" at the time when that light was emitted, led Shklovsky to suggest (1967) an interesting explanation of the puzzling predominance of values $z \approx 2$ among quasars: it is merely necessary to assume that the radius of the universe was for a comparatively long time quasi-stationary at approximately one-third of its present value (see Figure 30, where we also introduce the obvious notation $R(t_0) = R_0$, $R(t_1) = R_1$). We shall see that such "dachshund" universes are dynamically possible in GR. It should be noted, incidentally, from this example, that the red shift is not necessarily a faithful distance indicator for cosmic objects. One quasar could be several times as far away as another and yet exhibit practically the same red shift.

We can of course derive (86.1) directly, though less illuminatingly, from the RW metric (85.7). Any light signal satisfies $ds^2 = 0$; hence two successive signals from a galaxy at coordinate ρ_1 to the origin-galaxy will satisfy

$$\int_0^{\rho_1} \frac{d\rho}{(1 - k\rho^2)^{1/2}} = \pm \int_{t_1}^{t_0} \frac{c\,dt}{R(t)} = \pm \int_{t_1+\Delta t_1}^{t_0+\Delta t_0} \frac{c\,dt}{R(t)}, \qquad (86.2)$$

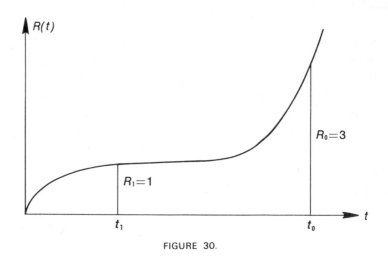

FIGURE 30.

which implies

$$\frac{\Delta t_0}{\Delta t_1} = \frac{R(t_0)}{R(t_1)} .$$ (86.3)

If we identify the two "signals" with successive wavecrests, formula (86.1) results.

As another application of the rubber model we briefly illustrate two of the *horizon* concepts used in cosmology.* For definiteness we consider a universe of positive curvature, though the argument applies equally in all three cases. In the first diagram of Figure 29 we have marked our own galaxy and a photon on its way to us along a geodesic. It can happen that "the balloon is blown up" at such a rate that this photon never gets to us. As Eddington has put it, light is then like a runner on an expanding track, with the winning post (us) receding forever from him. In such a case there will be two classes of photons on every geodesic through us: those that reach us at a finite time and those that do not. They are separated by the aggregate of photons that reach us exactly at $t = \infty$ —shown in the diagram as a dashed circle, but in the full model these photons con-

*Further details can be found in W. Rindler, *Monthly Notices of the Royal Astronomical Society* **116**, 662 (1956).

stitute a spherical light front converging on us. This light front is called our "*event horizon*," and its existence and motion depend on the form of $R(t)$. Events occurring beyond this horizon are forever beyond our possible powers of observation (that is, if we remain on our own galaxy). It is sometimes loosely said that at the horizon galaxies stream away from us at the speed of light, in violation of special relativity. But it must be remembered that special relativity need not apply on the cosmological scale and that we and our horizon are certainly not contained in a common inertial frame.

The same diagram can also be made to illustrate the concept of a "*particle horizon*." Suppose the very first photons emitted by our own galaxy at a big-bang creation event are still around, and now let the dashed circle in the diagram represent their present position. As this light front moves outward over more and more galaxies, these galaxies see us for the very first time. By symmetry, however, at the very cosmic instant when a galaxy sees *us* for the first time, we see *it* for the first time. Hence at any cosmic instant this light front, called the particle horizon, divides all galaxies into two classes relative to us: those already in our view and all others.

It is quite easy to obtain the relevant formulae from the RW metric. The equation of motion (ρ,t relation) of a photon emitted towards the origin-galaxy ("us") at coordinates ρ_1, t_1 is seen to be, as in (86.2),

$$\int_\rho^{\rho_1} \frac{d\rho}{(1 - k\rho^2)^{1/2}} = \int_{t_1}^t \frac{cdt}{R(t)} . \qquad (86.4)$$

If ρ never attains the value zero as $t \to \infty$, the photon was emitted at or beyond the event horizon. The condition for the existence of such a horizon is clearly that

$$\int_{t_1}^\infty \frac{dt}{R(t)} < \infty , \qquad (86.5)$$

and the coordinate ρ_1 of the horizon at any time t_1 is then given by

$$\Sigma(\rho_1) \equiv \int_0^{\rho_1} \frac{d\rho}{(1 - k\rho^2)^{1/2}} \equiv \left\{ \begin{array}{ll} \sin^{-1}\rho_1 & (k = 1) \\ \rho_1 & (k = 0) \\ \sinh^{-1}\rho_1 & (k = -1) \end{array} \right\} = \int_{t_1}^{\infty} \frac{c\,dt}{R(t)},^*$$

$$(86.6)$$

where $\Sigma(\rho_1)$ is defined by the first equation. For the steady state model (85.8), for example, we find that an event horizon exists at

$$\rho_1 = (c/H)\, e^{-Ht_1}. \tag{86.7}$$

Milne's model (84.7), on the other hand, has *no* event horizon.

A particle horizon will exist if there exists a finite coordinate ρ_1 such that no light front emitted by "us" in the past has yet swept over it. For this we need

$$\int_0^{t_1} \frac{dt}{R(t)} < \infty, \quad \text{or} \quad \int_{-\infty}^{t_1} \frac{dt}{R(t)} < \infty, \tag{86.8}$$

the latter in cases where the definition of $R(t)$ extends to negatively unbounded values of t. For a photon going *away* from us, (86.4) applies with a minus sign on one side; analogously to (86.6) we then find the equation of motion of the particle horizon:

$$\Sigma(\rho_1) = \int_0^{t_1} \frac{c\,dt}{R(t)}, \quad \text{or} \quad = \int_{-\infty}^{t_1} \frac{c\,dt}{R(t)}. \tag{86.9}$$

Some models have an event horizon only (e.g., the Bondi-Gold model), some have a particle horizon only, some have both (e.g., the "dachshund" models of GR), and some have neither (e.g., Milne's model).

87   Comparison with Observation

Astronomers observe galactic red shifts directly, and correlate them with galactic "magnitude," which, in astro-

---

*When $k = 1$, ρ in the RW metric is restricted to be less than unity, whereas the time integral here may exceed $\pi/2$. In this case we may have to go beyond the antipode, or even several times round the universe, before we come to the horizon. Though statements about horizons retain their *formal* correctness also in this case, their practical significance is subject to modification. (E.g., a photon from the event horizon *does* reach us at $t = \infty$, but it may have passed us several times previously during its trips round the universe.)

nomical usage, means apparent luminosity normalized in a certain way. For these and other observations to be compared with theory, it is necessary for theory to predict relations between observables. Several such relations will be derived in the present section.

First we digress briefly to discuss some concepts of "distance" in cosmology. As in Schwarzschild space (cf. Section 74), various "sensible" definitions of distance turn out to be inequivalent. One can, for example, define the *proper distance* between two galaxies P and Q: this would be measured by a chain of fundamental observers on the spatial geodesic between P and Q laying rulers end to end at *one* cosmic instant. The proper distance σ from the origin to a galaxy at coordinate ρ, at time t, is then given by

$$\sigma = \int_0^\rho d\sigma = R(t) \int_0^\rho \frac{d\rho}{(1 - k\rho^2)^{1/2}} = R(t)\, \Sigma(\rho), \quad (87.1)$$

(see (85.1), (85.6), and (86.6)). For example, the event horizon (86.7) of the Bondi-Gold model is at constant proper distance c/H from the observer. More strikingly, the "spherical boundary" in Milne's universe, which is at distance ct from each observer in his private Minkowskian coordinates, is always at infinite *proper* distance from him.

The practical methods of measuring distance in astronomy are, for example, by parallax, by radar, by apparent size, or by apparent luminosity. Only the last two will interest us here. The (uncorrected) *distance from apparent size*, S, of an object of cross-sectional area A, which is seen subtending a small solid angle $d\omega$, is *defined* by

$$S = (A/d\omega)^{1/2}, \quad (87.2)$$

i.e., by the *naive* formula which deliberately ignores any possible deviation of the space geometry from Euclidicity. And, similarly, the (uncorrected) *distance from apparent luminosity*, L, of an object of known intrinsic luminosity B and apparent luminosity b, is *defined* by

$$L = (B/b)^{1/2}, \quad (87.3)$$

again deliberately ignoring all possible deviations from the classical, static situation. (B is energy flux per unit area per unit time at unit distance from the source, and b is the same at the distance of the observer.*)

By (85.6), the area of a sphere at coordinate ρ_1 and time t_1 is evidently $4\pi R_1^2 \rho_1^2$, and its solid angle at the origin is 4π. Consequently, by isotropy and proportionality, the solid angle subtended at the origin by the spatial geodesics to a spherical area A at coordinate ρ_1 at time t_1 is $d\omega = A/R_1^2 \rho_1^2$; and this is the solid angle which A is seen to subtend when the light emitted at t_1 arrives at the origin.† Hence

$$S = R_1 \rho_1. \qquad (87.4)$$

Suppose, next, that a source of intrinsic luminosity B is placed at the *origin* and that its light is observed on a comoving sphere at radial coordinate $\tilde{\rho}_1$, at time t_0. If the sphere were stationary, the total flux of energy per unit time through it would be independent of its radius, and thus it would be $4\pi B$, since *near* the source Euclidean geometry holds with sufficient accuracy. But, because of the motion of the sphere, the energy gathered per photon is diminished by a Doppler factor ("Planck effect") and, moreover, the number of photons arriving per unit time is also diminished by a Doppler factor ("number effect"). From (86.1), therefore, the total flux through the sphere is $4\pi B R_1^2/R_0^2$, and that through a unit spherical area is

$$b = B R_1^2/\tilde{\rho}_1^2 R_0^4. \qquad (87.5)$$

By symmetry, the radial coordinate ρ_1 of the source relative to the observer (at the sphere) will equal that of the observer relative to the source, and thus we conclude from (87.5), by reference to (87.3) and (87.4), that

$$L = \rho_1 R_0^2/R_1 = S(1 + z)^2. \qquad (87.6)$$

We shall now combine this equation with (86.1) in order to relate z with L, or, equivalently, z with b. Introducing, *for the present section only*, the notation

*Astronomical "magnitude" m is related to b thus: $m = -2.5 \log_{10} b + $ constant.

†The balloon model should help to clarify that the solid angle is determined at the cosmic moment of *emission*.

$$R_0 = R, R_0 - R_1 = \Delta, \qquad (87.7)$$

we can cast (86.1) into the form

$$R_1 = R(1 + z)^{-1} = R(1 - z + z^2 - \cdots),$$

provided $|z| < 1$ (which, of course, is *not* true for some recent observations), whence

$$\Delta = R(z - z^2 + \cdots). \qquad (87.8)$$

Next, using (86.4) and the notation (86.5), we have, for a signal reaching the origin at t_0,

$$\Sigma(\rho_1) = \int_{t_1}^{t_0} \frac{c\,dt}{R(t)} = \int_{R_1}^{R_0} \frac{c\,dR}{R(t)\dot{R}(t)}, \qquad (87.9)$$

where a dot here and in the sequel denotes d/dt. Regarding the last integral as a function f of R_1, we can expand it as a Taylor series about R_0 with increment $-\Delta$,

$$\Sigma(\rho_1) = f(R) - f'(R)\Delta + \tfrac{1}{2}f''(R)\Delta^2 + \cdots,$$

and, remembering that the derivative of an integral with respect to its lower limit is minus the integrand, we find

$$\Sigma(\rho_1) = \frac{c}{R\dot{R}}\Delta + \frac{c}{2}\frac{R\ddot{R}/\dot{R} + \dot{R}}{R^2\dot{R}^2}\Delta^2 + \cdots, \qquad (87.10)$$

where, consistently with our convention (87.7), R and its derivatives are evaluated at t_0. Since $\rho = 1$ corresponds to the antipode of the origin in the positive-curvature model, it is clear that $\rho \ll 1$ for most observed galaxies even if $k = 0$ or -1; thus $\Sigma(\rho_1) = \rho_1 - \tfrac{1}{6}k\rho_1^3 + \cdots \approx \rho_1$ if we retain second powers only. Hence, substituting from (87.8) into (87.10), we find

$$\rho_1 = \frac{c}{\dot{R}}z + \frac{c}{2}\frac{R\ddot{R} - \dot{R}^2}{\dot{R}^3}z^2 + \cdots, \qquad (87.11)$$

which in turn can be substituted into the following variant of (87.6):

$$L = R\rho_1(1 + z);$$

this yields

$$\frac{L}{c} = \frac{R}{\dot{R}}z + \frac{1}{2}\frac{R^2\ddot{R} + R\dot{R}^2}{\dot{R}^3}z^2 + \cdots, \qquad (87.12)$$

or finally, on inversion,

$$z = \frac{\dot{R}}{R}\frac{L}{c} - \frac{1}{2}\left(\frac{\ddot{R}}{R} + \frac{\dot{R}^2}{R^2}\right)\frac{L^2}{c^2} + \cdots .^* \qquad (87.13)$$

All "sensible" distance definitions become equivalent in the limit of small distances; assuming also that for small distances the classical Doppler formula $z = u/c$ applies, we can read off from (87.13), as a check, Hubble's law $u = HL$ (cf. (85.3)) in first approximation. The usual way in which (87.13) is compared with (z, b) observations is to substitute $(B/b)^{1/2}$ for L and to *assume* that B is a certain constant for all galaxies, at all times, at least over the range of the observations.

Substituting from (87.6) into (87.12) we find the following series expansion for S, the distance from apparent size,

$$\frac{S}{c} = \frac{R}{\dot{R}}z + \frac{1}{2}\frac{R^2\ddot{R} - 3R\dot{R}^2}{\dot{R}^3}z^2 + \ldots, \qquad (87.14)$$

which, on inversion, yields

$$z = \frac{\dot{R}}{R}\frac{S}{c} - \frac{1}{2}\left(\frac{\ddot{R}}{R} - \frac{3\dot{R}^2}{R^2}\right)\frac{S^2}{c^2} + \ldots . \qquad (87.15)$$

When we replace S by $(A/d\omega)^{1/2}$, and assume that A is essentially constant (for galaxies, or clusters of galaxies), this formula can be compared with observational $(z, d\omega)$ relations, which, however, are less reliable than the usual (z, b) relations.

Formulae (87.13) or (87.15), which can be continued to any order, could in principle yield through observations the present values of $\dot{R}/R, \ddot{R}/R, \ldots$, and of k/R^2 (this appears in the third-order terms). In fact, however, the practical difficulties are so great that only Hubble's constant, $\dot{R}/R$, is

---

*To gain some idea of the convergence of this (and similar) series, we can calculate the exact values of the terms in (87.13) for some specific models, e.g., (i) $R(t) = \exp(Ht), k = 0$; (ii) $R(t) = t, k = 0$. The results for a red shift $z = 0.25$, and to one more term than is shown in (87.13), are as follows:

(i) $0.25 = 0.312 - 0.097 + 0.061 + \cdots$,
(ii) $0.25 = 0.278 - 0.039 + 0.014 + \cdots$.

For smaller z, of course, the convergence improves.

known with any certainty; it is not even known for sure whether $\ddot{R}$ is positive or negative. A restriction to bear in mind is that for very distant objects ($z > 1$) the above series expansions become invalid, and observations must be compared with particular models in nonapproximate (integral) form.

Another empirical relation obtained by the astronomers (both optical and radio) is the number of galaxies, per unit solid angle of sky, whose red shift is less than some given z. Such "nebular counts" evidently probe the galactic distribution radially. We shall assume that $R(t)$ is a monotonically increasing function so that larger z corresponds to larger distance (cf. (86.1) and Figure 30). Consider a cone of solid angle ω issuing from the origin of public space, and terminating at radial coordinate ρ_1. As we saw earlier in this section, the area which this cone cuts from a sphere at coordinate ρ at the "present" time t_0 is $\omega R^2 \rho^2$, and hence the present proper volume of the cone is given by

$$V = \omega R^3 \int_0^{\rho_1} \rho^2 \frac{d\rho}{(1 - k\rho^2)^{1/2}}$$

$$= \omega R^3 \int_0^{\rho_1} \rho^2 (1 + \tfrac{1}{2} k\rho^2 + \cdots) d\rho.$$

Multiplying V by the present particle density n_0, which can be estimated locally, we obtain the total number N of galaxies presently in the cone—and this, of course, is the number in it independently of time *if* there is local conservation:

$$N = n_0 V = n_0 \omega R^3 (\tfrac{1}{3} \rho_1^3 + \tfrac{1}{10} k \rho_1^5 + \ldots). \quad (87.16)$$

The coordinate ρ_1 corresponding to a galaxy now observed with red shift z was obtained in (87.11). Substituting this into (87.16) gives us the required formula for the number N of galaxies seen in a solid angle ω of sky at red shift less than z:

$$N = n_0 \omega c^3 \left\{ \frac{R^3}{\dot{R}^3} \frac{z^3}{3} + \left(\frac{\ddot{R} R^4}{\dot{R}^5} - \frac{R^3}{\dot{R}^3} \right) \frac{z^4}{2} + \cdots \right\}. \quad (87.17)$$

The corresponding formula for the steady state theory (where local particle conservation is violated) is easily found to be*

$$N = n_0 \omega c^3 H^{-3} \int_0^z z^2 (1 + z)^{-3} dz$$

$$= n_0 \omega c^3 H^{-3} (\tfrac{1}{3} z^3 - \tfrac{3}{4} z^4 + \cdots). \qquad (87.18)$$

Radio-astronomical number counts have long been in apparent conflict with this result.

88 *Cosmic Dynamics According to Pseudo-Newtonian Theory*

We now turn to the dynamical study of the RW model. Since the "lumpiness" of the material contents of the actual universe is not very amenable to mathematical treatment, one generally adopts the theoretical device of grinding these contents into dust and redistributing the dust homogeneously. The assumption is that such a "smoothed out" dust universe, and another in which the same dust is gathered into lumps, will, on the whole, behave identically under their own gravitation. It will be remembered (cf. Section 60) that "dust" refers technically to a continuous medium that has density but no internal stress, not even pressure. The proper motions of the galaxies, and the possible intergalactic presence of undetected neutrinos, magnetic fields, cosmic rays, quanta (e.g. gravitons), hydrogen, etc., are not usually considered to add a significant pressure. (As we shall see, the theoretical effect of pressure is in any case only through the mass-equivalent of its energy, which *slows* expansion, rather than through any direct elastic action.) Hence the idealization by dust would

---

*Let $R(t) = e^{Ht}$, $k = 0$, and $t_0 = 0$. Then, from (87.9) and (86.1), the coordinate ρ, time of emission t, and red shift z are related by $(H/c)\rho = e^{-Ht} - 1 = z$, (I). The number of galaxies per unit proper volume is constant, say n_0. Hence, the number in a solid angle ω between coordinates ρ and $\rho + d\rho$ at emission time t is $n_0 \omega e^{3Ht} \rho^2 d\rho$. From this, and (I), (87.18) follows at once.

seem to be justified, except in the very early stages of a universe that was much denser then.

In order to apply Newtonian gravitational theory to the universe as a whole, it is only necessary to give up the idea of absolute space and substitute for it that of local inertial frames (one set determined by each fundamental observer), in which Newtonian theory holds in its local form, i.e., as Poisson's equation. No modification of that equation is necessary. It is also possible to retain the absoluteness of time, the flatness both of public space and of each observer's extended rigid rest frame, and the local applicability of the Galilean transformation. Light can be assumed to propagate rectilinearly in public space, with constant local velocity c relative to the fundamental observers; this is equivalent to classical propagation in an ether that partakes of the expansion of the universe. All this was pointed out in essence by Milne and McCrea in 1934.

It is instructive to study the resulting "pseudo-Newtonian" theory *before* taking up general-relativistic cosmology, because it leads to essentially the same equations and to some identical models; and since we understand the Newtonian equations and models intuitively, they help us understand the GR models and equations, which arise in a much more abstract way. With a little hindsight we can even see why local Newtonian theory *should* give models which, even in the large, coincide with GR models: In the limit of slow motions and weak fields, GR reduces to Newtonian theory; but locally the cosmic fields *are* weak and the cosmic motions *are* slow, hence locally Newton's and Einstein's cosmic dynamics are equivalent; and finally, in a homogeneous universe local knowledge *is* global knowledge.

We now take as our starting point the ubiquitous RW model (with $k = 0$), although it is not hard to arrive at its main features quickly from scratch, on the basis of the pseudo-Newtonian assumptions.* We assume Poisson's

*See, for example, H. Bondi, "Cosmology," Chapter IX, Cambridge University Press, 1961. This is an extremely readable reference on all aspects of cosmology.

equation

$$\nabla^2 \phi = 4\pi G\rho, \qquad (88.1)$$

with the density ρ a function of absolute time but not of position. Since we suppose spherical symmetry about any fundamental observer P, and since ϕ cannot locally become infinite in a continuous medium, we seek (as in Section 82) a solution of the form $\phi = a + br + cr^2 + dr^3 + \cdots$, where r is the (Newtonian) distance from P, in P's local inertial frame. We find that this solution is unique, apart from an arbitrary additive constant, namely

$$\phi = \tfrac{2}{3}\pi G\rho r^2. \qquad (88.2)$$

For any radial potential the Newtonian equations of motion reduce to $\ddot{r} = -d\phi/dr$, and so, in our case,

$$\ddot{r} = -\tfrac{4}{3}\pi G\rho r = -M'G/r^2, \qquad (88.3)$$

where M' is the mass contained in a sphere of radius r. (Thus a particle is attracted to the center of any sphere through itself as though the mass of that sphere were concentrated at its center and none were outside.) If r refers to the position of a nearby galaxy Q relative to P, then $M' =$ constant (in time), since galaxies neither enter nor leave this sphere as public space expands. (This is the relevant version of the Newtonian "equation of continuity.") Now the distance r between a pair of galaxies such as P and Q is a multiple of $R(t)$, say $hR(t)$; substituting this into (88.3) yields the following differential equation for $R(t)$:

$$\ddot{R} = -MG/R^2, \qquad (88.4)$$

where $M = M'/h^3$ is the mass inside a sphere of radius $R(t)$. From now on we again write, where convenient, $R, \dot{R}, \ddot{R}$, etc., for the *general* values of these functions, *not* specialized by $t = t_0$ as in Section 87.)

In order to facilitate later comparison with the relativistic models, we can generalize the theory one step further by assuming a modified Poisson equation (82.5). As we have seen in (82.6), this leads to an additional r^2 term in ϕ, which, however, is arbitrary unless $A = 0$. We therefore prefer the more restrictive form (82.4), whose only regular spherically symmetric solution is

$$\phi = \tfrac{2}{3}\pi G \rho r^2 - \tfrac{1}{6}c^2 \Lambda r^2, \qquad (88.5)$$

apart from an additive constant. If we now proceed as from (88.2) to (88.4), we obtain, instead of (88.4),

$$\ddot{R} = -GM/R^2 + c^2 \Lambda R/3.* \qquad (88.6)$$

Multiplying this differential equation by $2\dot{R}$, we immediately find a first integral,

$$\dot{R}^2 = \frac{C}{R} + \frac{\Lambda c^2 R^2}{3} - \tilde{k}c^2, \qquad (88.7)$$

where

$$C = 2GM = \tfrac{8}{3}\pi G\rho R^3, \qquad (88.8)$$

and $-\tilde{k}c^2$ is simply a constant of integration, written in this form for later convenience. Since R is not intrinsically normalized (remember, $k = 0$) we can now impose a normalization on it, at least in the cases where $\tilde{k} \neq 0$: we choose the scale of R so that

$$\tilde{k} = \pm 1 \text{ or } 0. \qquad (88.9)$$

In fact, $\tilde{k}$ is an indicator of energy. *If* $\Lambda = 0$, we see from (88.7) that two galaxies reach infinite separation with finite or zero relative velocity according as $\tilde{k} = -1$ or 0; if $\tilde{k} = +1$, that separation cannot become infinite, and the universe falls back on itself. Thus, since the Λ term must be negligible locally, $\tilde{k} = \pm 1$ distinguishes between galaxies having locally more or less than the "escape" velocity.

We shall presently derive an equation formally identical with (88.7) on the basis of GR; accordingly we postpone the further discussion of the solutions of this equation until then.

Cosmic Dynamics According to General Relativity   89

The dynamics of general relativity are expressed in Einstein's field equations, which for cosmological purposes we

---

*One can further generalize this equation by including the effect of possible pressure: see the remark after equation (89.13) below.

shall take in their general form (79.10), i.e., *with* the so-called cosmological term $\Lambda g^{\mu\nu}$. Various arguments have at times been given *against* the inclusion of this term: (i) that it was only an afterthought of Einstein's (but: better discovered late than never); (ii) that Einstein himself eventually rejected it (but: authority is no substitute for scientific argument); (iii) that with it the well-established theory of SR is not a special case of GR (but: locally the Λ term is totally unobservable); (iv) that it is *ad hoc* (but: from the formal point of view it belongs to the field equations, much like an additive constant belongs to an indefinite integral); (v) that similar modifications could be made to Poisson's equation in gravity and Maxwell's equations in electrodynamics (but: locally the Λ term is ignored, and cosmologically Poisson's and Maxwell's equations may well need similar modification); (vi) that it represents a space expansion *uncaused* by matter (but: in GR, matter and space are intimately related by the field equations, and no mechanical picture is correct); (vii) that one should never envisage a more complicated law until a simpler one proves untenable (but: in cosmology—especially in the RW case—the technical complication is trivial, and there is the possibility of finding the actual value of Λ empirically, without prejudice).*

These general field equations, then, must be satisfied jointly by the metric of spacetime and by the matter-tensor —relative to this metric—of the contents of spacetime. In cosmology we are fortunate to be able to restrict the metric considerably by symmetry arguments alone. In fact, as we have seen, the RW metric applicable to all homogeneous and isotropic model universes contains but *two* free elements: the expansion function (or "radius of the universe") $R(t)$, and the curvature index k. The field equations will be seen to impose restrictions on these two elements.

As we explained in the last section, it is usual to treat the cosmic matter as "dust." The matter tensor of dust is given

---

*In this connection we may quote Eddington's mystical argument *for* the Λ term (Mathematical Theory, page 154): "An electron could never decide how large it ought to be unless there existed some length independent of itself for it to compare itself with."

by (60.2), i.e., $M^{\mu\nu} = \rho_0 \, U^\mu \, U^\nu$, where ρ_0 is the proper density and U^μ is the four-velocity $dx^\mu/d\tau$ of the dust. In the RW model the dust is at rest everywhere with respect to the local fundamental observer, and so we write ρ for ρ_0; U^μ is the velocity of the substratum, whence $U^\mu = (0, 0, 0, 1)$ if we take

$$(x^1, x^2, x^3, x^4) = (r, \theta, \phi, t). \tag{89.1}$$

(We shall use the form (85.5) of the RW metric.) Consequently the only nonvanishing component of $M^{\mu\nu}$ is $M^{44} = \rho$, which implies

$$M_{\mu\nu} = \mathrm{diag}(0, 0, 0, c^4\rho). \tag{89.2}$$

The main labor in applying the field equations (79.10), which we shall use in their "covariant" form (i.e., with subscripts rather than superscripts), lies in the computation of the "Einstein tensor" components

$$G_{\mu\nu} = R_{\mu\nu} - \tfrac{1}{2} Rg_{\mu\nu} + \Lambda g_{\mu\nu}.* \tag{89.3}$$

However, for various standard forms of the metric these are listed in the literature.† For the metric (85.5) one finds

$$G_{11}/g_{11} = G_{22}/g_{22} = G_{33}/g_{33} = -\frac{2\ddot{R}}{Rc^2} - \frac{\dot{R}^2}{R^2c^2} - \frac{k}{R^2} + \Lambda, \tag{89.4}$$

$$G_{44}/g_{44} = -\frac{3\dot{R}^2}{R^2c^2} - \frac{3k}{R^2} + \Lambda, \tag{89.5}$$

and $G_{\mu\nu} = 0$ when $\mu \neq \nu$. Substituting (89.4), (89.5) and (89.2) into the field equations

$$G_{\mu\nu} = -(8\pi G/c^4) M_{\mu\nu}, \tag{89.6}$$

we obtain the following two conditions:

$$\frac{2\ddot{R}}{Rc^2} + \frac{\dot{R}^2}{R^2c^2} + \frac{k}{R^2} - \Lambda = 0, (= -8\pi Gp/c^4), \tag{89.7}$$

*The R in this formula must not be confused with the expansion factor R. Unfortunately the traditional notations clash here.

†See, for example, R. C. Tolman, "Relativity, Thermodynamics, and Cosmology," formulae (98.6), Oxford University Press, 1934. Tolman's "mixed" components $8\pi T_1^1$, $8\pi T_2^2$, etc., here correspond to G_{11}/g_{11}, G_{22}/g_{22} etc. On the following pages Tolman reproduces Dingle's expressions for the T_ν^μ of a very general line element, and it is worth remembering where these can be found.

$$\frac{\dot{R}^2}{R^2 c^2} + \frac{k}{R^2} - \frac{\Lambda}{3} = \frac{8\pi G\rho}{3c^2}. \qquad (89.8)$$

In (89.7) we have parenthetically exhibited—without proof —a pressure term on the right-hand side instead of zero, to indicate the only modification that equations (89.7) and (89.8) would suffer if a pressure p were present.

Multiplying the left-hand side of (89.8) by R^3, and differentiating, we get $\dot{R}R^2$ times the left-hand side of equation (89.7), and thus zero. Consequently

$$\frac{8}{3}\pi G\rho R^3 = C = \text{constant}. \qquad (89.9)$$

(Cf. equation (88.8).) This evidently expresses the constancy of the mass contained in a *small* comoving sphere of radius hR, say. (For large spheres, volumes may be non-Euclidean, frames noninertial, and kinetic energy contributing to mass, all of which complicates the interpretation.) Hence (89.9) is the relativistic equation of continuity, and it should be noted how in GR it is a corollary of the field equations rather than a separate assumption. Substituting (89.9) into (89.8) yields an equation formally identical with the pseudo-Newtonian equation (88.7):

$$\dot{R}^2 = \frac{C}{R} + \frac{\Lambda c^2 R^2}{3} - kc^2. \qquad (89.10)$$

Equations (89.7) and (89.8), then, imply (89.9) and (89.10). Conversely, (89.9) and (89.10) imply (89.8), obviously, and also (89.7) *unless* $\dot{R} = 0$ (for the result of differentiating (89.10) is equivalent to $\dot{R}$ times (89.7)). Equation (89.10) is known as *Friedmann's differential equation*, after the first author who deliberately investigated expanding universes (1922). Together with (89.9) it essentially represents the GR restrictions on the "dust-filled" RW model. We discuss its solutions in the next section.

In GR the curvature index k replaces the "energy index" $\tilde{k}$. In all Newtonian models we assumed *flat* public space ($k = 0$), since by no stretch of the Newtonian imagination could we interpret $\tilde{k}$ in (88.7) as related to curvature. Hence only those GR models which have $k = 0$ can have *exact*

Newtonian analogs (choosing $\tilde{k}$ = 0). GR models with $k = \pm 1$, though locally similar to their Newtonian counterparts with $\tilde{k} = \pm 1$, i.e., having the same functional form of $R(t)$, have *curved* public space. This comparison shows that an excess of the local kinetic energy over the escape energy produces negative curvature in GR, whereas a deficit produces positive curvature.

Another interesting result of the Newtonian analogy is the *interpretation* of the relativistic effect of a possible pressure. The difference of equations (89.7) and (89.8) (without the pressure term) is equivalent to (88.6), in which the right-hand side is essentially the *force*, producing the *acceleration* on the left. The two force terms on the right of (88.6) have already been interpreted. The presence of the relativistic pressure term would correspond to a *third* force term

$$-4\pi GpR/c^2 \qquad (89.11)$$

in (88.6), acting in the same direction as gravity. Thus pressure *slows* expansion, and it apparently does so because its mass equivalent increases the effective density. But why does pressure *qua* pressure have no effect? The explanation is that a uniform pressure never causes motion; only a pressure *gradient* does—at least in a given inertial frame. Still, why cannot pressure push the inertial frames apart, just as gravity pulls them together? The answer, of course, is that gravity is unique among forces in this property. Hence pressure must be considered locally in a single inertial frame, and there, indeed, homogeneous pressure has no effect.

Our method of getting equation (89.9) in the *absence* of pressure, yields the equation

$$\frac{d}{dt}\left(\frac{8\pi G\rho R^3}{3c^2}\right) = -\frac{8\pi Gp\dot{R}R^2}{c^4} \qquad (89.12)$$

in the presence of pressure. Letting V stand for the volume $\frac{4}{3}\pi(hR)^3$ of a small comoving sphere, we can write this last equation in the form

$$d(c^2\rho V) = -pdV, \qquad (89.13)$$

whose interpretation is clear: as the small sphere expands, the pressure inside does work pdV on the matter outside, and thus energy is lost inside; $c^2\rho$ stands for the total effective energy density. *Because* of this interpretation we can posit (89.13) *a priori* simply on the basis of "$E = mc^2$" and use it, working backwards, to include a pressure term in the pseudo-Newtonian theory, which then becomes formally identical with the relativistic theory even in the presence of pressure.

McCrea has suggested an ingenious dynamics for the steady state theory, based on the GR equations (!) (89.7) and (89.8) *with* the pressure term. He postulates $\Lambda = 0$ and, of course, $k = 0$, $\rho = $ constant, *and* $p = $ constant. Equations (89.7) and (89.8) then imply

$$R = \exp(Ht), \quad H = (\tfrac{8}{3}\pi G\rho)^{1/2}, \quad p = -c^2\rho. \quad (89.14)$$

This vast negative pressure remains unexplained. Still, whereas a positive pressure in an expanding universe *does* work, a negative pressure *absorbs* work. The energy so absorbed by a sphere of fixed proper radius is continually converted into mass and escapes with the expanding universe, leading to local conservation of energy! The negative pressure is equivalent to negative mass, thereby producing the gravitational repulsion that drives the expansion. Not only is the idea in itself attractive, but even the numbers come out more or less right: if we take the value $H = 100$ km/sec/Mpc ($\approx 3 \times 10^{-18}$ cm/sec/cm), equation (89.14) (ii) gives a density $\rho = 1.6 \times 10^{-29}$ gm/cm^3, which is not too far from that observed in the actual universe.

These numbers are encouraging in a wider context: they show that, with the primitive assumptions $k = \Lambda = 0$, equation (89.8) is roughly satisfied by the actual universe, and that our dynamical approach, therefore, is probably not entirely wrong. We see further such encouragement in the fact that a model which has been *uniformly* expanding since creation ($R \propto t$, as in Milne's model—again the most primitive case) would now be at age $t = R/\dot{R} = 1/H$. And this comes to $\sim 10^{10}$ years, again not *too* far from empirical estimates.

The Friedmann Models   *90*

We shall now discuss the solutions of Friedmann's differential equation (89.10), with a view to obtaining and classifying *all* GR "dust" universes that are isotropic and homogeneous. It will be convenient to employ units in terms of which $c = 1$, so that Friedmann's equation reads

$$\dot{R}^2 = \frac{C}{R} + \frac{\Lambda R^2}{3} - k = F(R), \quad \left(C = \frac{8}{3}\pi G\rho R^3\right). \quad (90.1)$$

The symbol $F(R)$ is simply an abbreviation for the three terms preceding it; the parenthesis is a repeat of equation (89.9), whose sole function is to determine ρ once R is found from the differential equation. We can *formally* write down the solution at once by quadrature,

$$t = \int \frac{dR}{\sqrt{F}}, \quad (90.2)$$

and we could proceed to the full solution by using elliptic functions. That solution depends on the three parameters C, Λ, k, and also on an initial value of $R(t)$. In special cases the solution can be obtained in terms of elementary functions, as we shall see. In the general case it will be enough for us, and more instructive, to give a qualitative rather than an exact analysis. We preface our discussion with two general remarks:

(i) Since $R = 0$ is a singularity of the Friedmann equation, no regular solution $R = R(t)$ can pass *through* $R = 0$. Regular solutions are therefore entirely positive or entirely negative. Moreover, the solutions occur in matching pairs $\pm R(t)$: this is because, for physical reasons, we must insist on $\rho \geq 0$, which implies that the sign of C must be chosen to be the same as that of R—but then equation (90.1) is insensitive to the change $R \rightarrow -R$, and this proves our assertion. Since only R^2 occurs in the RW metric, we therefore exclude no solutions by insisting, as we shall, that $C \geq 0$ and $R \geq 0$.

(ii) Equation (90.1) also enjoys invariance under either of the changes $t \rightarrow -t$ or $t \rightarrow t +$ constant. The first implies that to every solution $R(t)$ there corresponds a "time-reversed" solution $R(-t)$ (e.g., to every expanding universe there corresponds a collapsing one); and the second implies that each solution $R(t)$ represents a whole set of solutions $R(t +$ constant), which simply expresses the "homogeneity of time," i.e., the fact that the zero-point of time is physically irrelevant. Bearing these properties in mind, we shall so normalize our solutions that of the pair $R(\pm t)$ we exhibit the expanding one in preference to the collapsing one, and of the set $R(t +$ constant) we exhibit, if possible, that member which has $R = 0$ at $t = 0$.

The Static Models. It is well to clear out of the way the static models first, i.e., those which have $\dot{R} \equiv 0$. As we remarked after (89.10), this is the exceptional case in which Friedmann's equation is insufficient and both its parent equations (89.7) and (89.8) must be satisfied separately. These equations permit $\dot{R} \equiv 0$ provided

$$k/R^2 = \Lambda = 4\pi G\rho, \quad (\sim 10^{-57}\,\mathrm{cm}^{-2}). \qquad (90.3)$$

(In parenthesis we give the value of $4\pi G\rho$ corresponding to $\rho = 10^{-30}\,\mathrm{gm/cm^3}$, which illustrates the typical smallness of Λ.) Equations (90.3) of course imply $\rho = $ constant, and for a physically meaningful solution we need $\rho > 0$, and thus $k = +1$. This gives the so-called *Einstein universe*, the very first GR model to be proposed (by Einstein, in 1917). To its inventor at that time it had every desirable feature. As a realistic model, however, it had to be abandoned with the discovery of the expansion of the universe.

The only other possibility of satisfying (90.3)—less physical but still acceptable as a limiting case—is $k = \Lambda = \rho = 0$, $R = $ any constant. The transformation $Rr \rightarrow r$ in the RW metric then leads to a standard metric for Minkowski space, and the model consequently represents static "test" dust ($\rho = 0$) homogeneously filling an inertial frame.

The Empty Models. Models with zero density, like Milne's or the above, are unrealistic, but they provide instructive and transparent examples of various geometric possibilities. We therefore classify them next. Setting $C = 0$ reduces (90.2) to the elementary form

$$t = \int (\tfrac{1}{3}\Lambda R^2 - k)^{-1/2} \, dR, \qquad (90.4)$$

which has the following solutions (apart from (a)—which we obtained above):

(a) $\Lambda = 0$, $k = 0$, R = arbitrary constant
(b) $\Lambda = 0$, $k = -1$, $R = t$
(c) $\Lambda > 0$, $k = 0$, $R = \exp \alpha t$
(d) $\Lambda > 0$, $k = 1$, $R = \alpha^{-1} \cosh \alpha t$ $\left.\right\}$ $\alpha = (\tfrac{1}{3}\Lambda)^{1/2}$
(e) $\Lambda > 0$, $k = -1$, $R = \alpha^{-1} \sinh \alpha t$
(f) $\Lambda < 0$, $k = -1$, $R = \beta^{-1} \sin \beta t$, $\beta = (-\tfrac{1}{3}\Lambda)^{1/2}$.

Models (a) and (b) we already know: (a) is the empty static model, and (b) is Milne's model; these have identical space-time backgrounds (M_4) but different substrata (i.e., motion patterns). The same is true also of the three models (c), (d) and (e): these all have the de Sitter space S_4^- (see Section 80) for their spacetime background.* This is *a priori* clear, since, as we saw in Section 80, S_4^- is the *unique* empty spacetime satisfying Einstein's modified field equations with $\Lambda > 0$ and isotropic about every point; and each of the three models in question has these properties. (It is for this reason that they are sometimes confusingly referred to as "static" models.) Of course, their substrata differ. Model (e), for example, is the analog of Milne's model in S_4^- (which is locally almost indistinguishable from M_4): in S_4^- it is an expanding ball of dust, bounded by a spherical light front, which, however, moves ever faster because of the Λ repulsion. The analogy with Milne's model (84.7) is clear from the fact that the RW metric of (e) is practically identical with (84.7) for small t. Model (f), incidentally, and by the same reasoning, is the analog of Milne's model in S_4^+: slowed by a Λ *attraction*, this dust ball finally stops expanding and collapses again. Like Milne's model, both

---

*Such a situation, however, can *only* arise with empty models; nonempty models with different substrata also have different spacetimes.

(e) and (f) are evidently "incomplete." And again, like Milne's model, (e) and (f) must be filled with *point* particles to permit the "dust ball" interpretation.

Model (d) at $t = 0$ is analogous to the static model in M_4; but then the Λ repulsion causes expansion to set in. For $t < 0$ the behavior of the model is the temporal mirror-image of its behavior thereafter. Like its counterpart in M_4, (d) is easily seen to be complete.

Model (c) is the well-known *de Sitter universe*. Kinematically it is identical with the steady state universe (85.8). (Thus, for example, it has an event horizon.) Though unrealistic in GR because of its emptiness, it constitutes a kind of limit to which *all* indefinitely expanding models with $\Lambda \neq 0$ must tend. For indefinite expansion ($R \rightarrow \infty$) in a general model causes the Λ term ultimately to predominate on the right-hand side of equation (90.1), which implies (i) $\Lambda > 0$, and (ii) $R \sim \exp{(\frac{1}{3}\Lambda)^{1/2} t}$ (a multiplicative constant can be absorbed by a translation of t); the curvature k/R^2 of the model and its density $3C/8\pi GR^3$ become ultimately small, and thus even $k = 0$ and $\rho = 0$ provide a good approximation *locally*. This proves our assertion. For example, *all* indefinitely expanding models with $\Lambda \neq 0$ consequently possess an event horizon.

There exists an interesting representation* of the three models (c), (d) and (e). Each of these corresponds (with its θ and ϕ dimensions suppressed) to all or part of a hyperboloid of revolution H with equation $X^2 + Y^2 - T^2 = a^2$ and metric $dT^2 - dX^2 - dY^2$ (see Section 80), whose two families of straight-line generators represent light paths. The substratum of (d) covers all of H, being represented by the meridians (the intersections of H with planes through the T-axis). The substratum of (e) is represented by the intersections of H with planes through the Y-axis, restricted by $T \geq 0$, $Y > 0$, and $-a < X/T < a$. The de Sitter model (c) corresponds to just half of H, namely that part which lies above the asymptotic plane

*See H. P. Robertson, *Rev. Mod. Phys.* **5**, 62 (1933), especially Note D.

$T + Y = 0$; its substratum is represented by the inter-sections of H with planes through the line $T + Y = 0 = X$; de Sitter cosmic time equals $\log (T + Y)$ in H, and de Sitter proper distance from the origin equals X. The horizon of the origin-galaxy $X \equiv 0$ is at $X = \pm a$ for all three models. Since in the cases (c) and (e) not *all* of H is covered by the respective substrata, it is evident that these two models are incomplete. For we can easily specify events on H, *outside* the substrata, from which light can be sent *into* the sub-strata.

Nonempty Models with $\Lambda = 0$. The substitution of $\Lambda = 0$ and a finite value for C into (90.1) leaves us with essentially three types of equation, depending on the choice of k. In each case a solution in terms of elementary func-tions is possible. When $k = 0$ this is very simple:

$$R = (\tfrac{9}{4}C)^{1/3} t^{2/3}, \quad (k = 0).$$

The corresponding model is called the *Einstein-deSitter universe*. The other two possibilities are

$$\left. \begin{array}{l} t = C[\sin^{-1} \sqrt{X} - \sqrt{(X - X^2)}], \quad (k = 1) \\ t = C[\sqrt{(X + X^2)} - \sinh^{-1} \sqrt{X}], \quad (k = -1) \end{array} \right\} X = R/C.$$

The first of these can be re-expressed in the form

$$R = \tfrac{1}{2}C(1 - \cos \psi), \quad t = \tfrac{1}{2}C(\psi - \sin \psi),$$

and is thus recognized as a cycloid; it is sometimes called the *Friedmann-Einstein universe*. The qualitative behavior of the second is most easily read off from the differential equation directly: $\dot{R}$ decreases from infinity and approaches unity. The graphs of all three models are shown in Figure 31. Note that for small R the C term *always* dominates the right-hand side of (90.1), whence *all* nonempty "big-bang" models share the behavior $R \sim (\tfrac{9}{4}C)^{1/3} t^{2/3}$ at $t = 0$. In particular, therefore, it can be seen that they all have a particle horizon.

Nonempty Models with $\Lambda \neq 0$. If we allow arbitrary values of Λ, the variety of possible models increases sub-stantially. We again assume $C \neq 0$. A qualitative solution

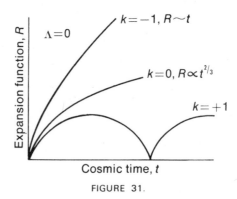

$k=-1, R \sim t$

$\Lambda = 0$

$k=0, R \propto t^{2/3}$

$k=+1$

Expansion function, R

Cosmic time, t

FIGURE 31.

of Friedmann's equation can most easily be obtained by the device of plotting the locus of $\dot{R}^2 = F(R) = 0$ in a (Λ, R) diagram (see Figure 32). This locus has one of two characteristic shapes according as $k = 1$ or not. In both cases it begins by peeling off the negative Λ axis and ends by approaching the R axis asymptotically; but only in the first case does it *cross* the R axis and attain a maximum at

$$R = \frac{3C}{2}, \quad \Lambda = \Lambda_E = \frac{4}{9C^2}. \quad (90.5)$$

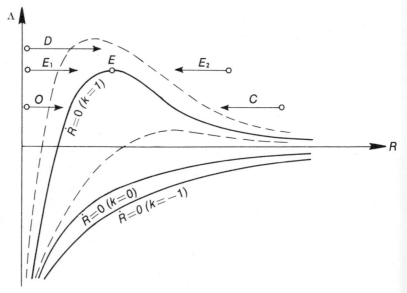

FIGURE 32.

This value of Λ is, in fact, the Λ of the Einstein universe. The reader may usefully imagine contour lines of $\dot{R}^2 =$ constant > 0 *above* the relevant loci of $\dot{R}^2 = 0$ (stippled lines in the diagram); *below*, they correspond to $\dot{R}^2 < 0$ and are therefore unphysical.

Now each Friedmann model is characterized by $\Lambda =$ constant. We therefore obtain solutions by choosing any physically possible starting point in the diagram, and proceeding horizontally. The contour lines tell us $\dot{R}$ and thus the slope of the solution-curve. For example, if we start at $R = 0$ and $\Lambda > \Lambda_E$ (for a "$k = 1$" model), $\dot{R}$ decreases at first from infinity and then increases again: thus we get a "dachshund" universe (D), more usually called a *Lemaître universe*; the same general behavior results from the assumptions $k = 0$ or -1 and $\Lambda > 0$. By choosing Λ close enough to Λ_E in the case $k = 1$, the "body of the dog" can be made arbitrarily long, and thus the universe arbitrarily old with given present conditions.

If we start at $R = 0$ and $\Lambda < \Lambda_E$ (when $k = 1$), $\dot{R}$ decreases to zero, and we get half of an oscillating universe before we hit the locus $\dot{R}^2 = 0$; the other half corresponds to going back along the same line (O) in the (Λ, R) diagram. (*Any* universe with two zeros of R is called "oscillating," even though the mathematics does not imply a repetition of the cycle: $R = 0$, after all, is a singularity. It may be noted that *every* oscillating universe is time-symmetric: for, given any value of R, say R_{max}, and C, k, Λ, the solution is unique and reversible.) If we start at the same level of Λ $(< \Lambda_E)$ but on the other side of the "hump" (i.e., with large R), and go to the left, $\dot{R}$ decreases to zero, and we get half of a "catenary" universe (C); the other half corresponds to going back along the same line in the (Λ, R) diagram. Again there is time-symmetry. Thus for the *same C, k, Λ* we can get two *different* types of model, depending on an initial value of R (*if* $k = 1$ and $0 < \Lambda < \Lambda_E$).

Corresponding to $k = 1$ and $\Lambda = \Lambda_E$ there are *three* different models: one is the static Einstein universe (E); the other two *approach* the Einstein state asymptotically from below (E_1) or from above (E_2). These, as well as all other possibilities, are shown schematically in Figure 33, in which the various curves are labeled according to the signs of Λ and k, in this order. (The dashed curve, contrary to

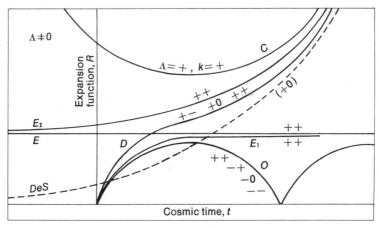

FIGURE 33.

our premise $C \neq 0$, represents the empty de Sitter universe: it is included as the "asymptote" to all expanding models.) It can be seen from both Figures 32 and 33 that the Einstein universe is unstable: a slight perturbation will set it on the course E_1 (in collapsing form), or on the course E_2 (expanding). The physical reason for this instability is clear: a slight contraction causes the density ρ to increase, whereas the "permanent" density $-\Lambda/4\pi G$ stays the same, which ends their balance and results in further contraction. The opposite perturbation for the same reason leads to further expansion. In fact, the expanding universe E_2 is sometimes regarded as the result of a disturbed Einstein universe, and on this interpretation it is called the *Eddington-Lemaître universe*; it too has the property of allowing an indefinitely large past age with given present conditions.

As we have seen, all models with $C = 0$ or with $\Lambda = 0$ allow representation by elementary functions. The same is true of models with $k = 0$, and for completeness we give the results:

$$R^3 = (3C/2\Lambda)[\cosh(3\Lambda)^{1/2}t - 1], \quad (\Lambda > 0),$$
$$R^3 = (3C/-2\Lambda)[1 - \cos(-3\Lambda)^{1/2}t], \quad (\Lambda < 0).$$

Finally, we must make some remarks on models which have an apparent creation-event or "big bang," i.e., which start from $R = 0$ at $t = 0$. First, we do not expect Friedmann's equation to apply in the neighborhood of $R = 0$, if only because *pressure* cannot then be neglected. But, as we have seen, pressure acts like extra density and would even hasten the collapse, if we look at the model in time-reversed form. Thus mathematically $R = 0$ will occur even if pressure is allowed for. However, $R = 0$ does *not* correspond to a point-event. For example, in Milne's model, the limit $a \longrightarrow 0$ of the public spaces $\tau = a$ is the entire light cone through the creation-event, as Figure 28 shows. The general case ($\rho \neq 0$) is even more complicated: there are *different* light cones emanating from the different fundamental particles at $t = 0$, as is shown by the occurrence of a particle horizon relative to each galaxy (—a particle horizon is precisely a "creation light cone"). Hence, kinematically, $R = 0$ is a complicated singularity rather than a single event. Of course, dynamically, it cannot occur. Matter will be tightly packed *before* $R = 0$ is reached. In closed universes this may correspond to a very small initial volume which then explodes. But in open universes the "big bang" must be pictured as already having infinite spatial extent.

Once Again, Comparison with Observation   *91*

Now that we have subjected the RW metric to dynamical conditions, we still find ourselves left with an embarrassingly large choice of possibilities. But whereas observations have little impact on the unrestricted RW models, they can, in principle, decide between the dynamically possible ones.

It is convenient to work with the following three functions of cosmic time:

$$H = \dot{R}/R, \quad q = -\ddot{R}/RH^2 = -R\ddot{R}/\dot{R}^2, \quad \sigma = 4\pi G\rho/3H^2, \tag{91.1}$$

where q and σ are dimensionless, while H has the dimension (time)$^{-1}$. H, of course, is Hubble's "constant," or better: *Hubble's parameter*; q is called the *deceleration parameter*, and σ—which is necessarily positive—is called the *density parameter*. In principle, the present values of these parameters can be determined by observation: H and q from relations such as (87.13), and σ from an estimate of ρ.

In terms of these functions we can now rewrite (i) equation (89.9), (ii) the difference of (89.7) and (89.8), and (iii) the difference of (89.7) and three times (89.8) (we still work in units in which $c = 1$):

(i) $\sigma = C/2H^2R^3;$ $C = 2\sigma_0 H_0^2 R_0^3$ (91.2)

(ii) $\sigma - q = \Lambda/3H^2;$ $\Lambda = 3H_0^2(\sigma_0 - q_0)$ (91.3)

(iii) $3\sigma - q - 1 = k/H^2R^2;$ $k = H_0^2 R_0^2(3\sigma_0 - q_0 - 1).$
(91.4)

The second entry in each line represents a solution for one of the constants C, Λ, k; and since these *are* constants, we can evaluate their representative functions at *any* time, in particular at the present time $t = t_0$: that is the significance of the suffix zero. Note that

$$\Lambda = 0 \leftrightarrow \sigma = q, \tag{91.5}$$

and *if* this obtains,

$$k \gtreqless 0 \leftrightarrow \sigma, q \gtreqless \tfrac{1}{2}, \quad (\Lambda = 0). \tag{91.6}$$

From the second entries in (91.2)–(91.4) it appears that if we know H_0, q_0, and σ_0, we can first determine Λ and k/R_0^2 (which yields k *and* R_0), and finally C. And, of course, Λ, k, C and R_0 determine a *unique* Friedmann model. But unfortunately this persuasively simple plan does not work out in practice: the uncertainties in the current determinations of q_0 and σ_0, and, to a lesser extent, of H_0, are so great that no direct conclusions are possible from these equations. H. P. Robertson* had the ingenious idea of coupling these three uncertain data with a fourth: t_0, the age of the universe. Some models can be eliminated simply because they are "too young." And in any case there are interesting relations between H_0, t_0, σ_0, and q_0.

We first remark on a rather specialized "age problem." Consider a graph of $R(t)$ against t, as in Figure 33. The tangent at t_0 intersects the R axis at a point $R_0/\dot{R}_0 = 1/H_0$ units to the left of t_0 (we assume $\dot{R}_0 > 0$). If $\ddot{R}$ has been negative *until* t_0, the curve lies to the right of its tangent, and the model has a present age *less* than $1/H_0$. But this is incompatible with such empirical values as $H_0 = 100$ km/ sec/Mpc ($1/H_0 = 9.7 \times 10^9$ years) and $t_0 > 2 \times 10^{10}$ years. In an expanding universe both ρ and p decrease. It is therefore clear from the difference of (89.7) and (89.8) that $\ddot{R}_0 < 0$ implies $\ddot{R} < 0$ throughout the past. Hence we must reject either models with $\ddot{R}_0 < 0$ or the above numerical data. Rejecting $\ddot{R}_0 < 0$ inevitably means accepting $\Lambda > 0$, even if we allow for pressure, since nothing but Λ can prevent deceleration. (This can be seen formally from the difference of equations (89.7) and (89.8).) Of course, this is a "problem" only for those who reject the Λ term on principle; present data are perhaps sufficiently uncertain to make that position still tenable.

Returning now to the general case, and essentially following Robertson (and R. Stabell and S. Refsdal†), we substitute from (91.2)–(91.4) into Friedmann's equation (90.1), obtaining

$$\dot{y}^2 = H_0^2\{2\sigma_0 y^{-1} + (\sigma_0 - q_0)y^2 + 1 + q_0 - 3\sigma_0\},$$
$$y = R/R_0. \quad (91.7)$$

Like the original equation, this can be solved at once by quadrature; and since we are interested here in *present* ages of models with *finite* age, we assume $R(0) = 0$ and perform

* *Publ. Astron. Soc. Pac.* **67,** 82 (1955); *Helv. Phys. Acta* Suppl. IV, 128 (1955).

† *Monthly Notices of the Royal Astronomical Society* **132,** 379 (1966).

a definite integration:

$$H_0 t_0 = \int_0^{t_0} H_0 \, dt = \int_0^1 \{ \ \}^{-1/2} \, dy = f(\sigma_0, q_0); \quad (91.8)$$

the empty brace denotes the braced expression of (91.7), and $f(\sigma_0, q_0)$ is defined by the last equation. This function can easily be machine evaluated, and thus one can tabulate corresponding values of σ_0, q_0, and $H_0 t_0$.

As far as (91.7) goes, σ_0 and q_0 determine $R(t)$ up to independent scale changes in R and t; but equation (91.4) shows that unless $k = 0$ these changes must be the same. Now since σ_0, q_0, and $H_0 t_0$ are related by (91.8), any two of them serve to determine a big-bang Friedmann model up to the above scale change. (For certain σ_0, q_0 there are *two* Friedmann models—one with finite and one with infinite past, like O and C in Figures 32 and 33. The present analysis omits the latter.) Following Tinsley, we choose $H_0 t_0$ and $\log \sigma_0$ as "coordinates" for the Robertson diagram,* Figure 34, on which each point corresponds to a Friedmann model. The limitations on ρ_0 and t_0 then single out a zone in which all acceptable models must occur; and these limitations appear at present to be more firmly established (cf. Section 81) than those on q_0. Nevertheless, we have superimposed on the Robertson diagram some level curves of q_0,† thus adding the fourth "observable" to σ_0, t_0, and H_0.

The diagram shows the important demarcation lines between models with $\Lambda > 0$ and $\Lambda < 0$, and between models with $k > 0$ and $k < 0$; they are easily obtained from (91.3) and (91.4), respectively. Also strictly separated in the

---

*Robertson used t_0 and $\log \rho_0$, assuming a definite value for H_0. But Tinsley's coordinates (Beatrice M. Tinsley, Ph.D. Dissertation, University of Texas, 1967), have the advantage that the diagram need not be recalibrated whenever a new value of H_0 is announced. Furthermore, the empirical density restrictions are on σ_0 rather than on ρ_0: The dynamical mass determinations of clusters of galaxies depend on observing relative motions, and these satisfy $v^2 \propto m/r$; but v is directly observable as red shift, whence $m \propto r$. The density involves a further division by (distance)^3, so that $\rho \propto$ (distance)$^{-2} \propto H^2$—since the uncertainty in Hubble's parameter $\dot{R}/R$ is only in the denominator, the numerator being again observable as a red shift.

†Making use of computational results given by Stabell and Refsdal, *loc. cit.*

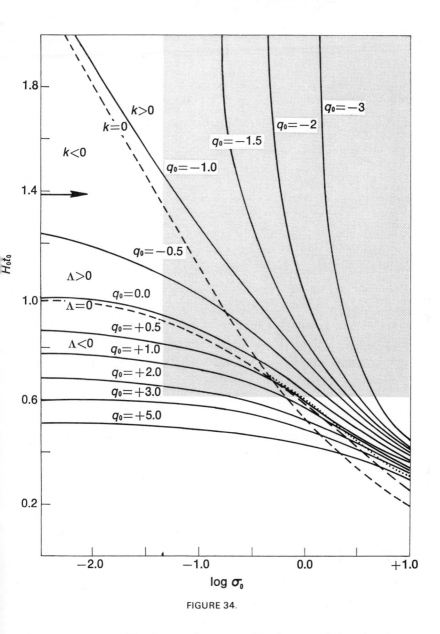

FIGURE 34.

diagram are oscillating and nonoscillating models: As is clear from Figure 32, the relevant demarkation line, on or above which models do not oscillate, is $\Lambda = 0$ for models with $k \leq 0$ and $\Lambda = \Lambda_E$ for models with $k > 0$. The equation of the former curve is

$$\sigma_0 - q_0 = 0, \tag{91.9}$$

while that of the latter is

$$27(\sigma_0 - q_0)\sigma_0^2 = (3\sigma_0 - q_0 - 1)^3, \tag{91.10}$$

as we find from (91.2)–(91.4) by setting $\Lambda = \Lambda_E = 4/9C^2$ and $k = 1$. These two curves, as well as the curve

$$3\sigma_0 - q_0 - 1 = 0, \tag{91.11}$$

corresponding to $k = 0$, all cross each other at the point $\sigma_0 = q_0 = \frac{1}{2}$. It is therefore easily seen that in the Robertson diagram all points below the line compounded of the locus $\Lambda = 0$ for $\sigma_0 < \frac{1}{2}$ and the locus (91.10) for $\sigma_0 > \frac{1}{2}$ (dotted in the diagram) correspond to oscillating models, while all points on or above this line correspond to nonoscillating models. [For each oscillating model there are, of course, *two* cosmic times (symmetric with respect to the time of maximum extension) that correspond to any pair of values σ_0, q_0. The Robertson diagram gives the earlier time, corresponding to the ascending limb; for it is based on the *positive* root in (91.8), i.e. on $H_0 > 0$, the one *certain* empirical fact.]

The shaded area in the diagram represents the age and density limitations, which we have chosen rather liberally as follows:

$$H_0 t_0 > .62 \text{ (e.g., } H_0 > 60 \text{km/sec/Mpc, } t_0 > 10^{10} \text{ years)},$$
$$-1.33 < \log \sigma_0 < 1.45 \text{ (e.g., } H_0 = 75 \text{ km/sec/Mpc,}$$
$$10^{-30} < \rho_0 < 6 \times 10^{-28} \text{ gm/cm}^3).$$

The former combines the lowest figure ever put forward for H_0 with the lowest possible age of our galaxy. More realistic lower limits would be $H_0 > 67$ km/sec/Mpc and $t_0 > 2 \times 10^{10}$ years, which implies $H_0 t_0 > 1.38$ (see arrow in diagram). The limitations on ρ_0 are those we quoted in Section 81, due to Abell, who assumed $H_0 = 75$ km/sec/Mpc in his calculations.

The few conclusions that emerge with fair probability from the diagram (using the higher $H_0 t_0$ limit) are that *if* our universe is represented by a Friedmann big-bang model without pressure, that model must have $k = 1$, $\Lambda > 0$, and $q_0 < -1$. The inclusion of pressure, important only in the early stages of the universe, has the effect of making the early $\dot{R}$ even more negative (cf. (89.7) minus (89.8)), and hence the model somewhat younger; the net result is a slight stretch of the $H_0 t_0$ axis in the diagram and a corresponding upward motion of the shaded zone, which only reinforces our conclusions.

Writing $h = (H_0/100)$ km/sec/Mpc, we can calculate from (91.3) and (91.4) that

$$\Lambda = 3.5 \times 10^{-56} h^2 (\sigma_0 - q_0) \text{cm}^{-2},$$
$$k/R_0^2 = 1.2 \times 10^{-56} h^2 (3\sigma_0 - q_0 - 1) \text{cm}^{-2}.$$

Since the Robertson diagram suggests $q_0 < -1$ and we know $\sigma_0 > .05$, it therefore appears probable (with $h = 1$) that

$$\Lambda > 3.5 \times 10^{-56} \text{cm}^{-2}, \quad k/R_0^2 > 1.8 \times 10^{-57} \text{cm}^{-2}.$$

Given the following useful numerical relation, $\sigma = 2.66 \times 10^{28} \rho/h^2$, and using $\rho < 6 \times 10^{-28}$ with $h = .75$ (Abell), we have $\sigma < 30$; if, moreover, $h < 2$ and $|q| < 20$, as seems highly probable, we can also conclude

$$|\Lambda| < 7 \times 10^{-54} \text{cm}^{-2}, \quad |k/R_0^2| < 7 \times 10^{-54} \text{cm}^{-2}.$$

[As we go to press, a new publication by A. Sandage (*Astrophysical J.* **152,** L149 (1968)) suggests that $H_0 = 75.3$ $(-15, +19)$ km/sec/Mpc, and that H_0 could be even as small as 50 km/sec/Mpc. It was not possible to incorporate these results into the text above.]

Mach's Principle Re-Examined 92

Now that we have come to the end of our survey of relativity, it may be fitting to return briefly to Mach's principle, and to see whether this principle, which strongly influenced Einstein in his invention of GR, has in fact been vindicated by GR. It will be recalled that, according to Mach, space as such played no role in physics and thus did not exist. In GR, on the other hand, space *does* play a role, though now in the guise of four-dimensional spacetime. Spacetime *fully* determines all free motions (i.e., motions under inertia and gravity); the question is whether the matter distribution, in turn, *fully* determines spacetime. For if it did, spacetime could be regarded as a mere mathematical auxiliary, and, as demanded by Mach, only the relative configuration of masses would count.

Before we enter into that question, however, we may note that GR has at least met what many regard as the strongest of the Mach-Einstein objections to *absolute* space, namely that it acts but cannot be acted upon: spacetime both acts *on* mass (as a guiding field) and is acted upon *by* mass (suffering curvature). And it may be that Mach's followers will have to be content with such a nonabsolute space rather than with no space at all.

For, as things stand, spacetime certainly is *not* a mere auxiliary. For example, according to the field equations, flat Minkowski space is consistent with the total absence of matter, and yet it determines all free motions in it. Furthermore, there are *other* nonsingular solutions beside Minkowski space of the unmodified vacuum field equations (e.g., Taub-NUT space* and Ozsváth-Schücking space†). Hence the *same* matter configuration (namely, *no* matter) can give rise to inequivalent fields. This is possibly connected with the existence of gravitational waves: Minkowski space with a gravitational wave (curvature!) going through it is *not* the same as Minkowski space; and yet it also satisfies the vacuum field equations.

The total absence of matter, of course, is not a realistic situation. But even when matter is present, we have no guarantee of a unique solution. Einstein's field equations are *differential* equations, and thus their solutions necessarily involve some arbitrariness which can only be removed

---

*See, for example, C. W. Misner, in "Relativity Theory and Astrophysics," J. Ehlers, editor, p. 160, Vol. I, Providence, R. I., American Math. Soc., 1967.

†I. Ozsváth and E. Schücking, in "Recent Developments in General Relativity," p. 339, New York, Pergamon Press, 1962.

through further information, e.g., boundary conditions. In the case of Schwarzschild's solution, as we have seen, spherical symmetry and local compatibility with Newton's theory suffice to ensure uniqueness. In cosmology, too, if we assume the Robertson-Walker symmetries and the value of Λ, spacetime is uniquely determined by the density and energy at one cosmic instant. It is not clear, however, that in the case of more general (i.e., less symmetrical) mass distributions, different boundary conditions could not lead to different solutions. In other words, it is conceivable that there could be two *different* solutions corresponding to the *same* matter content—e.g., the same local field joined smoothly to two different vacuum continuations to infinity.

Beyond these uncertainties, there exist explicit "anti-Mach" solutions of the field equations with matter. By this we understand model universes in which the local "compass of inertia" (e.g., a Foucault pendulum) rotates relative to the global mass distribution. The best-known among these is the Gödel universe* (important also in cosmology as an example of a homogeneous though nonisotropic model), but others have been discovered more recently.†

It is possible that additional axioms could be found and incorporated into GR to prevent such un-Machian situations as (i) spaces without matter, (ii) inequivalent spaces with the *same* matter, and (iii) anti-Mach spaces. But until that happens, we are forced to the conclusion that only *part* of Mach's program for a new gravitational theory has been realized by GR: Instead of abolishing space altogether, Einstein merely made it nonabsolute; and, ironically, instead of explaining inertial forces as gravitational (i.e., as matter pulling on inertial "charge") in the spirit of Mach, Einstein explained gravitational forces as inertial, i.e., as "space-guided."

Under these conditions it is not quite clear why GR nevertheless reproduces, at least to some extent, the pure

*K. Gödel, *Rev. Mod. Phys.* **21**, 447 (1949).

†See, for example, I. Ozsváth and E. Schücking, *Nature* **193**, 1168 (1962).

Machian effects of Section 16. *Either* the space-modifying effect of matter suffices for this purpose, *or* the relevant situations in GR already satisfy the still unknown axioms which would make all of GR purely Machian.

It must be said, in fairness, that today's quantum theoreticians (as well as many others) have little sympathy with Mach's principle. They point out that not only matter is the stuff of physics, but also fields, and that the whole of spacetime is occupied by the fields of the elementary particles. Even in the absence of matter, the fields of the *virtual* particles constitute an all-pervasive background which can in no way be eliminated. In fact, matter is only a small perturbation of it. This background, which possesses Lorentz invariance locally, can be looked upon as a modern ether. Since it possesses no net energy it makes no contribution to curvature, and hence it has no direct effect in general relativity. But it does suggest the *a priori* existence of spacetime, which matter merely modifies and does not create.

Be this as it may, if Einstein really sought to find a framework for Mach's principle in his general relativity, one would probably have to conclude that he, like Columbus, failed in his purpose. And yet, in the one case as in the other, how rich the actual discovery and how forgotten, by comparison, the original purpose!

Exercises

(Problems in relativity should generally be worked in units in which $c = 1$. The "missing" factor c can either be inserted later throughout, or simply at the answer stage by using it to make the physical dimensions balance. See the final remarks of Section 29.)

CHAPTER 1

1-1. A river of width l flows at speed v. A certain swimmer's speed relative to the water is V ($>v$). First he swims from a point P on one bank to a point on the same bank a distance l downstream, and thereupon immediately swims back to P. Prove that the total time taken is $2Vl/(V^2 - v^2)$. Next he swims from P to a point directly opposite on the other bank, and back to P. Prove that now the total time taken is $2l/(V^2 - v^2)^{1/2}$.

1-2. In the light of the preceding exercise, consider the following simplified version of the Michelson-Morley experiment. A laboratory flies at speed v through the supposed ether. Inside there are two identical rods, one placed along the direction of the "ether drift," and the other at right angles to it. *If* light travels at constant speed c relative to the ether, and *if* lengths in the direction of the ether drift shrink by a factor $(1 - v^2/c^2)^{1/2}$ (Lorentz theory), prove that light signals sent along either rod and reflected back from the far end are observed to take the same total times. [Anyone who remembers his trigonometry and doesn't shrink from a little calculating can now attempt to show that for a given rod placed in *any* direction in this laboratory the to-and-fro light travel times are the same; he must remember that only that component of the rod's length is shortened which is parallel to the ether drift.] Suppose, next, the observer compares these light travel times with an observer at rest in the ether who performs the same experiments with identical rods. Show that the two observers' measured times can agree only if it is assumed that clocks traveling through the ether at speed v go slow by a factor $(1 - v^2/c^2)^{1/2}$ (Lorentz theory).

1-3. According to the Lorentz theory, length contraction and time dilation assure that the measured two-way speed of light equals c in all directions in a laboratory S even if this moves through the ether frame AS at some speed $v < c$. Show, however, that if the clocks in S are synchronized so that simultaneous events in AS correspond to simultaneous events in S, the *one*-way speed of light in S varies with direction. Then prove that even the one-way speed of light in S can be made c in all directions provided the clock settings in S are arranged so that clock simultaneity on each plane perpendicular to the line of motion agrees with simultaneity in AS, but clocks on planes a distance x apart in S differ in their zero settings by vx/c^2 S-time units from those of AS. Prove this for signals along and across the line of motion only, if the general case is too difficult. The more ambitious reader can now prove that the transformation equations between S and AS are the Lorentz equations as given in Section 42.

1-4. It is well known that a straight electric current gives rise to circular magnetic lines of force around it, so that a compass needle suspended above a horizontal current takes up a horizontal position at right angles to the current. Using the relativity principle, deduce that in general a small magnet experiences a torque when it is moved through a static electric field.

1-5. An electric charge moving through a static magnetic field experiences a force orthogonal to both its motion and the field. From the relativity principle deduce that it must therefore be possible to set a stationary electric charge in motion by moving a magnet in its vicinity.

1-6. If Mach's principle is correct, the centrifugal force field f at any point inside a massive shell rotating with angular speed ω (cf. Figure 2(ii)) must be proportional to ω^2 and to the perpendicular distance r from the axis of rotation—at least in first approximation. Why? Assume, moreover, that it is proportional to the mass M of the shell and to the reciprocal of its radius R, i.e., $f = k\omega^2 r M/R$, where k is a constant. If the universe is oversimplified to an enormous ball of tenuous matter of density 10^{-30} gm/cm^3 and radius 10^{28} cm, prove that $k \approx 1.6 \times 10^{-27}$ in cgs units. (In several theories of cosmology there exists such an "effective" radius of the universe around *each* observer.) Thirring, in a well-known paper based on general relativity theory, obtained the value $4G/15c^2 \approx 2 \times 10^{-29}$ for k, G being the constant of gravitation. The order-of-magnitude agreement of these results is far more significant than their apparent discrepancy.

1-7. In a certain Cartesian coordinate system at rest relative to the fixed stars, a bar magnet occupies the z axis from

$z = -1$ to $z = 1$; an electrically charged pith ball is placed at the point (1, 0, 0); and this system is surrounded by a spherical mass shell centered on the origin. According to Mach's principle, which way will the pith ball tend to move as the shell is rotated about the z axis? (Take into account the polarization of the magnet, the sign of the charge, and the sense of the rotation.)

1-8. In Newtonian theory, inertial mass (m_I) and active and passive gravitational mass (m_A, m_P) are not only numerically equal in suitable units, but also all positive. Consider now the possibility of negative masses. Could the m_I of *all* particles be negative? (Remember that "force" can be regarded as a conventional quantity.) Could particles exist which have negative m_I while others have positive m_I? (Consider the action of a spring on a particle, and energy conservation.) Now assume m_I is positive for all particles. How would a normal particle and an "abnormal" particle (with $m_A = m_P < 0$) move under their mutual gravitation? How would two abnormal particles move under their mutual gravitation? How would an abnormal particle move in the earth's gravitational field? Would the existence of abnormal particles violate either Newton's third law or Galileo's principle? How would a normal particle and one with (i) $m_A > 0$, $m_P < 0$, (ii) $m_A < 0$, $m_P > 0$, move under their mutual gravitation? Would the existence of particles of these latter kinds violate either Newton's third law or Galileo's principle?

1-9. Knowing that radiation issues from an electric charge which accelerates through an inertial frame, would you expect, from the equivalence principle, that a charge held at rest in the earth's gravitational field radiates? Does your answer violate energy conservation? From the EP, would you expect that a charge allowed to fall freely in the earth's gravitational field radiates? Would a prerelativistic physicist have expected either of such charges to radiate? [Note that radiation is evidently not as simple and local a phenomenon as one may have thought; global considerations enter into its definition.]

1-10. In the elevator experiment discussed in the second paragraph of Section 21, prove that the relative velocity of observers A and B is gl/c, where g is the gravitational acceleration and l the height of the cabin. There exist Mössbauer apparatuses capable of measuring with tolerable error optical Doppler shifts corresponding to source velocities of 10^{-4} cm/sec.(!) A source of light at rest at the top of a solid tower is examined by such an apparatus placed at its foot. How high must the tower be to make the "gravitational Doppler effect" measurable? [$\sim$ 30 meters.]

CHAPTER 2

2-1. Assume you know about the conservation of energy, but not of momentum. Use Newtonian relativity (as in Section 24) and symmetry considerations to prove that if one billiard ball hits a second stationary one head-on, and no energy is dissipated, the second assumes the velocity of the first while the first comes to a total stop. Could you solve this problem directly, under the stated conditions?

2-2. A heavy plane slab moves with uniform speed v in the direction of its normal through an inertial frame. A ball is thrown at it with velocity u, from a direction making an angle θ with its normal. Assuming that the slab has essentially infinite momentum (no recoil) and that there is no dissipation of energy, use Newtonian relativity to show that the ball will leave the slab in a direction making an angle ϕ with its normal, and with a velocity w, such that

$$\frac{u}{w} = \frac{\sin \phi}{\sin \theta}, \quad \frac{u \cos \theta + 2v}{u \sin \theta} = \cot \phi.$$

2-3. In Newtonian mechanics the mass of each particle is *invariant*, i.e., it has the same measure in all inertial frames. Moreover, in any collision, mass is *conserved*, i.e., the total mass of all the particles going into the collision equals the total mass of all the particles (possibly different ones) coming out of the collision. Establish this law of mass conservation as a *consequence* of mass invariance, momentum conservation, and Newtonian relativity. [Hint: let Σ^* denote a summation which assigns positive signs to terms measured *before* a certain collision and negative signs to terms measured *after* the collision. Then momentum conservation is expressed by $\Sigma^* m\mathbf{u} = 0$. Also, if primed quantities refer to a second inertial frame moving with velocity $\mathbf{v}$ relative to the first, we have $\mathbf{u} = \mathbf{u}' + \mathbf{v}$ for all $\mathbf{u}$.] Prove similarly that if in any collision the kinetic energy $\frac{1}{2}\Sigma\, mu^2$ is conserved in *all* inertial frames, then mass *and* momentum must also be conserved.

2-4. (i) Draw a reasonably accurate graph of $\gamma(v)$ against v for speeds v between zero and c. (ii) Establish the approximation for γ mentioned in Section 29(iii). [Hint: $1 - v^2/c^2 = (1 - v/c)(1 + v/c)$.]

2-5. Establish the following useful formulae:
$$\gamma v = c(\gamma^2 - 1)^{1/2}, \qquad c^2 d\gamma = \gamma^3 v\, dv, \qquad d(\gamma v) = \gamma^3 dv.$$

2-6. If two events occur at the same point in some inertial frame S, prove that their temporal sequence is the same in all inertial frames, and that the least time separation is assigned to them in S. Solve this problem first by algebra and then illustrate it by a Minkowski diagram—or vice versa.

2-7. Prove that the temporal sequence of two events is the same in all inertial frames if and only if they occur at the same point in *some* inertial frame. Solve this problem by algebra and illustrate it by a Minkowski diagram. [Hint: cf. the paragraph containing (28.4).]

2-8. Consider the two events whose coordinates (x, y, z, t) relative to some inertial frame S are $(0,0,0,0)$ and $(2,0,0,1)$

in units in which $c = 1$. Find the speeds of frames in standard configuration with S in which (i) the events are simultaneous, (ii) the second event precedes the first by one unit of time. Is there a frame in which the events occur at the same point? $[\frac{1}{2}c, 4c/5.]$

2-9. Invent a more realistic arrangement than the garage and pole described in Section 33 whereby length contraction could be verified experimentally, if only our instruments were delicate enough.

2-10. Consider a rod of rest length L sliding with Lorentz factor 10 over a hole of diameter $\frac{1}{2}L$ as in Section 33. Draw some diagrams, or "snapshots," illustrating what happens in the frame of the table, on the assumption that in this frame the edges of the rod remain parallel to themselves during the fall. Try to deduce from these a series of snapshots in the frame of the rod, from the moment the front end passes over the hole to the moment the back end "knows" that an obstacle has been encountered. A *qualitative* description and argument will be enough. [Hint: any phenomenon which occurs everywhere simultaneously in S sweeps over S' at velocity c^2/v in the negative x direction. This general result follows at once from the LT, but it is also instructive to illustrate it with a Minkowski diagram.]

2-11. Two uniformly moving standard clocks pass each other with relative velocity v. An observer on one clock keeps the other in sight. By what factor does the *visually* observed rate of the other clock lag behind that of his own? What does he observe if the velocity of the receding clock is suddenly reversed to $-v$? Solve this problem algebraically and illustrate it by a Minkowski diagram. $[(c - v)^{1/2}/(c + v)^{1/2}.]$

2-12. Write a scenario for a short educational animated film explaining time dilation and length contraction, based on the ideas of Figure 5. For example, you could show "rods" on which are fixed at regular intervals a number of "lights" which could "flash" either simultaneously, or in sequence so as to illustrate the progress of a signal. Furthermore, you could consider the alternative situation in which simultaneity at two points is defined by the reception of light signals from their midpoint.

2-13.   A computer at MIT has been programmed to exhibit on a cathode ray display screen the effect of an *active* Lorentz transformation through an arbitrary velocity $v < c$ on events in the (x,t) plane.   Orthogonal x and t axes are permanently displayed with units chosen so that $c = 1$; the operator marks various points, representing events, with his lightpen and then "presses" the "velocity button" until the desired value of v—which increases continuously from zero —is reached; as he does so, the events move to their new positions, determined by their new x and t coordinates. Prove: (i) each individual point traces out a hyperbola, (ii) points on the bisectors b_1 and b_2 of the angles between the axes move along these bisectors, (iii) any three collinear points remain collinear, (iv) two parallel lines of points remain parallel, (v) a line of points perpendicular to b_1 (other than b_2) moves transversely along b_1.   Finally suggest how this facility can be used to demonstrate length contraction and time dilation.

2-14.   Two particles move towards one another, each having speed $\frac{1}{2}c$ relative to a certain inertial frame.   Find their speed relative to each other.   [$4c/5$.]

2-15.   Two particles move collinearly in an inertial frame S. B has speed $\frac{1}{2}c$ relative to A and A has speed $\frac{1}{2}c$ relative to S.   What is B's speed relative to S?   [$4c/5$.]

2-16.   A rod of proper length 8 cm moves longitudinally at speed $.8c$ in an inertial frame S.   It is passed by a particle moving at speed $.8c$ through S in the opposite direction.   In S, what time does the particle need to pass the rod?   [10^{-10}

sec. Hint: the mutual speed between rod and particle in S is $1.6c$!]

2-17. How many successive velocity increments of $\frac{1}{2}c$ from the instantaneous rest frame are needed to produce a resultant velocity of (i) $.99c$, (ii) $.999c$? [5, 7. Hint: use (29.2) and the remarks following (29.6). You will have to consult tables of $\tanh x$ extending to $x = 3.8$.]

2-18. In the situation illustrated in Figure 7, find the relative velocity between the frames S and S' and the distance between neighboring clocks in either frame. [$(2\sqrt{2}/3)c$, $\sqrt{2} \times 300{,}000$ km.]

2-19. S and S' are two inertial frames in standard configuration. Prove that at any instant there is just one plane in S on which the clocks agree with those of S', and prove that this plane moves with velocity $u = (c^2/v)\{1 - (1 - v^2/c^2)^{1/2}\}$ in S. Then verify that $u \dotplus u = v$ and interpret this fact. [Hint: see Figure 7.]

2-20. S and S' are in standard configuration. In S' a straight rod parallel to the x' axis moves in the y' direction with velocity u. Show that in S the rod is inclined to the x axis at an angle $-\tan^{-1}(\gamma uv/c^2)$. Show also that a rod moving arbitrarily while remaining parallel to the y' axis in S' remains parallel to the y axis in S.

2-21. S and S' are in standard configuration. In S a slightly slanting guillotine blade in the (x, y) plane falls in the y direction past a block level with the x axis, in such a way that the intersection point of blade and block travels at a speed in excess of c. In some S', as we have seen, this intersection point travels in the *opposite* direction along the block. Explain, from the point of view of S', how this is possible. [Hint: modify the first result of the preceding exercise.]

2-22. *S* and *S'* are in standard configuration. In *S* a searchlight sweeps over high level clouds in such a way that the spot of light travels in the *x* direction at a speed in excess of *c*. In some *S'*, as we have seen, the spot travels the same path *backwards*. Explain, from the point of view of *S'*, how the light can be turned forward while the spot moves backwards.

2-23. Is Figure 8 correctly drawn in that the four hyperbolas cut each horizontal "rod" (except the one on the *x* axis) into three *unequal* portions? Support your answer (a) by a physical and (b) by a mathematical argument.

2-24. Consider the rectilinear motion with constant proper acceleration α described in equations (37.3)–(37.5). Let τ be the time elapsed on the moving particle, with $\tau = 0$ when $t = 0$. Then, from the clock hypothesis, $d\tau/dt = (1 - u^2/c^2)^{1/2}$. Now establish the following formulae:

$$\alpha t/c = \sinh(\alpha\tau/c), \qquad \alpha x/c^2 = \cosh(\alpha\tau/c),$$
$$u/c = \tanh(\alpha\tau/c), \qquad \gamma(u) = \cosh(\alpha\tau/c).$$

2-25. Given that g, the acceleration of gravity at the earth's surface, is ~ 980 cm/sec², and that a year has $\sim 3.2 \times 10^7$ seconds, verify that, in units of years and light years, $g \approx 1$. A rocket moves from rest in an inertial frame *S* with constant proper acceleration g (thus giving maximum comfort to its passengers). Find its Lorentz factor relative to *S* when its own clock indicates times $\tau = 1$ day, 1 year, 10 years. Find also the corresponding distances and times traveled in *S*. If the rocket accelerates for 10 years of its own time, then decelerates for 10 years, and then repeats the whole maneuver in the reverse direction, what is the total time elapsed in *S* during the rocket's absence? [$\gamma = 1.0000036, 1.5431, 11012; x = .0000036, .5431, 11011$ light years; $t = .0027, 1.1752, 11012$ years; $t = 44048$ years. To obtain some of these answers you will have to consult tables of $\sinh x$ and $\cosh x$. At small values of their arguments a

Taylor expansion suffices.] Note: because of the limitations on the extent of actual inertial frames, even if local irregularities are tolerated, SR can be expected to give reasonably accurate answers to such problems only on the subcosmic scale, say to about 10^8 light years. Beyond that, a theory of cosmology must be taken into account.

CHAPTER 3

3-1. In prerelativistic days, a simple telescope on an earth supposedly flying through the ether was aimed at a star and then filled with water: the star was still found centered on the cross-hairs. Show qualitatively that this could happen, on the ether theory, only if the ether were partially dragged along by the water. [Airy's experiment, 1871.] The more ambitious reader can derive the value of the drag coefficient from this result. [Hint: For simplicity assume the telescope points vertically upwards. When the water is present, allowance must be made for three effects: the difference of the (small) angles which the ray makes with the vertical outside and inside the telescope (*before* allowance is made for ether dragging) in accordance with Snell's law $\sin \theta / \sin \phi = n : 1$; its slowing down in the ratio $n : 1$; and, of course, the dragging.]

3-2. From (40.4) and (41.2) derive the following interesting relation between Doppler shift and aberration: $\lambda / \lambda' = \sin \alpha / \sin \alpha'$.

3-3. Let Δt and $\Delta t'$ be the time separations in the usual two frames S and S' between two events occurring at a freely moving photon. If the photon has frequencies ν and ν' in these frames, prove that $\nu / \nu' = \Delta t / \Delta t'$. Would you have guessed the ratio the other way round? [Hint: use the result of the preceding exercise.]

3-4. By interchanging primed and unprimed symbols and replacing v by $-v$ in the Doppler formula (40.4), obtain the aberration formula $\gamma^2(1 + (v/c)\cos\alpha)(1 - (v/c)\cos\alpha') = 1$. Derive the same result from (41.2). Why is this a valid technique for obtaining new formulae?

3-5. Describe a situation in which the classical and the relativistic formulae predict Doppler shifts in opposite directions, i.e., $D > 1$ and $D < 1$. [Hint: cf. (40.1).]

3-6. A man of height h runs very fast (with speed v) through an open door of height $h + a$. Prove that he sees the top of the door ahead of himself until he is a distance $av\gamma(v)/c$ *beyond* the door. Prove this result twice: once in the rest frame of the door, and once in the rest frame of the man.

3-7. A firework exploding from rest scatters sparks uniformly in all directions. But a firework exploding at high speed will evidently scatter most of its sparks in the forward direction. It is much the same with a source of light which radiates isotropically in its rest frame. Prove that when it moves at speed v, one-half of the total number of photons will be radiated into a forward cone whose semi-angle is given by $\cos\theta = v/c$. [This angle may be quite small; for obvious reasons the phenomenon is called the "headlight effect."]

3-8. A ray of light is reflected from a plane mirror which moves in the direction of its normal with velocity v. Prove that the angles of incidence and reflection, θ and ϕ, are related by $\sin\theta/\sin\phi = (\cos\theta + v/c)/(\cos\phi - v/c)$. [Cf. exercise 2-2.]

3-9. In a frame S, consider the equation $x\cos\alpha + y\sin\alpha = -ct$. For fixed α this represents a plane propagating in the direction of its normal with speed c, this direction being parallel to the (x, y) plane and making an angle α with the negative x axis. We can evidently regard this plane as a light front. Now transform x, y, and t directly to the usual frame S', and from the resulting equation deduce at once the following aberration formula: $\tan \alpha' = \sin \alpha / \gamma (\cos \alpha + v/c)$, which is equivalent to (41.1) and (41.2).

3-10. Make a rough sketch, using Figure 9 and projections, to demonstrate how some inertial observers could see the outline of a uniformly moving wheel (or disc) boomerang-shaped. How must a straight rod move relative to an observer in order to be seen straight?

3-11. Make a qualitative argument to determine how a prerelativistic physicist, believing himself at rest in the ether, would expect to see the outline of a sphere that moves transversely to his line of vision at a high constant velocity. Then show, again qualitatively, how the introduction of length contraction could restore circularity. Remember that light from the front of the sphere takes less time to reach the observer's eye than light from the sides, and also that light from beyond the geometrical points of tangency to the observer's eye (in other words, from the back of the sphere) may reach that eye.

3-12. A cube with its edges parallel to the coordinate axes moves with Lorentz factor 3 along the x axis of an inertial frame. A "supersnapshot" of this cube is made in a plane $z =$ constant by means of light rays parallel to the z axis. Make an *exact* scale drawing of this supersnapshot.

CHAPTER 4

4-1. A four-vector has components (V_1, V_2, V_3, V_4) in an inertial frame S. Write down its components (i) in a frame which coincides with S except that the directions of the x and z axes are reversed; (ii) in a frame which coincides with S except for a $45°$ rotation of the (x, y) plane about the origin followed by a translation in the z direction by 3 units; (iii) in a frame which moves in standard configuration with S.

4-2. Use the fact that $U = \gamma(u, 1)$ transforms as a four-vector to rederive the transformation equations (36.3) and (36.6). Recall that our earlier derivation of (36.6), which is essentially equivalent to (36.5), was quite tedious.

4-3. Establish the form (44.7) of the four-acceleration components in the rest frame. A particle moves along the circle $x^2 + y^2 - r^2 = 0 = z$ at constant speed u in an inertial frame S. Find the components of its four-acceleration when it crosses the negative y axis. Find the corresponding components in the rest frame of the particle (with axes parallel to those of S) and also the three-acceleration in the rest frame. [In all cases the second component is $\gamma^2 u^2 / r$, and all others vanish.]

4-4. A particle has the following worldline relative to a given inertial frame: $\alpha x = \cosh \alpha \tau$, $\alpha t = \sinh \alpha \tau$, with $\alpha = $ constant and units chosen to make $c = 1$. Prove that τ is the particle's proper time. Write down the components of the four-velocity and of the four-acceleration, and deduce that α is the proper acceleration. [Cf. exercise 2-24, and also (44.12).]

4-5. "In three dimensions a particle has a three-velocity u *relative* to some observer; in four dimensions a particle has a four-velocity U, period." Comment. [Distinguish between a vector and its components.]

4-6. An inertial observer O has four-velocity U_0 and a particle P has (variable) four-acceleration A. If $U_0 \cdot A \equiv 0$, what can you conclude about the speed of P in O's rest frame? [Hint: look at the datum in O's rest frame.]

4-7. Establish *formally* the results mentioned in the final paragraph of Section 46. [Hint: let $V = (a, b, c, d)$ in some arbitrary inertial frame; rotate the spatial axes to absorb b, c; then show that a LT can be found to make the first component vanish, say; etc.]

4-8.   Prove that any four-vector orthogonal to a timelike or null vector (other than the null vector itself in the latter case) must be spacelike, but that two spacelike vectors can also be orthogonal. [Hint: use the results of the preceding exercise.]

4-9.   Prove that the sign of the fourth component of a timelike or null four-vector is invariant under *general* LT's. According as this sign is negative or positive, such vectors are said to be past- or future-pointing.   Illustrate this with a three-dimensional Minkowski diagram.

4-10.   Prove that the sum of two timelike four-vectors which are isochronous (i.e., both pointing into the future or both into the past) is a timelike vector isochronous with them. Is this result still true if one or both vectors are null? Illustrate with a three-dimensional Minkowski diagram. [Hint: use the results of exercise 4-7.]

4-11.   Prove that the vector join of any two events in an inertial observer's instantaneous space t = constant is orthogonal to his time axis.

4-12.   "Even if every local physical experiment were fully deterministic, and an observer had at his disposal the most perfect data gathering instruments and the most perfect records left by devoted predecessors, he could never predict his future with certainty."   Justify.   [Hint: consider the observer's light cone.]

CHAPTER 5

5-1.   How fast must a particle move before its *kinetic* energy equals its *rest* energy? [.866 c.]

5-2.   A particle moves at speed .995 c. How fast must it be made to move to double (i) its *kinetic* energy, (ii) its *total* energy? [.99861 c, .99875 c.]

5-3. An electron has rest mass $.9 \times 10^{-27}$ gm; when it traverses a potential difference of one volt it gains 1.6×10^{-12} ergs of energy. How many volts are necessary to increase its energy a thousand times over its rest energy? [$.5 \times 10^9$ volt.]

5-4. The mass of a hydrogen atom is 1.00814 amu, that of a neutron is 1.00898 amu, and that of a helium atom (two hydrogen atoms and two neutrons) is 4.00388 amu. Find the binding energy in one gram of helium expressed in calories. (One calorie $= 4.18 \times 10^7$ ergs $=$ heat energy per degree Kelvin in one gram of water.) Compare this with the *total* energy in one gram of *any* substance. [1.6×10^{11}, 2.5×10^{13}.]

5-5. A particle with four-momentum **P** is observed by an observer with four-velocity $\mathbf{U}_0$. Prove that the energy of the particle relative to the observer is $\mathbf{U}_0 \cdot \mathbf{P}$. [Hint: look at components in a suitable frame.]

5-6. A particle of constant proper mass moves *rectilinearly* in some inertial frame. Show that the product of its proper mass and its instantaneous proper acceleration equals the magnitude of the relativistic three-force acting on the particle in that frame. [Hint: (37.2), (57.1).] Show also that this is not necessarily true when the motion is not rectilinear.

5-7. A particle of instantaneous rest mass m is at rest and being heated in a frame S', so as to increase its energy at the rate of q units per second. From the definition (57.1) find the relativistic force on the particle in the usual second frame S. What is that force if, after being heated, the particle *cools* at a rate q?

5-8. Show that the equations (57.9) are *equivalent* to (57.8) in the sense that they represent the vector components of the force (57.8) in the instantaneous plane of the motion.

[Hint: "dot" (57.8) first with **u** and then with a unit vector coplanar with **u** and **a** and orthogonal to **u**.] Find the relativistic three-force acting on a particle which moves in the (x,y) plane with vector velocity **u** $= (3,4)$ and vector acceleration **a** $= (-2,2)$.

5-9. (The relativistic harmonic oscillator.) A particle of constant proper mass m_0, moving along the x axis of an inertial frame, is attracted to the origin by a relativistic force $-m_0k^2x$. If the amplitude of the resulting oscillation is a, prove that the period T is $(4/c) \int_0^a \gamma(\gamma^2 - 1)^{-1/2}dx$, where $\gamma = 1 + \frac{1}{2}k^2c^{-2}(a^2 - x^2)$. [Hint: supply the details of the following calculation. $\gamma^3 du/dt = -k^2x$, where $\gamma = (1 - u^2/c^2)^{-1/2}$; $u\gamma^3 du = -k^2xdx$, $\gamma = $ constant $- \frac{1}{2}k^2x^2 = $ answer given; $T = 4 \int_0^a (1/u)dx = $ answer given.]

5-10. As a rule of thumb, does relativistic mechanics result from Newtonian mechanics by simply replacing each Newtonian m by the relevant $m_0\gamma$? Give a careful and detailed answer.

5-11. Show *directly* by the method of exercise 3-9 that the aberration of the wave normal of a wave traveling at speed c^2/u (cf. (47.8)) is precisely the same as that of the track of a particle traveling with speed u. [Hint: for the latter adapt the argument leading to (41.1).]

5-12. If a photon with four-momentum **P** is observed by two observers having respective four-velocities U_0 and U_1, prove that the observed frequencies are in the ratio $U_0 \cdot P/U_1 \cdot P$. Hence rederive formula (40.4).

5-13. Prove that the outcome of a collision between two distinct particles (of finite *or* zero rest mass) cannot be a single photon. [Hint: conservation of four-momentum.]

5-14. Prove that no particle of finite rest mass can disintegrate into a single photon.

5-15. Radiation energy from the sun is received on earth at the rate of 1.94 calories per minute per cm². Given the distance of the sun (150,000,000 km) and the fact that one calorie = 4.18×10^7 ergs, find the total mass lost by the sun per second, and also the force exerted by solar radiation on a disc of the same diameter as the earth (12,800 km) at the location of the earth. [4.3×10^9 kg, 5.8×10^{13} dyne. Hint: force equals momentum absorbed per unit time.]

5-16. Suppose a part, m, of the earth's total rest mass M is transmuted into photons and radiated directly ahead into the earth's orbital direction, so that by the reaction the remaining mass comes to a complete halt (and thereupon falls into the sun). If the earth's orbital speed is u (~ 18.5 mile/sec) show that $(M - m)/M = (c - u)^{1/2}/(c + u)^{1/2}$, whence $m/M \approx u/c \approx 1/10{,}000$. Show also that if mass is ejected in the form of matter rather than light, a greater proportion of rest mass must be sacrificed. [Hint: let the *total* energy and momentum of the ejected photons be E and E/c and appeal to the conservation of energy and momentum.]

5-17. If one neutron and one pi-meson are to result from the collision of a photon with a stationary proton, find the threshold frequency of the photon in terms of the rest mass n of a proton or neutron (here assumed equal) and that, m, of a pi-meson. [$\nu = c^2(m^2 + 2mn)/2hn$.]

5-18. A particle of rest mass m decays from rest into a particle of rest mass m' and a photon. Find the separate energies of these end products. [$c^2m'\gamma$, $c^2(m - \gamma m')$, with $\gamma = \gamma(u)$, $u = c(m^2 - m'^2)/(m^2 + m'^2)$.]

CHAPTER 6

6-1. Write down the equations inverse to (61.11) and (61.12), i.e., those giving the unprimed components of the field in terms of the primed.

6-2. If at a certain event an electromagnetic field satisfies the relations $\mathbf{e} \cdot \mathbf{h} = 0$, $e^2 < h^2$, prove that there exists a frame in which $\mathbf{e} = 0$. Then prove that infinitely many such frames exist, all in collinear relative motion. [Hint: choose the spatial axes suitably and then use the transformation equations (61.11).]

6-3. If at a certain event $\mathbf{e} \cdot \mathbf{h} \neq 0$, prove that there exists a frame in which $\mathbf{e}$ and $\mathbf{h}$ are parallel. Then prove that infinitely many such frames exist, all in collinear relative motion. [Hint: the first special frame moves in the direction $\mathbf{e} \times \mathbf{h}$ relative to the general frame.]

6-4. Prove that the vacuum Maxwell equation

$$\frac{\partial e_1}{\partial x} + \frac{\partial e_2}{\partial y} + \frac{\partial e_3}{\partial z} = 0 \quad (1)$$

(i.e., div $\mathbf{e} = 0$) can hold in *two* inertial frames only if also the Maxwell equations

$$\frac{\partial h_3}{\partial y} - \frac{\partial h_2}{\partial z} = \frac{\partial e_1}{\partial t} \ (2), \quad \frac{\partial h_1}{\partial z} - \frac{\partial h_3}{\partial x} = \frac{\partial e_2}{\partial t} \ (3),$$

$$\frac{\partial h_2}{\partial x} - \frac{\partial h_1}{\partial y} = \frac{\partial e_3}{\partial t} \quad (4)$$

(i.e., curl $\mathbf{h} = \partial \mathbf{e}/\partial t$) hold in *both* frames. (The units are chosen so as to make $c = 1$.) [Hint: use

$$\frac{\partial}{\partial x} = \gamma \left(\frac{\partial}{\partial x'} - v \frac{\partial}{\partial t'} \right), \quad \frac{\partial}{\partial y} = \frac{\partial}{\partial y'}, \quad \frac{\partial}{\partial z} = \frac{\partial}{\partial z'}$$

(why is this true?) and the inverse of (61.11) to transform (1), thus obtaining (2) in S'. Then simply permute axes in both frames ($x \longrightarrow y$, $y \longrightarrow z$, $z \longrightarrow x$) to derive (3), and once again to derive (4), in S'. Conversely, beginning with (1) in S' evidently yields (2)–(4) in S.]

6-5. What is the path of an electrically charged particle which is projected into a uniform (parallel) magnetic field at an angle other than a right angle to the lines of force? Support your answer with exact arguments.

6-6. There are good reasons for saying that an electromagnetic field is "radiative" if it satisfies $\mathbf{e} \cdot \mathbf{h} = 0$ and $\mathbf{e}^2 = \mathbf{h}^2$. Show that the field of a very fast moving charge ($v \approx c$) is essentially radiative in a plane which contains that charge and is orthogonal to its motion.

6-7. In a frame S, two identical particles with electric charge q move abreast along lines parallel to the x axis, a distance r apart and with velocity v. Determine the force, in S, that each exerts upon the other, and do this in two ways: (i) by use of (63.3) and (61.1), and (ii) by transforming the Coulomb force from the rest frame to S by use of the four-vector property of (57.3), with $dm/dt = 0$ (why?). Note that the force is smaller than that in the rest frame, while each mass is evidently greater. Here we see the physical reasons for the "relativistic focusing" effect whose existence we deduced from purely kinematic considerations before. (See the last paragraph of Section 34.) Do these physical arguments lead to the expected time dilation of an "electron cloud clock"? Also note from (i) that as $v \longrightarrow c$ the electric and magnetic forces each become infinite, but that their effects cancel.

6-8. Instead of the equal charges moving abreast as in the preceding exercise, consider now two *opposite* charges moving at the same velocity but one *ahead* of the other. By both suggested methods determine the forces acting on these charges, and show that they do *not* act along the line joining the charges but, instead, apparently constitute a couple tending to turn that join into orthogonality with the line of motion. [Trouton and Noble, in a famous experiment in 1903, unsuccessfully looked for this couple on charges at rest in the laboratory, which they presumed to be flying through the ether. The fact that force and acceleration are not necessarily parallel was unknown then, and the null result seemed puzzling. However, it contributed to the later acceptance of relativity.]

6-9. According to Maxwell's theory, charge is not only *invariant* (i.e., each charge has the same measure in all frames), but it is also *conserved* (i.e., the total charge involved in an experiment remains the same at all times). Explain why it is nevertheless possible for a current-carrying straight wire to be electrically neutral in one frame while possessing a net charge in another (as we saw in Section 64).

6-10. We have asserted that the components of the electromagnetic field, arranged in the pattern (61.13) in every inertial frame, constitute a tensor transforming according to the scheme (45.3). Test this assertion by so transforming to the usual frame S' a pure electromagnetic field of intensity e in the z direction in S, and checking the result by use of the transformation formulae (61.11) and (61.12).

CHAPTER 7

7-1. Say which of the following are intrinsic relative to a two-dimensional surface:
  (i)   The property of a line being straight.
  (ii)   The angle at which two curves intersect.
  (iii) The property of two curves being tangent to each other at a given point.
  (iv)   The length of a curve between two of its points.
  (v)   The shortest distance, in the surface, between two given points.

(vi) The normal curvature of the surface in a given direction (i.e., the curvature of the section obtained by cutting the surface with a plane containing the normal at the point of interest).

(vii) The area contained within a closed curve.

(viii) The "geodesic" curvature of a curve on the surface (i.e., the curvature, at the point of interest, of the projection of the curve onto the tangent plane at that point). [In fact, it can be shown that the geodesics on a surface are precisely those curves whose geodesic curvature vanishes everywhere.]

7-2. The curvature of a plane curve (or, indeed, any curve) is defined as the rate of turning of the tangent (in radians) with respect to distance along the curve; it can be shown to equal $\lim(2z/r^2)$ as $r \to 0$, where r is the distance along the tangent at the point of interest and z is the perpendicular distance from the tangent to the curve. Now, the equation $z = f(x, y)$ of an arbitrary surface, if sufficiently well-behaved, can be expressed as a Taylor series $z = a + bx + cy + dx^2 + exy + fy^2 + \ldots$ for small x, y. If we choose a tangent plane to the surface as the (x, y) plane and the point of contact as the origin, that equation assumes the simpler form $z = Ax^2 + Bxy + Cy^2$ (neglecting cubes and higher powers), and even this can be further reduced to $z = Fx^2 + Gy^2$ by a suitable rotation of the x and y axes. Use this fact to prove that the maximum and minimum of the normal curvature of a surface (cf. exercise 7-1(vi)) occur in orthogonal directions.

7-3. In the plane, the total angle Δ through which the tangent of a closed (and not self-intersecting) curve turns in one circuit is evidently always 2π. On a curved surface, the corresponding Δ (increments of angle being measured in the successive local tangent planes) generally differs from 2π. According to a deep and beautiful theorem (Gauss-Bonnet), $2\pi - \Delta$ equals $\int\int K dS$, the integral of the Gaussian curvature over the enclosed area. Consider a sphere of radius a and on it a "geodesic triangle" formed by three great-circular arcs making a right angle at each vertex. Test the theorem for *both* the areas that can be considered enclosed by this triangle.

7-4. Consider a sphere of radius a and on it a "geodesic circle" of radius r, as in Figure 17. To find the total angle Δ through which the tangent of this circle turns in one circuit (increments of angle always being measured in the local tangent plane), construct the cone tangent to the sphere along the given circle and then "unroll" this cone and measure the angle at its vertex. Thus prove $\Delta = 2\pi \cos(r/a)$. Then verify that this accords exactly with the Gauss-Bonnet theorem of the preceding exercise—as applied to *both* possible "insides" of the circle.

7-5. It is often thought that the sphere is the only two-dimensional surface of *constant* curvature that is both finite and unbounded. Nevertheless, a plane surface, too, can be finite and unbounded. One need merely draw a rectangle in the plane, discard the outside, and "identify" opposite points on opposite edges. The area of the resulting surface is evidently finite, yet it has no boundary. Each point is an internal point, since each point can be surrounded by a circle lying wholly in the surface: a circle around a point on an edge appears in two halves, yet is connected because of the identification; around the vertices—all identified—such a circle appears in four parts. Unlike the plane, however, this surface has the topology of a torus, and thus lacks global isotropy. (Consider, for example, the lengths of geodesics drawn in various directions from a given point.) Still, it is *locally* isotropic in its planeness.

A similar though rather more complicated construction can be made on a surface of constant negative curvature. Issuing from one of its points, we draw eight geodesics of equal length r, each making an angle of 45° with the next. Then we draw the eight geodesics which join their endpoints. What can you say about the angles at the vertices of the resulting "geodesics octagon" in terms of its total area? Deduce that r can be chosen to make these angles 45°, and chose r so. Labeling the vertices successively A,B,C,D,E,F,G,H, identify the following directed geodesics: $AB = DC, BC = ED, EF = HG, FG = AH$. Draw a picture and verify that (i) each point on an edge other than a vertex is an internal point, (ii) the eight vertices are all identified and constitute an internal point, (iii) at all these points the curvature is the same as "inside." Can the same trick be worked with a four- or six-sided polygon?

Analogous constructions exist, obviously, for flat three-space and also, much less obviously, for three-spaces of constant negative curvature.

7-6. Derive the formulae (66.1) for the surface and volume of a small geodesic sphere centered on an isotropic point in a curved three-space.

7-7. In a three-space of constant positive curvature $1/a^2$, the geodesics of any geodesic "pencil" spread exactly like geodesics on a sphere of radius a, e.g., like the meridians issuing from the north pole. Use this fact to establish quantitatively the various properties of a hypersphere stated in the third paragraph of Section 66.

7-8. Suppose we suspect that spacetime, instead of being Minkowskian, is a four-space of constant curvature. In principle, how could we test this hypothesis? Comparing the radius and surface of a geodesic two-sphere could be part of the test, but this would *not* probe the spread of time-like or null geodesics, nor of spacelike geodesics with time-like separation. How would you check on all these? [Hint: draw a three-dimensional Minkowski diagram to develop your ideas.]

7-9. In Figure 20 we have shown a triangular light path (in a static field) which has the property that the coordinate time for light to travel along two of the sides is less than that along the third side—which would be impossible in Minkowski space, i.e., in the absence of gravitation. Consider the gravitational field of a single concentrated spherical mass, and in it indicate a "triangle" to which the data of Figure 20 might apply, qualitatively. [Hint: Remember that standard clocks at low gravitational potential go slow relative to those at zero potential; what does this imply about the *coordinate* speed of light at low potential?]

7-10. In Newtonian theory, every gravitational field relative to AS is completely described by a scalar potential $\phi = - \int \int \int (\rho/r)dV$, evaluated instantaneously over all space, the field itself being $- \operatorname{grad}\phi$. If the field is stationary, ϕ is independent of time, and thus there exist no stationary fields which are not also static. For example, a "gravitational" field like that found by an observer at rest on a uniformly rotating turntable has no analog in Newtonian AS. Nevertheless, it is possible to define a conservative scalar potential on the turntable, corresponding to the centrifugal force only, since the Coriolis force acts at right angles to a particle's motion and thus does no work. The centrifugal force being $\omega^2 r$ (ω = angular velocity, r = distance from the center), the potential is $-\frac{1}{2}\omega^2 r^2$. If we substitute this in (69.4), we obtain a frequency shift between a point at radius r and the center which agrees, *to first order*, with our previously found result (40.2). However, the agreement is not exact. This is because we have ignored the fact that the force on a unit rest mass at rest in the field, measured by an observer at rest in the field, is not $\omega^2 r$, but rather $\omega^2 r \gamma^2(\omega r)$. Why? Show that the corresponding potential is $\frac{1}{2}\log(1 - \omega^2 r^2)$, and that this, when substituted in (69.4), agrees exactly with (40.2). The present example, like that of the linear acceleration field, is interesting in that it allows a given noninfinitesimal frequency shift to be interpreted alternatively by purely kinematic or purely gravitational considerations.

7-11. A satellite is in circular orbit of geocentric radius r around the earth (radius R), satisfying equation (70.5). A standard clock C on the satellite is compared with an identical clock C_0 on earth. Prove that the ratio of the rates of these clocks is given by

$$\frac{\nu}{\nu_0} \approx 1 + \frac{Gm}{Rc^2} - \frac{3Gm}{2rc^2} ,$$

and note that this exceeds unity only if $r > 3R/2$ (i.e., $r - R > 3184$ km). [Hint: compare C first with a clock C_1 at rest at a point on its orbit (appealing to the usual SR time dilation effect), and then compare C_1 with C_0.]

7-12. Gravity evidently affects the rate of a pendulum clock. In a stronger field, does a given pendulum clock go faster or slower? Is this in any way connected with gravitational time dilation?

CHAPTER 8

8-1. For the polar metric of the plane, $dr^2 + r^2d\theta^2$, work out the Christoffel symbols Γ^i_{jk} (put $r = x^1$, $\theta = x^2$) and verify that $\theta = $ constant satisfies the geodesic equations (72.12).

8-2. Prove that the metric $y^2dx^2 + x^2dy^2$ represents the Euclidean plane. [Hint: work out the Christoffel symbols and verify that *all* components of the curvature tensor (72.16) vanish; do not forget the symmetries (72.17).]

8-3. Prove that the metric $ydx^2 + xdy^2$ represents a *curved* space. [Hint: find at least *one* component of the curvature tensor different from zero.]

8-4. Prove that for a concentrated spherical mass m, the *Newtonian* "escape velocity" (i.e., the minimum velocity at which a particle must be projected so as to reach infinity) is c at distance $r = 2Gm/c^2$ from the center. In the units of the metric (74.8) this corresponds precisely to the Schwarzschild radius $r = 2m$. [However, the physical analogy with the Schwarzschild situation is rather tenuous.]

8-5. Accepting the geodesic equations (75.3) and (75.4) for the Schwarzschild field, show that circular orbits are possible with any radius $r > 3m$, and that they must satisfy

$$\frac{m}{r^3} = \left(\frac{d\phi}{ds}\right)^2 \left(1 - \frac{3m}{r}\right).$$

Then, by direct use of the metric (74.8), show that this condition is equivalent to $(d\phi/dt)^2 = m/r^3$. Compare this with (70.5). What is the total proper time for such an orbit? What is the total coordinate time? What happens when $r = 3m$?

8-6. Suppose that at the instant a particle in circular orbit around a spherical mass passes through a certain point P, another freely moving particle passes through P in a radially outward direction, at the precise velocity necessary to ensure that it will fall back through P when also the orbiting particle next passes through P. By using the results of the preceding exercise, prove that it is certainly possible for these two particles to take *different* proper times between their two coincidences. (The precise amount of the difference is of little interest in the present context.) Note that here we have a version of the twin "paradox" in which both twins are permanently unaccelerated in their rest frames.

8-7. Reobtain the formula (76.3) for the acceleration (i.e., the force) felt by an observer at rest in the Schwarzschild field in the following way: First prove by use of (75.2) that the potential in the sense of (69.4), with zero-point at infinity, is $\phi = \frac{1}{2}\log(1 - 2m/r)$; then evaluate g as $-d\phi/d\sigma$, using the relation (76.1).

8-8. Consider the metric $ds^2 = X^2 dT^2 - dX^2 - dY^2 - dZ^2$ (which is, in fact, fully discussed in Section 77) purely on its own merits. By a method analogous to that leading to (75.2), obtain the frequency shift ν/ν_1 between two points on the X axis, one at arbitrary X and the other at $X = 1$. From this derive a potential in the sense of the preceding exercise and deduce that the force felt by an observer at rest at coordinate X is $-1/X$.

8-9. In the situation illustrated in Figure 26, show that *any* free particle must fall, sooner, or later, into the abyss beyond the "edge" E_2. (As in Schwarzschild space, the only way to survive is to accelerate against the field.) Prove also that a particle cannot avoid the abyss by any means once it has strayed into the region II. [Hint: use the diagram and argue graphically by use of light cones.]

8-10. In the situation illustrated in Figure 26, show that a particle dropped from rest at "level" $X = X_1$ to a lower level $X = X_2$ $(< X_1)$ always takes the same *proper* time, namely $(X_1^2 - X_2^2)^{1/2}$, and also the same *coordinate* time T, namely $\tanh^{-1} \{(X_1^2 - X_2^2)^{1/2}/X_1\}$. [Hint: The particle worldline will be tangent to the X_1 hyperbola. Why? Consider a LT which transforms the hyperbola into itself and the tangent into the vertex tangent.]

8-11. For the metric of exercise 8-8 work out the Christoffel symbols and hence the geodesic equations of motion in the X direction. Translate these equations by use of (77.11) into the Minkowskian coordinates x and t, and interpret the result.

8-12. Prove, by any method, (i) that light tracks in the space with the metric of the preceding exercise are semicircles, with typical equation $X^2 + Y^2 = a^2$, $X > 0$; (ii) that the *coordinate velocity* of light at all points with coordinate X is X in *all* directions; (iii) that there is no upper limit to the *coordinate time* for a light signal to travel in the X direction from X_0 (>0) to X_1 $(>X_0)$, or vice versa, provided that X_0 is sufficiently close to zero.

8-13. What is the *coordinate velocity* of light in the Schwarzschild space (74.8) at coordinate r, (i) in the radial direction, (ii) in the transverse direction? $[1 - 2m/r,$ $(1 - 2m/r)^{1/2}.]$

8-14. Obtain the integral

$$\Delta t = 2 \int_p^{r_0} \{\alpha^{-2} + \alpha^{-1}p^2(r^2 - p^2)^{-1}\}^{1/2} dr, \quad \alpha = 1 - 2m/r,$$

for the coordinate time it takes a light signal to travel along a path in the Schwarzschild space (77.1) which starts and ends at radial coordinate r_0, whose closest approach to the origin is at radial coordinate p, and whose equation is approximated by $r \cos \theta = p, \phi = 0$, i.e., by a line which is "straight" relative to the coordinates. Neglecting squares of m/p, one can quite easily show that this integral has the value

$$2x_0(1 - m/r_0) + 4m \log \{(r_0 + x_0)/p\}, \quad x_0 = (r_0^2 - p^2)^{1/2}.$$

Verify that this exceeds $2x_0$, i.e., the value when $m = 0$, and considerably so when p is small. Show how one can *immediately* modify the answer if, instead, the signal travels between two *unequal* values of r, say, r_0 and r_1. [The time delay discussed here is due to the slowing down of standard clocks *and* to the modified space geometry near the central mass—unlike the gravitational Doppler shift, which is due to the former only. This has recently led to a proposal (I.I. Shapiro, *Phys. Rev. Letters* **13**, 789 (1964)) for a "fourth test" of GR, which consists in comparing the time it takes for a radar signal to be bounced off a planet when the signal passes close to the sun, with the time it takes when the signal is practically unaffected by the solar field. For preliminary results, see *ibid.* **20**, 1265 (1968), **21**, 266 (1968).

8-15. Explain, *in principle only* but nevertheless in full detail, how you would solve a collision problem involving "test particles" (i.e., particles whose mass is too small to affect the *field*) in curved spacetime. Consider, for example, a fully elastic head-on collision of two test particles of different inertial mass in equal and opposite circular orbit in the Schwarzschild space due to a given object.

8-16. It is clear from the symmetry of the particular form (80.7) of the metric of de Sitter space, that "radial" light signals (satisfying θ, ϕ = constant) are possible. Because of the condition $ds^2 = 0$, they must also satisfy $dt = \pm dr/(1 - r^2/a^2)$, where $a^2 = 3/\Lambda$ (which is positive for S_4^-). For a suitable choice of initial conditions (which, however, does not restrict the generality), this leads to $\theta = \pi/2$, $\phi = 0$, $r = a\tanh(t/a)$. Translate these equations into a locus on the pseudo-sphere (80.9), and verify that that locus consists of a pair of straight-line "generators" of the "reduced" model of the pseudo-sphere, namely the hyperboloid of revolution $X^2 + W^2 - T^2 = a^2$. (A sketch of this surface on a Cartesian triplet of axes, $X, W, T,$ will be of help.) To anyone with a little experience of differential geometry, the null-geodetic character of this locus is evident *geometrically*, whereas it was *not* so relative to the metric (80.7).

8-17. The existence of closed timelike lines in an otherwise acceptable spacetime, which was discussed in the final paragraph of Section 80, is not quite as rare a phenomenon as might be suspected. In fact, it is quite easy to construct spaces with even closed timelike *geodesics*: let us, for example, in flat Minkowski space identify any events whose respective x, y, and z coordinates are equal but whose t coordinates differ by an integer. If desired, one can make the same kind of identification also in the x, y, and z dimensions and thus produce finite and unbounded spatial sections. Which are now the closed timelike geodesics? Apart from the obvious violation of causality (why?), can you see any other defects of these spaces?

CHAPTER 9

9-1. In connection with our cosmological scale illustrations (e.g., dimes for galaxies), prove the following theorem of Newtonian theory concerning scale models of systems of bodies moving under their mutual gravitation, in which each body is scaled down to one of *equal density*: the orbits of the bodies in the model, under *their* mutual gravitation, are similar in shape and identical in time to those of the original system. [Hint: consider at first only two of the original bodies and their counterparts in the model.]

9-2. By considering the volume and mass of a small sphere of constant *coordinate* radius r in the metric (85.8) of the steady state theory, prove that the mass dM created in volume V per time dt is given by $dM = 3H\rho V dt$. Assuming, in cgs units, that $H = 3 \times 10^{-18}$ and the density $\rho = 10^{-30}$, and knowing that one year is $\sim 3.2 \times 10^7$ and the mass of a hydrogen atom is $\sim 1.7 \times 10^{-24}$, prove that one new hydrogen atom would have to be created in a volume of one km^3 about every six years to maintain the assumed constant density.

9-3. For the metric (85.5) with $(x^1, x^2, x^3, x^4) = (r, \theta, \phi, t)$ and $c = 1$, prove that of the three Christoffel symbols Γ^4_{11}, Γ^4_{14}, Γ^4_{44} only the first is nonzero, and is in fact $-g_{11}\dot{R}/R$, where the dot denotes d/dt. These are all the Γ's you need in order next to deduce that *radial* geodesics (i.e., those with $\theta, \phi = $ constant), whose existence we take for granted from symmetry, must satisfy $t'' - (g_{11}\dot{R}/R)r'^2 = 0$, where each prime denotes d/ds. Use the metric itself to reduce this equation to the form $t''/(t'^2 - 1) = -\dot{R}/R$, and hence integrate it to find $t'^2 - 1 = A/R^2(t)$, with A an arbitrary (positive) constant, as the general differential equation for timelike radial geodesics. [See also exercise 9-8.]

9-4. Use the geodetic differential equation obtained in the preceding exercise to verify that each fundamental particle $(r, \theta, \phi = $ constant) in the RW metric (85.5) is in geodetic motion. [Hint: look at the metric with $dr = d\theta = d\phi = 0$.]

9-5. Prove that the velocity u of any radially moving particle in the RW metric (85.5) relative to the local rest

LIF is given by $u^2 = -g_{11}dr^2/dt^2$. Using this and the metric itself (again with $c = 1$), deduce that $t' = (1 - u^2)^{-1/2}, = \gamma$, say. Can you give reasons why this could have been written down *a priori*? Now cast the radial geodetic equation of exercise 9-3 into the form $\gamma u = B/R(t)$, $B = $ constant, and deduce that, in a model in which $R \rightarrow \infty$ as $t \rightarrow \infty$, *all* freely moving particles eventually come to rest relative to the substratum—which is certainly reasonable from the rubber-model point of view. Note, in particular, that the momentum of freely moving particles relative to the substratum varies as $1/R$.

9-6. By briefly checking the steps of the argument, verify that the geodetic equation obtained in exercise 9-3 applies equally to the form (85.6) of the RW metric. Hence test that geodetic equation for the case of Milne's model, by applying it directly to the metric (84.7), and then translating the answer into Minkowski space by use of (84.6).

9-7. Use Figure 28 to illustrate *graphically* in the case of Milne's universe the result of exercise 9-5 according to which any freely moving particle eventually comes to rest relative to the substratum. What is the coordinate ρ of the fundamental particle that will be reached only in the infinite future by a freely moving particle emitted at the spatial origin at time $\tau = a$ with velocity u? [$\rho = u(c^2 - u^2)^{-1/2}$.]

9-8. Fill in the details of the following heuristic rederivation of the radial geodetic equation in the form given in exercise 9-5. A small spherical shell with perfectly reflecting inner surface is filled with a "photon gas." It is then made to move freely in a radial direction in the RW metric. In the rest frame of this object, its total energy evidently remains constant; relative to the substratum, however, the enclosed photons lose energy, according to the cosmic Doppler effect, and thus momentum. Their momentum component in the radial direction, like their energy, is inversely proportional to the cosmic expansion factor $R(t)$. Hence the momentum of the shell itself must also vary as $1/R$, since the shell *with or without* the photons must execute the same motion. Consequently, if u is the (variable) velocity of the shell relative to the substratum, we are led to $\gamma u = B/R(t)$, precisely as in exercise 9-5. This would allow us, retrospectively, also to reobtain the equation of exercise 9-3. [Apparently there is no such simple "balloon" argument for getting these equations of motion as there is in the case of photons; photons enjoy the particularly simple property of having the same velocity relative to each fundamental observer, whereas there seems to be no heuristic kinematic way to predict the local velocity variation of material particles. No doubt this is due to the nonintuitive nature of the relativistic velocity addition law.]

9-9. According to Planck's law, the energy density distribution among the various frequencies of "black body" radiation is given by

$$du_0 = 8\pi h \nu_0^3 c^{-3} (e^{h\nu_0/kT_0} - 1)^{-1} d\nu_0, \qquad (1)$$

where k is Boltzmann's constant and T the absolute temperature. We have inserted the subscripts zero to indicate that we look at the various quantities at some given cosmic instant t_0. Now suppose that the radiation in question uniformly fills an RW model universe with expansion function $R(t)$, and suppose we can neglect its interaction with the cosmic matter. As the universe expands or contracts, will the radiation maintain its "black body" character (1), and, if so, with what temperature law? Fill in the details of the following argument: $\nu/\nu_0 = R_0/R$, $du/du_0 = R_0^4/R^4$, hence (1) without the subscript, provided $T/T_0 = R_0/R$. [As a result of radio-astronomical observations within the last four years, such black body radiation is, in fact, now believed to fill our universe, with $T \approx 3.5°$K. (For a résumé see, for example, P.J.E. Peebles in "Relativity Theory and Astrophysics," Vol. I, p. 274, J. Ehlers, editor, Providence, R.I., American Mathematical Society, 1967.) The temperature of the cosmic *matter* as a nonrelativistic gas, which is presently minute by comparison, falls off in the usual adiabatic way as $1/R^2$. Producing these two different temperature laws sufficiently far back in time and assuming the model reliable to that extent, one is led to thermal equilibrium between matter and radiation at some early cosmic time, after which decoupling must have occurred. Current theories of these effects agree reasonably well with the observational data against a background of some "big bang" RW models. This is taken by many as strong evidence in favor of the latter.]

9-10. Prove, either analytically or by reference to the rubber models (and preferably *both* ways), that if an RW model characterized by an expansion function $R(t)$ is run backwards in time, i.e., if we consider the "dual" model with expansion function $R(-t)$ and the same k, then the event horizon (if any) of the first model becomes the particle horizon of the second, and vice versa. [Note: for models culminating at finite t in point-annihilation, the definition of event horizons needs an obvious modification.]

9-11. Prove by reference to the rubber models: (i) If a model possesses no event horizon, then all events are observable sooner or later by any fundamental observer. (ii) Every galaxy but A eventually passes out of the event horizon of A. (iii) If a model possesses an event horizon but no particle horizon, then any observer can be present at any one preassigned event provided he is willing if necessary to detach himself from his original fundamental particle and provided he does so soon enough. Nevertheless, if two arbitrary events are preassigned it will generally be impossible for any one observer ever to observe both. (iv) If a model possesses an event horizon *and* a particle horizon, then there exists a class of galaxies never overtaken by the particle horizon of a given galaxy, and for any observer there exists a class of events absolutely beyond his cognizance, no matter how he journeys through space.

9-12. By reference to the rubber models, describe the most general (isotropic and homogeneous) universe in which it is possible for two given galaxies, seen simultaneously by a given observer in the same direction at one given instant t_0, to exhibit the same nonzero red shift and the same distance by apparent size, and yet for one to be at twice the proper distance σ_0 as the other, at that instant.

9-13. Fill in the details of the following derivation of a condition for the avoidance of Olbers' paradox in RW models: From (87.3) and (87.8), the energy flux b per unit area and unit time at the origin at time t_0, due to a source of intrinsic luminosity B, is given by $BR^2/\rho^2 R_0^4$ (dropping the subscript 1 and writing t for t_1 etc.). Let n be the number of galaxies per unit comoving coordinate volume (strictly constant in conservative models), and $B(t)$ the intrinsic luminosity of an average galaxy as a function of cosmic time (usually, though with less justification, also regarded as essentially constant). Then the energy flux at the origin through a spherical detector of unit proper radius, due to a shell of cosmic matter at coordinate radius ρ with coordinate thickness $d\rho$, is given by

$$du = \frac{B(t)R^2(t)}{\rho^2 R_0^4} \times \frac{n4\pi\rho^2 d\rho}{(1 - k\rho^2)^{1/2}}.$$

When we sum over all shells which contribute light to the origin at that instant, we must of course allow for the finite velocity of light, and count each contribution according to its emission time. From (85.6), $-c\,dt = R(t)d\rho/(1 - k\rho^2)^{1/2}$ for incoming light. Hence the total flux through the detector is given by

$$u = \frac{cn}{R_0^4} \int_{-\infty,0}^{t_0} R(t)B(t)dt,$$

where the lower limit of integration must be chosen according as the model exists for all negative cosmic times or only from some definite cosmic instant ($t = 0$) onward. If B is taken as constant, the condition for the avoidance of Olbers' paradox is thus the convergence of the integral $\int R(t)dt$ for the model's entire *past*. (Note: (i) the spatial curvature k does not affect the result; (ii) in the case of closed universes, each galaxy may contribute several times to the total flux measured at the origin, its light having circumnavigated the universe several times; (iii) no allowance has been made for possible absorption of emitted light on the way to the origin.) Under the present assumptions, which of the Friedmann models (see Section 90) have an Olbers problem?

9-14.   Adapt the argument of the preceding exercise to prove that in the steady state theory $u = c\tilde{n}B/4H$, where $\tilde{n}$ is the constant number of galaxies per unit proper volume, and B is the constant intrinsic luminosity of an average galaxy.

9-15.   Prove, from the formulae, that for all RW models with $k = 0$, the proper distance σ and the distance S from apparent size coincide. By use of the rubber models illustrate why this is so, and also why it is *not* so in the cases $k = \pm 1$.

9-16.   For Milne's model (84.7) (which, in the notation of (85.6), has $R(t) = ct$ and $k = -1$), prove that $\Sigma(\rho_1) = \log(t_0/t_1)$ and hence derive the following relation between the three "distances" described in Section 87 of an object at cosmic time t_1: $L/S = \exp(2\sigma/ct_1)$. Prove also that S coincides with the "ordinary" distance of the object at *its* proper time t_1 in the Minkowski rest frame of the observer; and that both σ and L for particles near the observer's "boundary" of the universe become arbitrarily large.

9-17.   For the steady state model (85.8) prove the following relation between S and L: $L/S = (1 - HS/c)^{-2}$. Use this to rederive the distance of the event horizon, $\sigma = S = c/H$. Why does the infinite value of L indicate an event horizon in this model but *not* in the Milne model?

9-18. Fill in the details of the following proof that the only (zero-pressure) Friedmann models which have constant curvature *as four-spaces* are precisely the six empty ones: Consider two particular neighboring timelike geodesics issuing from the origin, namely the worldlines of two galaxies at equal radial coordinate r, separated by a small comoving coordinate distance dl. The cosmic time t, being proper time at each fundamental particle, serves as "distance" along these geodesics if we take $c = 1$. All their spacelike joins at fixed t, of magnitude $\eta = R(t)dl$, are orthogonal to them.   Evidently $\ddot{\eta} = \ddot{R}(t)dl = (\ddot{R}/R)\eta$. Comparison with (66.2) now shows that we cannot have constant curvature *unless* $\ddot{R} = -KR$, i.e., $\dot{R}\ddot{R} = -KR\dot{R}$, i.e., $\dot{R}^2 = -KR^2 +$ constant. Comparison with (89.8), and the fact that ρ varies as $1/R^3$ (cf. (89.9)) finally leads to $\rho = 0$ (and, incidentally, to $K = -\Lambda/3$). Hence only the empty models *can* have constant curvature. Reference to the list following (90.4) shows that, in fact, they all *do* have constant curvature. [It can be shown quite apart from the restriction of the field equations that these six RW metrics are the only ones with constant curvature; see, for example, H. P. Robertson and T. W. Noonan, "Relativity and Cosmology," Sections 14.7 and 16.3, Philadelphia, W.B. Saunders Co., 1968.] Note particularly that in these models the constant curvature K of the full spacetime does not coincide with the constant curvature k/R^2 of the cosmic sections (except in the trivial case of the static Minkowski universe). By considering the specially simple example of Milne's model, try to explain why this is so.

9-19. Explain *in principle only*, but nevertheless in full detail, how a problem such as exercise 2-25 (concerning the distance covered by a rocket moving with large constant proper acceleration) would have to be worked if one assumed an RW background and were interested in voyages between galaxies whose cosmic proper distance increases significantly during the trip.

9-20. A qualitative analysis similar to that illustrated in Figure 32 can be made also for models *with* pressure. The main task again is to find the exremals of the curve $\dot{R} = 0$ plotted on a (Λ, R) diagram. To this end, deduce from (89.12) the relation $dp/dR = -3(\rho + pc^{-2})/R$ and then, from (89.8), derive the condition

$$d\Lambda/dR = -6k/R^3 + 24\pi G c^{-2}(\rho + pc^{-2})/R = 0$$

for the extremals in question. If $k = 0$ or -1, no extremal is possible, as before, if we assume $\rho, p \geq 0$. For $k = 1$, however, the analysis is complicated by the fact that $(\rho + pc^{-2})$ is now not known explicitly as a function of R. It can be shown that there may be several extremals for positive R instead of the single one when $p = 0$. (See, for example, R. C. Tolman, "Relativity, Thermodynamics, and Cosmology," Section 157, Oxford University Press, 1934.)

9-21. Prove that the theorem of exercise 9-1 is true in all pseudo-Newtonian universes characterized by eq. (88.7), even for nonzero Λ. Is there, in fact, any difference between such a universe and a scale model of it constructed according to the hypothesis of that theorem? Prove that the theorem (with "cosmic time" taking the place of "time") is true for the relativistic models characterized by eq. (89.10) if and only if $k = 0$.

Index

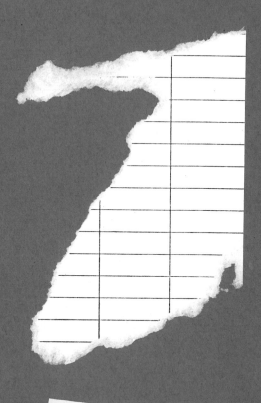